UNDERST.
MENTAL HEALTH AND
MENTAL ILLNESS

The question of whether someone is psychologically healthy or mentally ill, and the fundamental nature of mental health underlying that question, has been debated in cultural, academic, and clinical settings for millennia. This book provides an overview of how people have conceptualized and understood mental illness through the ages.

The book begins by looking at mental illness in humanity's evolutionary past then moves through the major historical epochs: the mythological, the Classical, the Middle Ages, the Renaissance, the Enlightenment, the modern, and the postmodern. At each point, it focuses on major elements that emerged regarding how people judged sanity and insanity and places major emphasis on the growing fields of psychiatry and psychology as they emerged and developed. As the book moves into the twenty-first century, Dr. Jenkins presents his integrated model of knowledge, a systemic, holistic model of the psyche that creates a conceptual foundation for understanding both psychological wellness and disorder and approaching assessment and diagnosis.

This text provides a valuable exploration of mental health and illness across the ages and gives those already well versed in the subject matter a fresh perspective on the past and new model of knowledge and assessment for the future.

Paul H. Jenkins, PsyD, is a licensed clinical psychologist with more than 30 years of professional experience in the assessment, diagnosis, and treatment of mental illness. He is a professor of psychology at National University, USA and enjoys teaching students the fundamentals of assessment, treatment planning, and psychotherapy.

"In this deeply probing work, Paul Jenkins investigates and analyses the constructs of mental health and mental illness. Drawing from multiple perspectives based in a rich and deep knowledge of the relevant scholarship from an array of relevant fields, Jenkins deconstructs and assesses the theories and underlying epistemologies that have been applied to mental health and mental illness. He takes the reader on an insightful historical voyage through the development of these concepts over time, concluding with an integrative synthesis grounded in a new variation on the biopsychosocial model. This is a book that should be read by every thoughtful student or practitioner in a mental health field."

Jay L. Lebow, *PhD, ABPP, senior scholar and clinical professor, The Family Institute at Northwestern University, USA*

UNDERSTANDING MENTAL HEALTH AND MENTAL ILLNESS

AN EXPLORATION OF THE PAST, PRESENT, AND FUTURE

Paul H. Jenkins

Routledge
Taylor & Francis Group

NEW YORK AND LONDON

First published 2021
by Routledge
52 Vanderbilt Avenue, New York, NY 10017

and by Routledge
2 Park Square, Milton Park, Abingdon, Oxon, OX14 4RN

Routledge is an imprint of the Taylor & Francis Group, an informa business

© 2021 Taylor & Francis

Library of Congress Cataloging-in-Publication Data
Names: Jenkins, Paul H., author.
Title: Understanding mental health and mental illness: an exploration of the past, present, and future/Paul H. Jenkins.
Identifiers: LCCN 2020035574 (print) | LCCN 2020035575 (ebook) | ISBN 9781138340664 (hardback) | ISBN 9781138340756 (paperback) | ISBN 9780429440526 (ebook)
Subjects: LCSH: Psychiatry. | Mental health.
Classification: LCC RC454.4 J46 2021 (print) | LCC RC454.4 (ebook) | DDC 616.89 – dc23
LC record available at https://lccn.loc.gov/2020035574
LC ebook record available at https://lccn.loc.gov/2020035575

ISBN: 978-1-138-34066-4 (hbk)
ISBN: 978-1-138-34075-6 (pbk)
ISBN: 978-0-429-44052-6 (ebk)

Typeset in Baskerville
by Apex CoVantage, LLC

To my parents, John and Ann Jenkins, who always encouraged me to reach for my dreams, my wife Jennifer for her love and patience, and my children Chris and AnnMarie, for their love, laughter, and smiles.

CONTENTS

INTRODUCTION   1

1   PREHISTORY   19

2   THE MYTHOLOGICAL ERA   40

3   THE CLASSICAL ERA   53

4   THE MIDDLE AGES   70

5   THE RENAISSANCE   87

6   THE ENLIGHTENMENT   102

7   THE MODERN AGE   134

8   THE POSTMODERN ERA   181

9   THE TWENTY-FIRST CENTURY   217

10 NOW AND INTO THE FUTURE   263

References   *307*
Index   *321*

INTRODUCTION

Imagine yourself sitting on a bus. You are ten years old. You are just sitting there, watching the town roll by, when you notice something going on behind you. You turn your head and see a man sitting in the back of the bus. He is by himself but he is talking. In fact, he is having an argument, and it appears to be with his own reflection in the window of the bus. It is not clear what he is arguing about or with whom, but he is really angry, yelling in fact. He seems oblivious to everyone else in the bus.

I was the ten-year-old child and I remember feeling nervous and uncomfortable – the man's behavior was so strange and vaguely threatening. What if he noticed me and decided to start yelling at me? Like everyone else on the bus, I pointedly ignored him until my stop came up. I gave him a quick glance as I got off the bus, but he never noticed me. He was lost in his own world.

From the moment I noticed that man and for years afterward, I wondered what was wrong with him. Something must have been – there was nobody there for him to be arguing with, and he did not seem to be aware of how he appeared to the people around him. Those were the pertinent variables as I understood them at the age of ten. Together, they led me to conclude he was crazy. It was an easy conclusion to draw. But as the years went by in my childhood, I thought about him from time to time, and many more questions presented themselves to me. Was he on drugs? Was he usually like that, or was he having a really bad day? Did something horrible happen in his life that made him like that, or was he born that way? Later, when I became a student of psychology, a whole new series of questions emerged. What was his specific mental illness? Did what he was experiencing even fit a particular diagnosis? How do we come up with these diagnoses anyway? And most importantly, what was it about his behavior that led a ten-year-old child to almost immediately place him in the category of "crazy"?

This is a book about an idea, a concept, namely mental illness and its corollary, mental health. They exist as categories, organizational principles, and ways of conceptualizing human nature. In a wider sense, they are ways of interpreting the world. People often use the concept of sanity metaphorically, to interpret all sorts of events and situations that occur in life: "Did you see that concert last night? It was crazy!" Thus, almost any given psychological experience or behavior can be given the label of sane or crazy by the experiencer or an observer. Which one does one pick and why?

The use of the term "label" here is not spurious or random. It reflects the foundational nature of what is being explored in this book. Labels imply categories, and the categories people choose and how they are defined tell us how those people construct their reality. Lakoff and Johnson (1980) remind us that humans *have* to categorize things in order to understand the world and function in it. Creating categories is necessary to organize the otherwise chaotic flood of raw data human brains are inundated with every moment of their existence. Categorical thinking brings order to the chaos and reflects what people think is *true* about the world. Categorization also has a double-edged quality to it. On the one side, they have the aforementioned benefit of organizing human mentation in adaptive ways; they play a critical role in people being able to move through their lives efficiently and effectively. For instance, people need to be able to categorize some situations and/ or people as "safe" rather than "dangerous" in order to make quick decisions and avoid being seriously hurt or even killed. However, on the other side, the process of categorization highlights certain qualities or properties of phenomena and down-plays or ignores others. Categorization, therefore, tends to oversimplify the world. By narrowing down the available information about a phenomenon, it leads to stereotyping or "pigeonholing."

This dynamic is certainly in play when it comes to concepts regarding men-tal health and mental illness. Everyone has their implicit, mostly unconscious pro-cess of interpreting phenomena as sane or crazy. People categorize based on their underlying beliefs. This begs the question of how we know what is true; how do people decide on what is true for them? This is a particular problem for the concept of mental illness, which is notoriously difficult to define (Porter, 2013; Scull, 2015). Many definitions have been offered, both now and throughout history, leaving many even now in the awkward position of providing not one answer but a range of possibilities (Davidson, Campbell, Shannon, & Mulholland, 2016). This means that the exact nature of our topic of our text is not "settled science." It is an open question that needs to be explored.

This open question regarding the true nature of mental illness requires that we delve into questions of existence (ontology), knowledge (epistemology), and mean-ing (hermeneutics). We have to ask fundamental questions regarding mental illness. Does it actually exist as a natural entity? And If so, what is its nature, and how can it be differentiated from something we could then call mental health? On what basis can we have confidence in our answers? Given the conceptual nature of the topic, we need to start by developing an understanding of how to explore such questions. To do this, let's start by exploring how to figure out what is real or true regarding a topic as controversial, complex, and ultimately subjective as mental illness. After that, we will look at how these epistemological questions play out in regard to how people typically think and how large-scale systems of truth – paradigms – develop or change over time.

But first, we need to understand why it matters. Why bother with such a philo-sophical topic? We could also debate how many angels can dance on the head of a pin, right? Well, it turns out that what we think about mental illness *is* very import-ant, both within its own professional fields of clinical psychology and psychiatry and also in any given culture in general. From the professional perspective, what we think mental illness *is* serves as the foundation for its differentiation from mental health and the development of a categorical system, or nosology, of mental illness. The resulting descriptive system is used to develop assessment tools and ultimately treatments for mental illness. In other words, understanding the conceptual foun-dation for mental illness is extremely relevant for psychotherapists, mental health professionals in general, and everyone else who is impacted by the mental health system, which is basically everyone.

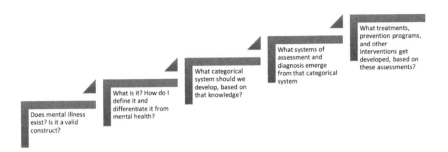

Part of the problem today is that many (not all) clinically oriented educational programs in psychology and psychiatry work backward, teaching students how to treat mental illness, with the implicit assumption that we already have commonly accepted and valid answers to the foundational questions. That is not true, and presuming it *is* true does a profound disservice to our students and to society in general. Consider this thought experiment: What if we still believed in witches? We would be teaching students how to identify and destroy witches based on our assumptions about all three levels of truth – that witches exist, that we know what they are, and that we know how to categorically identify them. With these assumptions in place, we are ready to "assess" and "treat" witchcraft! Of course, we would reject this approach to education as absurd because it is based on unsupportable assumptions, yet that is how we typically educate students of psychology and psychiatry today.

Instead, we need to question our assumptions about mental illness. Before we jump into treating the problem, we need to know what it really is. It is that word "really" that gives us trouble. It forces us to start at the most fundamental level of questioning. How do we know anything is "real"? This problem is an issue for all sciences, but it is particularly difficult one for the social sciences. Many academic and professional fields are strongly based on clear, objective, naturally occurring phenomena, providing their conceptual theories with a solid foundation of empirical data. In engineering, for instance, the value or validity of a piece of work depends on whether the product actually works. Does the building stand up? Does the air conditioner pump out cold air? It doesn't matter what people *think* or *feel* about it. All that matters are results in the real world – how well the product works. New ideas about engineering may emerge, but they are quickly supported or shot down by the real-world results of their application. Engineers probably do not spend much time at work discussing postmodern relativity. In their professional thinking, the real world is just that: real. Of course, the load bearing capacity for a particular column depends on a number of environmental factors, so there is some relativity involved, but the other factors are also considered real, objective, value-free things *themselves* that can be measured. Therefore, it is really about objective complexity rather than subjective relativity.

There are other academic/professional fields that are based on more subjective phenomena. They *do* depend on what people *think* is true and how they *feel* about things. In general, the social sciences are much more on the subjective side. As much as they try to be objective (and, in doing so, have become academic leaders in research design and statistical analysis), they can't escape the ultimate subjectivity of their field. This subjectivity stems from two primary sources. The first is related to the contrast between social reality and natural reality. In the earlier example of the engineer, we see how much more objective it is possible to be when dealing with material reality – the world of actual, physical things, even in their complex interactions with each other. Many of the "things" in the social sciences are much harder to measure or even define. For instance, most people would agree that love is important in their lives, but how does one measure it or even define it? The second source of subjectivity is the fact that the object of study is the same as that which is conducting the study. It is humans studying humans, so it is ultimately impossible to take the "objective position" required for empirical science. For instance, is it *better* for people to focus their lives on work or play? Productivity or joy? It depends on what one thinks is more important, or more *good*. It is a value judgment and it is very difficult, if not impossible to create an objective standard for personal values and study them scientifically. Making this more challenging is the fact that we all (1) have values, (2) think they are superior to other values, and (3) rarely if ever question where they come from or on what basis we think they are valid. The result is that conclusions based, even in part, on our values can never be more than personal opinions, invalid for anyone who doesn't happen to share them.

The social sciences try to rise above these problems in a number of ways. One way is to limit studies to those things which are thought to be more objective. This is done through a process. First, identify the topic or issue to study. Then attempt to operationalize that topic. To operationalize something, it needs to be manifested in a form that is objectively measurable. If it cannot be done, then the topic is dropped for something "better." That is why there are a lot more studies about sex than love. We can measure sex, but it is a lot harder to measure love. However, can we honestly say that sex is that much more important than love? Okay, some folks would say "yes," but you know what I mean. This "tyranny of metrics" (Muller, 2018) causes gross distortions in the field of psychology, as it spends tremendous time and energy on those things that can easily be measured and avoid those that cannot, no matter what their relative importance is to actual human lives. Even worse, the field may find itself minimizing, negatively judging, or denying the reality of things that happen to be hard to measure, like love or spirituality.

Another way to try to be more objective is to *create the appearance* of being objective about subjective phenomena by creating complex research designs, using questionable ways to measure things, and relying on ever-more-amazing and complicated statistics to gather and analyze data from phenomena which are anything but objective. In other words, the social sciences often go through the motions of objective science about things that are not. For instance, a questionnaire about love can be developed, with all sorts of items about romance, affection, and spiritual grace. It could be given to a thousand people, and then the resulting data can be analyzed using complex statistics, but can we really confirm that we have found out anything meaningful about "this thing called love"? Has the questionnaire really captured the "truth" of love? Has it done a good job of drawing out that truth from the people who took it? How would we even know without some gold-standard way of measuring human love with which to evaluate the quality of our questionnaire?

The consequence is that the field produces a lot of results from research for which the ultimate validity is highly questionable.

A third way social science tries to be more objective is to narrow the number of variables it studies for any given phenomenon. This is helpful in trying to be empirical. It will isolate the variables it is trying to look at and measure them in relation to each other. It can then see if variable A effects variable B. However, when it includes variables C, D, and E in the mix, it becomes very difficult, if not impossible, to know what effect variable A might have had. The problem is that in the real world, all of these variables (and many, many more) exist at the same time. So the more tightly limited the study, the less it resembles the real world. More advanced research models and statistics have helped by allowing for more variables to be considered and providing subtle ways of measuring their interactions. However, it still falls far short of how things work in reality, where we don't even know all the variables involved in as seemingly simple a process as deciding where to have breakfast this morning!

These three challenges – narrowing research to what is measurable, objectifying the subjective, and artificially limiting the number of variables that exist in the real world – run rampant in psychology. They all stem from the same source, an emphasis on a system of truth-finding (epistemology) that we call empiricism. Famously born from the work of a series of philosophers from the seventeenth and eighteenth centuries, including John Locke, George Berkeley, and David Hume, among others, this school of thought claimed that all *real* knowledge derives from sense-experience. The basic idea is that we should only believe things to be true if there is compelling, logical, and objective *data* to support the conclusion. In other words, things aren't true just because everyone else thinks so, authority figures say they are, they *feel right*, or well-known books say they are. We are supposed to put aside our feelings, our preconceptions, and social pressure to look at the data from the *real* world and follow it to its logical conclusions.

The logic of this approach is obvious. The early empiricists were responding to a situation in which much of what was thought to be true stemmed from concepts that were increasingly being questioned. Much of science at the time stemmed from authority-based belief systems, such as the humoral and Ptolemaic. Those systems relied on a combination of authority, logic, and superficial observation for their validity. We all know the story. In the era that we now call the Renaissance, newly emerging technologies such as the telescope, the modern mechanical clock, and the printing press provided new data that contradicted old beliefs, spread that knowledge quickly, and inspired new experiment and invention. The new empiricism set off an explosion of research and technology, each validating and invigorating the other, until the modern world as we now know it emerged.

Of course, some of the limits of the empirical approach to truth have already been discussed here. Also, even in the modern world, this is not the only way to go. In the years just prior to John Locke arguing that all truth must stem from sensory experience, subsequently organized by reason, Renee Descartes was saying something quite different. Descartes was a rationalist, believing that we should start with logical, self-evident, foundational ideas and then follow logical steps to their conclusions (1637/1998). The idea was that reality has an intrinsically logical structure, which can be discovered and understood by the human intellect. Rather than gathering raw data and letting them guide him to a given conclusion, he engaged in a purely rational, intellectual exploration, guided by logic. Descartes found he had to start with a position of radical doubt about knowing anything. After all, from a purely logical perspective, you have to start with a fundamental questioning of why we should hold any beliefs as true and then logically test them, one by one. As he worked through all the layers of things people tend to believe without questioning them, Descartes found each in turn to have no solid, underlying basis of truth. Finally, he was left only with the self-evident truth of each person's directly experienced reality of self-consciousness. "I know that I exist because I directly experience it. Everything else (including the existence of the outside world, or even my own body) is conjecture."

This approach, rationalism, is based on what is called deductive reasoning. One starts with a "strong premise" that leads logically to more specific conclusions. This assumes that the premise or intuition is true. Inductive reasoning, by contrast, follows a stricter empirical line, relying on the collection of raw data to lead to a conclusion. If we use deductive reasoning, for instance, we could say that all humans are mortal >> Socrates was a human >> therefore Socrates was mortal. The potential weakness of deductive reasoning is in the premise. It is too easy to start with ideas that seem self-evident to the believer but might not hold up in the bright light of empirical evidence. Or worse, they may be "self-fulfilling prophecies" that become true because the actions of believers *make* them true. This is particularly true in the social sciences. For instance, if a cultural group believes that women are not smart enough to engage in politics, then women will be denied education regarding political matters, rejected from public or private discussion of politics, and discouraged from reading books about politics. The result will be that most women in that culture will be relatively ignorant about political matters and thus *appear* to be not smart enough to engage in politics. That was the case in the Western world prior to the twentieth century, but it's been proven wrong in the years since.

This weakness in deductive reasoning has led most modern research in psychology to be based on inductive reasoning. A researcher has an idea, a hypothesis, that something *might* be true (this is necessary because you have to have some focus for your data collection – it cannot be random). He or she designs a controlled experiment or some other form of research to gather data that will support or reject the hypothesis. This means the phenomena must be objectively measurable with current knowledge and technology and that the study focuses strongly on the hypothesis and does not inadvertently end up measuring other things. These limitations lead to the problems with research discussed earlier.

So empiricism and rationalism are two ways to try and get to truth, each having its strengths and weaknesses. Are there other ways? Why yes, there are. One way that was particularly common in the ancient world and still holds sway in many areas of the world is reliance on authority. In this approach, truth is what the culturally powerful say it is. This typically takes place through traditional institutions such as a religious organization or a government. It can also take place through the soft power of a dominant cultural belief system. Most often, these two forces act in concert, working together to create and reinforce a belief set that maintains order, stability, cohesion, and continuity in a society. The belief set does not have to correspond to empirically known truths to be sustainable; it just has to make sense to its adherents. If the local chieftain says that a local volcano erupted because the god Wonan (totally made up) is angry with the village for not providing enough sacrificial offerings to him, and it is backed up by the other religious and cultural authorities in the village, then it will make sense to the villagers, and it will be their "truth." This form of truth has amazing resiliency, even in the face of contradictory data. People, in general, want truths that make them feel comfortable, correct, and corroborated. They don't like their beliefs to be challenged. They like to feel they are right (in the know), and they like to feel a part of a community of fellow believers (one of the cool kids). Ideas that threaten them with cognitive dissonance, make them feel stupid or ignorant, or lead to them being criticized or rejected by their peers are experienced as dangerous and easily dismissed, no matter what their empirical support.

Let's look at a modern-day example of this. The theory of evolution is a fully established, empirically supported idea that is now foundational to our understanding of human biology and a dozen other scientific fields. Ninety-eight percent of members of the American Association for the Advancement of Science believe that humans evolved exclusively through natural processes. On the other hand, only one-third of all Americans believe that. Seventy-six percent of Americans are aware that scientists believe in evolution, but they are unswayed by this (Pew Research Center, 2019a). This represents a conflict between a "truth" from empiricism and one from religious authority and cultural tradition.

Another way to approach truth finding is what is commonly called pragmatism. This epistemological idea was developed in the late 1800s in America. In some ways, it is a quintessentially American idea. Some of the founders of this doctrine, including William James, Charles Sanders Peirce, and John Dewey, are considered giants in American intellectual history (Menand, 2001). Rather than rely exclusively on logic (rationalism), data (empiricism), or reliance on authority, it asserts that the best we can do in approaching something we can call truth is *if it works*. If the practical application of a precept is effective, then we can call it true. Pragmatism tends to focus on issues involving solving real-world problems, making predictions, and taking effective action rather than metaphysical values or concepts. One way to think about it is as a hybrid of the empirical and rationalistic models. In some ways, it is rational, in that it emphasizes logical relationships between ideas and perceived reality and thus allows for multiple valid ways to conceptualize the world. In other ways, it is more empirical, in that all true knowledge needs to be justified by practical application in the real world – what we commonly call data.

Yet another way to approach truth finding is what is commonly referred to as the postmodern approach. There are many permutations of the basic idea that most, if not all, that people claim as truth is socially constructed. It is highly skeptical of empirical, rational, and even pragmatic approaches to truth, as they are all bound to what some refer to as the myth of objectivity (Lakoff & Johnson, 1980). This myth says that the world is made up of objects that have properties independent from how people experience them, and the categories we create reflect the reality of those properties. Conversely, postmodernism would assert that although objects may have independent qualities, we can never truly know them because all human attempts to do so are mediated through structures of meaning. All assertions of truth are contingent interpretations of something we call reality, and thus the closest we can get to truth is not by judging the correspondence of truth statements to reality but rather by understanding the values, interests, preconceptions of those making such statements.

Not only does postmodernism call into doubt the validity of any truth statements, it is important to remember that there are many ways that people struggle to even be logical and empirical when they are trying to figure out "the truth of things." People typically engage in a variety of cognitive techniques that can keep them in error but also develop the sense of meaning they crave in their lived experience of the world (Levy, 2010). It turns out that there is partial support for many notions that may or may not be true, and people tend to cling to them if they support what they want or already believe to be true. This is especially true in the social sciences, as was noted previously in relation to such dynamics as the self-fulfilling prophecy. There are a number of other ways people easily fool themselves into believing the untrue or exaggerating the partially true. One common dynamic related to this problem is known as the confirmation bias. People tend to seek out information that supports their preexisting beliefs. A closely related error people engage in is called the assimilation bias, in which they manipulate information to fit their existing beliefs. People also engage in hindsight bias when they look back in time and see themselves as almost always having been right, minimizing when they might have been wrong. People also utilize a number of cognitive shortcuts (heuristics) to reach conclusions about things that may not be right. These are very important, because people usually do not have the time to think things through in a thorough way, so to keep life flowing, they think quickly. The problem is that shortcuts often lead to bad destinations. So, for instance, people tend to overemphasize either the first or most recent information they get and disregard the bulk of information that may be more valid or pertinent. People also tend to overemphasize dramatic information and disregard the boring or mundane.

When discussing these dynamics with students, I often use the example of crime. When you ask people if crime is getting worse or better in America, the large majority of students (and people in general) say it is getting worse. They are often shocked to learn that violent crime rates have dropped significantly since the early 1990s. We then discuss the reality that news reports focus on highly dramatic and recent events. Historical crime statistics are boring, while a murder a few miles from your home is decidedly not! Memory of crime in the past fades, while recent events are fresh and emotionally vivid. This consistently gives people the false impression that crime is getting worse and the past was a "golden age" of better behavior (Heinberg, 1989). A quick look at history tends to show that the human world was never really better or less violent, and in many ways, places, and times, it was actually much worse (Pinker, 2011).

On a related note, my professional work leads me to talk with a lot of people in law enforcement and prisons. When the topic of crime rates comes up, I have found (very unscientifically) that almost all of them refuse to believe that crime is going down. I have always found this fascinating. Why is it so hard for people in law enforcement to believe that crime rates are going down?

A possible answer leads us into a field of philosophy a bit different than epistemology. Rather than looking at *how* we know what we know, the field of hermeneutics explores the way we draw meanings from the world around us (Zimmermann, 2015). We can do this at the micro level (text analysis, legal decisions, etc.) or at the macro level (religious, cultural, and even scientific beliefs). The focus of hermeneutics is to look at the various factors that lead to a given belief, so truth is not a thing, it is an event. In this view, we don't see "naked truth" before us; we interpret the world based largely on preunderstandings. These are underlying ways that we conceptualize the world prior to our conscious awareness and subsequent rational analysis of it. They combine to create a holistic experience of truth. I have often wondered, what are the factors, in the lived experience of being a correctional officer, that would lead one to cling tightly to the idea that crime is getting worse? To answer this fully would require a deep exploration of the experience and psyche of each officer, but clearly there is a meaning about criminality and society that many officers share and that may have drawn them to their work in the first place. Such meanings are deeply held and not easily shaken by statistics.

In that sense, hermeneutics is closely connected to phenomenology, which reminds us that our experience of phenomena comes to us already imbued with meaning. When we see a rose, we don't have to think through what it means. The multiple layers of meaning are already there, arising from the physiological/neurological experience of "seeing." Starting with the immediate "knowledge" of its basic form as a rose, we can choose to take our time and explore (bring into more conscious awareness) the other meanings it embodies for us. Does it represent beauty, love, nature, impermanence, a specific lover in our present or past, or all at the same time? How is my individual meaning/experience different from yours? How does ours differ from someone from another culture, another place, another time? It is important to remember that these meanings are vitally important to the human experience, but how could they be surmised from an empirical perspective? How could we measure the pain in one person's heart when they see a rose and it reminds them of a lost love and compare that to the joy in another when the rose reminds them of the rebirth of nature in spring?

There is an old story, which may or may not be true, that when the first Spanish ships approached the shores of the "new world," the Native Americans did not see them until they were very close. Why? Because they had no conceptual framework for the existence of large ships, so their minds simply could not register their reality until the visitors were right on top of them. Factual or not, this story exemplifies the power of preconception to shape reality in the mind of the observer. The social sciences tell us that this power is immensely amplified when the preconceptions are collective rather than individual. A common question at this point is whether hermeneutics is the same as relativity. The answer is no. While there is obviously a strong overlap between the two approaches, relativity stresses the lack of *any* real basis for reality outside the contextual relationship, or point of contact between one phenomenon and another. Hermeneutics posits that there *is* a universally valid basis for meaning. That basis may be a shared cultural foundation or, at a deeper level a shared human experience of life. For instance, there are transcultural experiences such as love, death, sickness, joy, parenthood, childhood, deprivation, plenty, etc. These provide a universal foundational context – adjusted by local cultural circumstances – for interpreting the meaning of various phenomena.

We have reviewed the basics of how we know what we think we know (epistemology), how we use cognitive shortcuts to develop or reinforce our belief system (heuristics), and how we use that imperfect knowledge to develop a sense of meaning in our knowledge (hermeneutics). Now we need to take the next step and explore how our larger understanding of scientific fields changes over time. This book is about what was believed about mental illness in the past, what we believe now, and how those beliefs are likely to evolve in the future. Therefore, it is important to look at how this process of intellectual and cultural change occurs.

The term *revolution* may be the most overused word in science (alongside paradigm), but it is an important one. It refers to a process of significant change, often accompanied by resistance and conflict, ending with a new situation that is quite different. This happens on a regular basis, in societies as well as in science. As we know, incorrect truths can have strong staying power, so it is important to explore the forces that keep them in place, as well as those that lead to change. While many writers have produced work on the process of change in the scientific fields (Alexander Koyre, Carl Popper, Martin Gellender, David Wooton, Susan Wise Bauer, and Richard DeWitt, to name just a few), none has had as much widespread and powerful impact as Thomas Kuhn. In *The Structure of Scientific Revolutions* (1962), he developed an outline for the process of how core beliefs about how the world works change over time. Kuhn criticized the then popular notion that historical progress in science was incremental, progressing steadily through an accumulation of discoveries and inventions.

Instead, as a student of history, he noted that groups of people tend to hold onto established beliefs about things for a long time, even when contradictory evidence is available and increasing. Every field has its own cultural elements that tend to reinforce continuity and resist change. Those elements start with the educational system future researchers learn from, establishing a set of beliefs delineating what questions can be asked (particularly fundamental ones) and what techniques can be utilized to answer them. These forces continue to impact them throughout their careers as they try to land and keep jobs and grants and get their results to be taken seriously or published at all. The social consequences of inclusion and honor versus rejection and ridicule are powerful forces in this process. It turns out that many of the techniques for establishing truth (as we reviewed earlier in the chapter) can continue to support existing beliefs, whether or not they reflect reality in the most accurate way.

Kuhn pointed out that the scientific method does not only produce *real truth*. Because it relies on and is often designed to reinforce a preexisting set of beliefs, research and observation can be framed to find at least some of the results sought by a researcher under the influence of a preexisting schema. For example, bloodletting is now known to be a completely ineffective treatment for schizophrenia, but some patients thus treated will experience spontaneous remission of symptoms, which will make it appear that the treatment was effective, at least for some.

Because, except in very rare cases, it turns out that research does not *establish* the fundamental beliefs in a field but rather is *based* on already existing ones, it is particularly important that a field value truly free enquiry. It must be *open* to the emergence of anomalies in the data, as well as limitations or distortions in its organizing concepts. It should not become complacent, accepting that what *might* be true, based on cherry-picked data, *is* true. This is part of the reason that Carl Popper insisted both that truth statements are descriptions of an underlying, theoretical framework and that any true belief or finding in a field of study must be falsifiable (1935/2002). If there is no way to establish if something is *not* true, it can never be confirmed that it really *is* true. As we will see later in this book, history is full of situations in which a given view of mental illness *seemed* true at the time, based on the data available, as seen from a particular belief set. Given that historical weakness, is there any reason to *not* question our current assumptions and continually seek better ways to square our beliefs with reality?

There is one more piece of this foundation of conceptual understanding of truth to explore, and that is systems theory. Epistemology helps us understand how we decide what is true. Heuristics shows us common shortcuts was take in making these decisions. Hermeneutics emphasizes the importance of the meanings we attach to truth propositions, and the idea of scientific revolutions helps us understand the process by which our truths change over time. Now we are ready to introduce a conceptual metaframework that can carry our enterprise of understanding mental health and wellness into the future. One of the underappreciated thinkers of the twentieth century, Ludwig von Bertalanffy, helped develop a new paradigm regarding human knowledge of the world and its operations (1969). He saw the whole world as a system, including a hierarchy of subsystems and general laws that controlled the processes implicit within the overall system. This approach to understanding how so much of reality is constructed and operates can be utilized to help us understand specific fields, such as clinical psychology, as well as their integrated relationship with other fields, such as neurology and sociology. A number of subsequent academics have worked on systems theory and the social sciences, including people like Ken Wilber, Roy Grinker, and more recently, Margaret Archer.

Systems theory provides the unifying framework for the central thesis of this book, which is that the future of our field lies in a dynamic integration of *both* various knowledge streams *and* various epistemological approaches to truth, within a conceptual model of stratified levels of phenomena. The model of mental illness that will presented here seeks to understand "wholes" rather than just parts. It seeks to develop a theory of mental illness, nested within a hierarchal system of human knowledge, including both individual and collective human functioning and the overall natural and metaphysical world. There are a number of benefits to this approach. It allows for the existence of a real, concrete world while at the same time acknowledging that much of our experience of that world is subjective and co-constructed. It accepts the reality of the natural world but acknowledges that not everything can be reduced to biology or physics. It allows for natural, systemic values and principles but acknowledges that values are largely co-constructed through cultural processes. It allows for the conditioning effects of both nature and nurture but acknowledges the existence of free will and agency. By taking a "metalevel" approach, systems theory is able to allow these different perspectives to coexist. For instance, when thinking about mental illness, biology is a level in the system, and it doesn't make sense to think about biology purely from a postmodern perspective. Neurons and DNA exist whether we are "invested" in their reality or not. However, culture is also a level in the system, and it does make sense to think about culture from a postmodern perspective, including how cultural beliefs impact the functioning of neurons and DNA. Taking a systems approach, we can look at mental illness from both a biological and a cultural viewpoint, considering both empirical and postmodern ways of knowing.

That returns us to the central focus of this book. We will be looking at both the conceptual understanding of and practical beliefs about mental health and mental illness through the combined lenses of history, epistemology, and hermeneutics and their emphases on (1) looking at the foundation of what people believe they know about mental illness and (2) exploring the cultural and local circumstances that create meaning around what people know. To do this, it is necessary to take a historical perspective. These foundations and meanings change over time. That process of change has led to our states of belief about these matters as they stand now and will continue to influence us into the future. In other words, we will look at just how the understanding of mental health and illness has changed over the course of time. We will explore some of the main factors that have driven those changes. We will outline just where we are today. And we will imagine where we are possibly headed into the future.

The importance of taking a historical approach to this task requires some explanation. This approach is appropriate and even necessary because of the dynamic, subjective, and contextual nature of the topic. As discussed at the beginning of the chapter, in some fields of study, there is very limited disagreement on the foundation validity of the subject matter, and as new truths are developed, old ones are simply cast off and forgotten. That is not true in the social sciences. As previously noted, there is a fundamentally subjective or relativistic nature to our field of study. This amplifies the profound disagreement between professionals and lay-people regarding mental health and mental illness. Cultural tradition and resistance to scientific revolution dictates that older ideas about these matters continue to exist and exert their influence on various groups of people, inside and outside the profession. While few people try to claim that mental illness does not exist at all (even Thomas Szasz did not go that far), there is serious debate about how to define it, how to differentiate it from mental health, how to measure it, and how to categorize it. The current debate is robust and grows out of the debates of the past. To change metaphors a bit, history provides the very foundation upon which any new house of understanding can be built.

Not only does the current understanding of mental illness struggle with its (partial) loyalty to the past, it also suffers from the all-to-modern problem of what is commonly called the silo effect (Tett, 2015). This refers to the difficulties that arise when specialists in different areas fail to cooperate, share information or resources, and integrate their findings. Rather than working together, there are often forces in play that support competition and even conflict between groups. This leads to reduced efficiency and poor outcomes. Sadly, this dynamic has developed in the academic and clinical fields over the last two centuries. Instead of seeking some form of unity and integration, there has largely been an atomization within the social sciences, referring to an explosion of different specialties and knowledge areas in both academia and the clinical professions. A hundred years ago, there were fewer than one hundred professional journals in the field of psychology. Today, PsycINFO lists 2,291 journals in its database, covering every imaginable subspecialty. This does not include all the electronic and open-access journals available to researchers for publication of their work. This also does not include journals in other social science fields with an overlap with the field of psychology, ranging from sociology to criminal justice. It also does not include any medically oriented journals that publish research related to psychology, ranging from neurology to genetics. Finally, it does not include the thousands of books published every year in this field, the vast majority of which address specific rather than general topics. This avalanche of new information makes it impossible for anyone to do anything but scratch the surface of professional knowledge and forces most to become highly specialized. Individuals can only know an adequate amount about a very limited number of topics. Professionals in mental health are virtually forced to be specialists.

That has created a sadly ironic situation. For most of the twentieth century, there was a professional demand to specialize in one's conceptual approach to psychology (behaviorism, humanism, psychoanalytic, biological/physiological) and take sides in the professional culture war between nature and nurture to explain human development, functioning, and, of course, mental health and illness. By the 1990s, this infighting had mostly ended, with the general acknowledgment that multiple approaches to understanding psychological functioning had relative merit, and the emergence of the biopsychosocial, integrated model, developed largely by George Engel (1977). This détente and new clinical model offered to provide a solid foundation for a truly integrated model of psychological wellness and pathology. However, at the same time that there was this increasing sense of a conceptual integration in the field, there was *also* a dramatic narrowing of focus in the field, driven by the rise in subspecializations and overall academic output that nobody could really keep up with. The result is that in order to be adequately knowledgeable and proficient, many students (and later professionals) enter specializations and learn more and more about less and less.

Students who enter clinical programs that focus on the assessment and treatment of psychological problems and disorders are often told that the field is moving toward integration but are not provided a solid foundation in a robust metatheory to achieve this integration. Faced with entering a profession in which it is impossible to keep up with the new information coming from a hundred different subfields, many of our students graduate feeling confused, overwhelmed, and underprepared. I am reminded of the famous scene in *I Love Lucy*, where Lucy is working at a chocolate factory, wrapping candies as they come by on a conveyer belt. She has to wrap each one in paper, but the conveyer keeps going faster and faster, and soon she cannot keep up, and she ends up shoving the chocolates into her mouth and her pockets in desperation. In the television scene, the resulting chaos is hilarious, but the situation in our field and with our students is not so funny. It would be one thing if we had a solid conceptual foundation to provide a structure to organize and make sense of the flow of information. The lack of such a structure makes it that much more confusing and overwhelming as the chocolates keep flying past us, faster and faster.

Where is that solid foundation to build our understanding of mental health and mental illness? It turns out we do have it. It has been lying all around us for years. We have thousands of years of recorded human experience. We have hundreds of years of professional development in the field of psychopathology. We have nearly a hundred years of development in epistemology, systems theory, and hermeneutics. We have nearly 30 years of development of the biopsychosocial model. We have our evolving understanding of how scientific revolutions occur. Together, these blocks of knowledge and conceptualization can be used to build a foundation for the future. The key to this endeavor is to seek inclusion and integration. Break down silos – look for congruence and confluence – find ways to conceptually and practically link disparate fields and subfields. A systemic model is the only way to bring different ontologies, epistemologies, and nosologies together under the same roof. It provides the structure of a metasystem for the underlying subsystems and subfields.

The major limitation of such an approach is that while providing such a foundation, it requires that a book like this must limit the amount of detail in each area as we piece them together. If we included everything in one text, or even a lot from each area, the book would be 10,000 pages long and could never be finished, because new information would keep emerging faster than it could be included. Instead, this text provides a brief introduction, designed to describe the problem, review the history of our attempts to solve it, and then use that as a springboard for the next step. The problem we are trying to solve is how to define and describe mental health and mental illness. The next step to its solution is to develop a truly integrated conceptual framework for the explosion of knowledge, which is very exciting but is currently overwhelming us.

One important way we will limit the detail, in order to stay manageably concise and focused, is to strenuously avoid talking about treatment. Including an exploration of the history, controversies, current practices, and future of mental health treatment both would be unnecessarily confusing and would grossly extend the length of the book. Instead, we will stay focused on the understanding of mental illness and health in and of itself. To the extent we will look at treatments, it will only be in how the *choice or development* of those treatments has and continues to reflect people's *understanding* of mental illness. Again, this runs counter to how students are often taught in our professional schools. They are typically taught treatments, with relatively little reflection on the concepts underlying those treatments. Since the end of the demand that therapists enter the field with a specific orientation (behavioral, psychodynamic, and humanistic being the most common), our training programs have become increasingly eclectic but lacking in a well-developed, integrated model of psychopathology. Schools teach the *Diagnostic and Statistical Manual of the American Psychiatric Association* (DSM), they teach counseling/psychotherapy skills, and they may introduce students to a few models of therapy. More recently, they will often make some space for the biopsychosocial and recovery models as well.

But the teaching of foundational theory is secondary to that of practical application and, in some cases, ignored all together.

There are two fundamental problems with this approach. The first is that offering brief introductions to a wide variety of theoretical models provides no solid foundation for the student to understand what he or she is doing – it is an aimless mish-mash of ideas and practices. Second, there is often no clear differentiation of theories of mental health/wellness from theories of psychotherapy. Although there is obviously substantial overlap between the two, theories of psychotherapy were developed and are taught with very different aims, concerns, and fundamental questions than are the related but different theories of mental health/illness. In clinically orientated programs, the emphasis tends to be on theories of psychotherapy, so the basic ideas are taught with little to no connection to their historical origins in beliefs about human nature and psychopathology. The result is graduates who are technically proficient but often lacking in a depth of knowledge in their chosen field. As noted at the beginning of this chapter, this is fine for practitioners in fields that have a solid ontological and epistemological foundation. Students of engineering have no need to explore the historical roots of their field to properly understand and question the current *truths* of their field. In fact, doing so would likely be a confusing waste of time in their studies. I am not a student of engineering, but I doubt if anybody in that department has seriously doubted the existence of buildings or ships! It is the *dynamic uncertainty* regarding the ontological and epistemological foundation of the mental health field that makes it necessary to take the journey this book proposes.

So we are ready to take off. How have humans approached the issue of what is crazy and what is sane? What answers have they come up with over the years, and why? Where does that story stand today? And what direction are we heading in the future? At each point, we will look at ontological issues (what is reality?), epistemological issues (how do we know it is real?), and hermeneutic issues (what does that reality mean to people?). We will explore these historical changes through the lens of our understanding of scientific revolutions (paradigms), and then utilize a systems model perspective to offer a vision of the future of an idea.

OUTLINE OF CHAPTERS

This story of the shifting paradigms of understanding and subsequent changes to nosology, assessment, and (just a little) treatment starts with the emergence of characteristically human cognition and society in the Neolithic age. Relatively little is known about this time, so it is difficult to figure out just what people thought in regard to mental health and illness. There are some clues, though, from still-existing tribal culture as well as from anthropology and a few other disciplines. What we do not have is a well-developed history, written by those who lived through it. Thus, we will call this the Prehistoric era.

The next shift came with the development of large-scale, complex societies and religious organizations. A clearer record emerges of what people thought about themselves and the forces they saw shaping their world, including their concepts of mental health and disorder. They left a more direct, written record of these dynamics, often through the lens of the mythological systems that they created. Thus, this will be called the Mythological era.

The next shift came with the Ancient Greek development of conceptualizations of the natural and human world beyond the mythological and instead based on reason and logic. For the first time in human history, we will see concepts of mental illness conceptualized as separate from cultural or religious conceptualizations and becoming medicalized. This dramatic change set the foundation for what would later emerge as the modern perspective on mental illness, and we will call it the Classical era.

The next shift came with the end of the Roman Empire, when the Western world became focused on the development of a Christian worldview. It retained the medical beliefs of the Greeks and Romans but tried to integrate them within a Christian theology. We will call this the Middle Ages era.

The next shift includes the combination of a rediscovery of Greek philosophy, the new advances coming from the Muslim world, and the philosophical and scientific advancements of the European world. This dramatic change was driven by a number of historical developments, including culturally disruptive wars and religious fissions. Europe in particular was transformed through this process, and the understanding of mental health and illness began to separate from its long dormancy in the classic humoral system and Christian theology. We will call this the Renaissance era.

The next shift grew out of the Renaissance and drove the emergent changes of that era to a new level. The resulting advances built upon those of the previous in regard to ways of knowing and beliefs and practices in politics, economics, philosophy, religion, medicine, art, and literature. They reflected a more rational and empirical approach to human knowledge. The study of mental health began to separate itself from general medical science and practice. We will call this the Enlightenment era.

The next shift involved the development of psychiatry as a fully separate medical discipline, based on observation and professional structures of training and treatment. At the same time, the industrial revolution and other forces were radically transforming how people lived and what they thought about mental health. The academic field of psychology began to emerge from philosophy and theology, with its own independent observations about human nature. We will call this the Modern era.

The next shift involved the emergence of psychology as an academic discipline and its battle with psychiatry for dominance in the field of understanding and treating mental illness. Psychology splintered into various subfields, each with its own understanding of mental health, placing them at odds with each other. At the same time, the limitations of modernism sparked a revolution in how many people conceptualized truth and reality itself. This shift also included the accelerating development of knowledge and its application within the biological sciences in the twentieth century. It involves dramatic developments in the fields of neurology, neuroimaging, psychopharmacology, genetics, and a dozen other related fields. We will call this the Postmodern era.

The next shift included advances in these areas of knowledge over the first two decades of the twenty-first century. The mental health field has grown and become more professionalized in general. The battles between the behaviorists, the humanists, and the psychoanalysts have mostly been left behind, as have some of the battles between the nature camp and the nurture camp regarding human nature. The field has become more interested in mental health and wellness, is embracing the populations it serves, is becoming more multicultural, and has seen neuroscience emerge as a powerful force in how we understand the brain and its role in maintaining mental health or triggering mental illness.

Finally, we will look at the field as it stands at this point in time and where we may be headed. This involves the most recent findings from cross-disciplinary research and the need to integrate various professional, academic, and cultural fields and movements into a more holistic understanding of mental health and mental illness. We will show how this movement is radically transforming the field, currently by challenging the primacy of any one approach and thus creating disruption, but over time, by leading to a more organized system of interdisciplinary conceptualization and practice.

As with all evolutions in conceptualization and practice, there is no simple, linear progression of understanding, acceptance, and practice. How or even *if* such evolution emerges will be strikingly different from place to place, group to group. There will be periods of stagnation or regression. The Middle Ages were such a time. Following the Classical era, sparked by the Greek and Roman thinkers and doctors, there was a fifteen-hundred-year period of time when the world changed relatively little in its understanding or treatment of mental illness. There are still groups today that appear to have changed little in their understanding and practice from those earlier times, begging the postmodern question of whether conceptual change actually reflect something called "progress" or simply changes in cultural perspectives. But that does not change the fact that revolutions occur. They reflect some form of *growing edge* of human understanding and beg a dynamic question whether they reflect a *better* understanding of reality or just a different one. They have an impact on virtually all people, in virtually all places, even when that impact is to inspire attempts to reject the change, isolate from the change, or integrate the change into existing modes of thought and belief.

An example of this type of challenge, of major importance to the conceptualization of mental health and illness, is the battle over evolution. As noted previously, this lens of understanding of human nature, development, and thus mental health and illness is well established as a scientific fact, yet it is rejected by two-thirds of Americans and many people around the world, especially those with a strong religious faith. The question is how or even whether this or any revolution of understanding taking place in academia will become integrated into the much larger *public consciousness*. Will the growing scientific understanding of human nature and mental illness float above people's heads like the island of Laputa in *Gulliver's Travels*? Or instead, will academia draw this island down and make it inhabitable by the wider public?

Obviously, my personal bias is for the latter. This is not just a story about a particular academic and professional discipline, it is about us – human beings – about how we think about who we are, what *makes us tick*, what it looks like when human nature is functioning well, and what it looks like when it goes bad. Ultimately, the theory and practice of psychiatry and clinical psychology need to correspond, at a fundamental level, with the general public's conceptualization of human nature. For mental health professionals to be effective, to be able to actually help people who are suffering, the public and professional understanding of what we think and, subsequently, what we think people should do (including taking medication, going to therapy, or living more healthy lifestyles) needs to be in sync.

So what follows is an exploration of the long history of that interplay of public and professional views of mental health and mental illness. As we move closer to our current time, there will be greater detail offered regarding the main professional positions on the issue. Finally, we will propose an updated model of mental health to help lead us into the future, taking a wider, more integrated view of the subject and its place in the spectrum of human knowledge than has previously been considered. Let's begin.

CHAPTER 1

PREHISTORY

In our review of the history of mental illness, it makes sense to start at the very beginning – that is, at the beginning of the human race. The world did not start with humanity in mind; it came into existence out of a swirling cloud of interstellar debris about 4.5 billion years ago. For the first half a billion years or so, it was molten and volcanic and held little oxygen. However, it was cooling down and, around 4 billion years ago, formed a crust and began to allow liquid water to pool. The first evidence of life emerged 3.5 billion years ago in the form of self-replicating, complex amino acids. Over the next 2 billion years, the world went through the eras of the arthropods, the fish, the amphibians, the reptiles (highlighted by our much-beloved dinosaurs), and finally the mammals. The first recognizable humans emerged about 2 million years ago.

For those who wonder how animals could have sprung so quickly from the primordial swamp, it should be noted that life on Earth remained microscopic for the first 3 billion years. It took another 50 million years to go from the beginning of multicellular life to the Cambrian Explosion, about 540 million years ago.

As previously noted, humans developed about 2 million years ago with the appearance of *homo erectus*. They then spent the vast majority of the subsequent time hunting and foraging in small groups. About 200,000 years ago, our modern form, *homo sapiens*, emerged in Africa and began to migrate through Eurasia around 60,000 years ago, replacing all the other *homo* species. Around 50,000 years ago, early humans began to leave traces of their psychological lives that reflected a conscious, self-reflective mind. Around 30,000 years ago, in the Upper Paleolithic period, humans began leaving evidence, in the form of cave art, of shamanistic religious thinking and practices, suggesting more advanced consciousness, art, mythology, and complexly structured society (Lewis-Williams, 2002).

Ideally, our formal story about mental health should start there, with self-descriptions of the mental states of early humans. The problem with telling this story is that until humans invented writing, about 5,000 years ago, what we have is what archeologists refer to as prehistory. With no written records to refer to, no recordings to study, we rely on clues – a chipped rock here, an ideographic cave painting there – to tell us all that can be known. The good news is that the field of archeological research has developed tremendously over the last 100 years and now provides a surprising amount of evidence, so much more is known about early human history than previously.

EVOLUTION AND EPISTEMIC AUTHORITY

The bad news is that there is a very limited archeological record of anything directly related to mental health or illness. The one exception to this is the practice of trephining, but before the text gets to that story, it is important to take a step back to epistemology again. This chapter has begun with the assertion of a 2.5-million-year history of human existence. That means it starts with a dramatically controversial theory to organize the exploration of its central topic. That theory is evolution. This immediately begs a number of ontological and epistemological questions. Does evolution exist, and how would one know, one way or another? Should this be approached empirically? If so, what natural evidence is required? Basically, to support the validity of the theory, there needs to be evidence that populations change over generations in response to environmental forces. There should be data indicating intermediate species, as well as the emergence of entirely new species. The good news for those who believe in evolution is that there is overwhelming evidence to support the reality of all three of those requirements (change, intermediate species, and new species), thus providing support for evolution as a general and foundational natural process that is very real and the source of human development as a species (Dawkins, 2004; Gould, 1993). This is why it has become the cornerstone of the biological sciences.

The primary competing theory, creationism, has virtually no support in the scientific community (National Academy of Sciences, 1999). There is no evidence, from the research in paleontology, geology, biology, or any other related scientific field, to support the idea that life originated approximately 6,000 years ago and has maintained itself in basically the same form from its beginnings. As a result, creationism is not considered *real science*. Not only is there no empirical support for creationism, it is not testable by the methods of science and thus is not falsifiable. Instead, it relies on authoritative belief, which cannot be superseded by new data or logical analysis.

From an empirical perspective, evolution is the clear winner in this competition, and this book will move forward on the assumption that evolution, not creationism, is *true*. However, it is important to point out that the debate between the two models represents a classic competition between two different epistemologies, because the tension between these two approaches to truth is central to the subject matter of this book. The belief in evolution is supported by empiricism, and the belief in creationism is supported by reliance on authority, sometimes called epistemic authority (EA) (Zagzebski, 2012). The first demands observable, naturally occurring data, that leads to a conclusion. The second requires an established authoritative source to provide the truth statement. The authoritative source for creationism is, of course, the Bible and other religious texts, as well as the statements of various religious authorities.

The differing epistemological foundations explain why both beliefs can exist at the same time – the arguments for their truths are completely different and thus unpersuasive to adherents of the other. The question then becomes, is there a basis for picking one epistemology over the other? Can we make an argument for either EA or empiricism being a better way to approach truth? Yes, we can make a strong case that empiricism is a *better* approach to truth than EA. The main reason is that, while empiricism relies on objective data to guide us logically to a conclusion, EA relies on a judgment of the veracity of the authority itself. This means that all truth statements stemming from authority are circular or tautological arguments and are vulnerable to any refutation of the legitimacy of the authority. Compare these two arguments. Why should I believe in evolution? Because over one hundred and fifty years of fossil (and other) evidence supports the theory, without a single contradictory piece of evidence emerging from any area of research related to the subject. Why should I believe in creationism? Because the Bible says it's true, and the Bible was written by God. How do you know the Bible was written by God? Because the Bible and religious authority figures say so. Could it have been written by someone else who wanted us to think the text had the authority of God? Yes, but I don't believe that. Which argument is more persuasive? Unless one is predisposed by religious faith and cultural tradition to believe in the divine authorship theory, the evolutionary argument, based on empiricism is much stronger.

That being said, there is an argument to be made for EA. This may come as a surprise to many who assumed that in the modern age, with the Enlightenment behind us, serious academics would universally reject reliance on authority as a strong or even minimally legitimate epistemological basis for truth. Linda Zagzebski (2012) took on this challenge. She agrees that EA is not taken seriously by modern epistemologists, but she thinks they are misguided. She points out that the rise of empiricism and rejection of EA were largely based on the Enlightenment's focus on the autonomous self. The more we empower individuals to make their own decisions about what is true, the more we come to distrust authority. The problem, as she describes it, is that this situation leaves us with no way to understand a wide variety of beliefs, including many religious ones that people continue to rely on, based on our trust of authority. She asserts that it is both rational and unavoidable that people have trust in the truth provided by authority figures. She points to self-reflective consciousness, the ability to think about ourselves, as a basis for the legitimacy of EA. The self-reflective person is naturally committed to a belief in authority (I don't know everything, and there are others who know more than me), and it is impossible to be completely epistemologically self-reliant (I can't test every possible truth assertion). Thus, we can and need to be able to trust ourselves to assess and trust certain external, authoritative sources of truth.

This is an important point, because the farther we go back in time, the more truth statements about mental illness tended to be based on EA. This is particularly true in the early phases of human history. Before the Enlightenment, beliefs about mental illness were typically *not* derived from systematic observation or empirical research. They grew out of heuristic reasoning and preexisting cultural beliefs. These beliefs were embraced, communicated, and enforced by authority figures in their respective cultures. These people would have been shamans, elders, chieftains, etc. It was their responsibility to maintain and implement the *truths* of the group. This dynamic is, of course, still in force today. People rely on cultural authority figures to maintain the integrity of their groups by conserving the *truth* of the world and carefully managing any change to that truth. As long as the known facts and beliefs are not challenged by new facts and beliefs, they can be maintained with relatively little change for hundreds or even thousands of years.

The emergence of empiricism was the result of just such a clash of new information with preexisting truths. During the late Middle Ages, increasing trade with the Far East and the Middle East brought new ideas to the West. Technological and methodological developments created new information as well. New concepts

about reality challenged the existing ones, and the new ones had actual data to
back them up. Anyone with access to a telescope could see the moons of Jupiter
that proved that not all the heavenly bodies orbited the Earth. At the same time,
advances in mathematics and experimental design brought more aspects of reality
into the realm of scientific study. By the time Charles Darwin came along in the
nineteenth century, the world was used to modern science announcing amazing
new ways of understanding reality, and the forces of received wisdom, or EA were
increasingly being doubted. Like previous revolutionary ideas such as a heliocentric
solar system, the new idea of evolution still produced a great deal of resistance. It
still does. However, like other scientific truths, it has overwhelming data to support
its validity.

Therefore, this book will proceed on the belief that evolution is ontologically
real and epistemologically valid. Further, we will proceed on the belief that evolution is a natural process that led to the emergence and development of the human
species. The generally accepted storyline of that development was that humans
evolved from small, apelike creatures that probably lived in small bands and were
hunter-gatherers. As areas of the African forest began to thin out, the only way
those early creatures could survive was by developing a big brain. Being smart was
their evolutionary advantage. Cognitive development was excellent for a number
of vital functions, including planning and coordination of hunting, food gathering,
and various communal activities such as cooking, food distribution, shelter building,
defense against predators, etc. As the communal life of these small, slow, but very
smart primates became more complex, basic rules of behavioral norms and even
collective attitudes and beliefs would naturally develop. Unlike "lower" animals,
in which such things are dictated by instinct, in "higher" primates today, many
of these rules are learned by youngsters, reinforced by parents and other elders,
and can be practiced flexibly within the group, and individuals are punished for
breaking them. It would make sense that very early on, individuals who exhibited
"strange" or "unusual" attitudes, beliefs, or behavior would cause concern and/or
upset in the community, leading to attempts to "help" or "punish" the individual.
In rare cases, the individual's differences from the group might be received as a sign
of superior functioning or insight, which could lead to special treatment and status,
perhaps as a leader or a shaman. More often, though, nonconformity would have
been seen as a problem, especially if it was associated with reduced functioning
(poor cooperation skills) or was in distinct contrast to established group beliefs.

TWO TYPES OF EVOLUTION

The concept of evolution is interesting not only because it produces so much controversy but because it is used in so many ways. Classical evolution refers to the
natural process by which biological populations genetically and physiologically
change in response to their environment. Evolutionary success is measured by survival, failure by death. This is an important point, because there is no such thing
as populations getting better and better, there is only survival or death. Evolution
is more Machiavellian than humanistic. Organisms that can respond effectively

to the challenges and opportunities of their environment thrive. For instance, the dramatic increase in size and change in structure of the brain in early hominids, a process called encephalization, provided the neurological and cognitive engine for behavioral changes that provided significant improvements in survivability. These changes include things like bipedalism, speech, use of symbols, etc. So far, this is a pretty standard understanding of evolution. Colin Renfrew (2007) refers to this as the *speciation phase* of human development. It reflects the development of basic cognitive capacities tied more or less directly to physiological evolution.

This phase is very slow, taking place over millions of years, but it provided the biological foundation for subsequent cultural changes, which he refers to as the *tectonic phase* of development. More commonly referred to as social evolution, this phase began to accelerate around 100,000 years ago. It is a much faster process than biological evolution and led to dramatic changes in how humans lived, compared to our (distant) primate cousins in the animal kingdom. While speciation has taken up most of the conversation about human evolution, especially in the public sphere, it is within the tectonic phase that most of the really interesting *action* has taken place in our evolution. It is the changes in collective social/cultural beliefs, traditions, and subsequent practices that have provided the most dramatic development of characteristically human ways of life and survival advantages. In other words, it is the evolution of culture versus the evolution of the brain itself. That does not mean that the mind, the creator of culture, is a completely separate entity from the brain. Instead, a better analogy, still only partly true, is that the human psyche is like a computer, with the brain being the hardware and culture being the software. The brain does the work, and what we call culture prescribes what work gets done and how it is to be done.

The idea of this two-part evolution has become increasingly accepted in the social sciences. The reason it has become important to the social sciences is that it turns out that the dynamics that drive biological evolution have a parallel reality and impact in the social and cultural spheres (Frank, 1998; Grinin, Markov, & Korotayev, 2013). This is likely because the two foci of evolution have an overlapping variable, the mind. What we call the mind is the activity of the brain and thus directly reflects its functioning. The mind does not exist without the brain, but it is not exactly the same thing *as* the brain, in the same way the informational output of a computer is impossible without the physical computer but is not the same thing *as* the computer. Culture represents the collective output of many minds coexisting in a social setting with a sense of mutual identity and thus developing collective beliefs and practices. It cannot exist without the individual minds, but it is not the same thing *as* individual minds. The three spheres of functioning are inextricably linked and must therefore share some common, naturally occurring dynamics. The most foundational of these is evolution. They are all flexible (changeable) over time, responding to the demands and opportunities of their surrounding environments, but can only do so within the constraints and capabilities of the others.

This brings us back to the concept of systems theory. In this case, we can think of brain > mind > culture as a system. Each is connected to, reliant upon, and, to some extent, overlapping with the others within a holistic, functional system. Trying to understand one without the others is as limited as studying computer design, but not software coding. You get part of the picture but not how the whole computer system works. In regard to our current topic, mental health and mental illness, it is important that we consider not just how the brain is embedded within the mind or how the mind is embedded within culture but how all three are embedded within a natural environment, which itself is always changing. The entire system is thus involved in the process of evolution. The question then becomes, what are the historical roots of the human experience of mental health and mental illness within the context of this unfolding evolutionary process?

COGNITIVE ARCHEOLOGY

This is a very important but very difficult question to answer. There is very little concrete data to answer it. Instead, there are clues and guesses. They lead to theories, which come to us from archeology, specifically cognitive archeology (Mithen, 1996; Renfrew, 2007; Renfrew & Bahn, 2016). This subfield seeks to understand the origins and development of human thinking and symbolic behavior. It focuses on what we can discover about ancient people's cognition, values, belief systems, and resulting political and social structures, as well as other behavioral dynamics. In other words, it uses material evidence to try and identify symbolic structures and subsequent adaptive behavior. Because very little of it can be linked *specifically* to mental health or illness, I will provide a brief overview of cognitive archeology, focusing on where linkages to ideas about mental health and mental illness are most appropriate.

The tectonic phase of development, focused on the evolution of the mind and culture, began in earnest around 100,000 years ago, produced a profound emergence of consciousness during the Paleolithic Period, but then went into hyper drive closer to 12,000 years ago. That was when early humans entered what is generally known as the Neolithic Revolution. While it looked different in various places, it typically involved the transition from a hunter-gatherer lifestyle to a more sedentary, village-based life, with agriculture, animal domestication, more sophisticated use of fire, more permanent buildings, production of pottery and art, and the development of more complex religious beliefs and practices. Renfrew and Bahn (2016) point out that sedentism (the practice of living in one place for a long time) was actually a necessary precursor for many of these developments, including intergroup trade, much larger cultural groups, more complex hierarchies and other social groupings, and individual specialization. All of these changes worked together to provide better common defense and food production. This gave the groups who moved in the direction of sedation a distinct advantage not only over the various challenges of the natural environment but over other human groups. More and more over time, human groups who practiced sedentism would enjoy tremendous success and represent an increasing percentage of the human population.

In regard to cognitive changes, the developments around that time likely included more extensive and sophisticated language, use of symbols, and self-consciousness as well as more complex and individually differentiated self-identities based on one's place in the economic, political, and social groupings within a given cultural population (Pinker, 1994; Dennett, 2017). In regard to language development, it probably included developing grammatical structures that reflected new types of cognitions, including a clear differentiation of past, present, and future. It also allowed for better communication about and the development of complex practices involving abstract thought. We know this development included ideas and practices involving religion (Lewis-Williams, 2002). The question is whether it also involved ideas and practices regarding mental health and disorder.

In order to begin answering that question, we need to keep digging into the cognitive developments that were occurring at that time. For instance, one of the core postulates of cognitive archeology is that an understanding of human cognition *cannot* be separated from the study of human society in general, because the two are deeply intertwined (Renfrew & Bahn, 2016). Shared beliefs about a wide variety of things are necessary for the effective functioning of a social group. Ideas about the correct or proper way to think, feel, and behave develop on a collective level, and deviations from those ideas are likely to be met with resistance, punishment, and correction. Even before the development of formal language, there must have been norms of behavior that developed in different groups, and deviation from them would have negative consequences, such as physical attack, shunning, and, in extreme cases, expulsion from the community. Without a written record of ancient people's language, we do not know what words might have been used to communicate culturally acceptable cognition and its censure, but we know that spoken language is not even necessary for this process to occur. We can see this in some of our closest existing cognitive relatives in the animal kingdom, including chimpanzees (Goodall, 2010).

Obviously, there would be differences from group to group regarding just what those behaviors and beliefs would be. Local conditions and the vagaries of history would lead to different religious, social, and political conventions, or cultural norms. These would need to reflect real conditions – gods that live in volcanoes need real local volcanoes to justify their existence. The group beliefs would also need to reflect adaptive behavior patterns, such as effective hunting, building, and agricultural strategies. Beliefs that strayed too far from these reality-based schemas would not only threaten group coherence but could easily be deemed irrational and potentially dangerous or fatal not just to the individual but to the entire group. This dynamic would lead to a conception of mental health as reflecting an alignment with what we now call groupthink. Staying *in line* would be thought of as sane and healthy by the group and would elicit more social support, lower levels of conflict with others, and thus a greater sense of peace, well-being, and success (higher status) within the group. The old truism "go along to get along" is true for a reason. Even in our hyperindividualized modern societies, in which we can choose to live virtually autonomous lives, avoiding intimate contact with others by staying in our houses and cars and staring at television and computer screens, we are still vulnerable to social ostracism through unconventionality. Imagine what it would be like to live in a much smaller-scale society, without all those technological buffers between the individual and others, what the level of pressure would be to fit in and the powerful reaction that being *different* would elicit. Some of the earliest words created probably reflected judgments of others being "of sound mind" or "crazy."

The bottom line here is that from the earliest times, it is quite likely that mental health was equated with cultural conformity.

A closely related concept is rank order. In general, the higher (smarter) the primate, the more they appear to be aware of, concerned about, and taking action in regard to the pecking order in their group. Obviously, many animal species engage in rank ordering (thus the origin of the term pecking order), but no species spends more time and effort engaged in more complex thoughts, feelings, and behavior related to this phenomenon than humans. At times, it can seem as if this is all we care about. We know from primate studies that where one stands in social status effects one's neurological circuitry (Noonan et al., 2014) and functional well-being, including access to food, mating opportunities, and even overall health (Shively & Day, 2015). In humans, we know that perceived social status impacts our overall functionality (Marmot, 2005), as well as our overall sense of psychological well-being (Haught, Rose, Geers, & Brown, 2015). Much more will be said about this dynamic in later chapters, but it is enough here to point out that, given its importance to primates, social status must have been an important factor in early humans' sense of psychological well-being. Not only that, but as early societies became more complex, the attainment and maintenance of social status must have become more complicated and, in some ways, more challenging.

Another important factor in the development of a working concept of mental health in these very early societies was the cognitive development of self-consciousness. The capacity for reflection upon one's own thinking, emotions, and behavior apparently developed extensively during the Neolithic period and introduced a number of important dynamics related to mental health. It would allow one to *pretend* to go along with the group but actually think and feel quite differently than the group wants or expects (Dennett, 2017). This is the "they would think I was crazy if they knew what I really thought" dynamic. It also leads to a variety of social emotions, such as sadness, shame, and even the complexity of what we think of as depression for not feeling *able* to stay in line with the expectations of others. This can lead to pretending to feel okay in front of others to avoid negative reactions from others, including pity or revulsion, and thus further shaming. The resulting *split self* then becomes a further source of suffering. The person doesn't feel whole or integrated. There is now a real self, a false self, an ideal self, and a despised self. The person wants to feel good about herself (self-esteem or healthy narcissism), but that is not possible without playing out several psychological games (defenses), such as conflating the ideal self with the real self and refusing to acknowledge the despised self (clinical narcissism). In other words, self-consciousness is the birthplace of neurosis. Without self-consciousness, there can still be psychological pain (primates and other mammals exhibit signs of sadness and even depression when mistreated or after a loss of a close support figure), but self-consciousness amplifies psychological suffering significantly. People are cognitively forced to *reflect* on their pain. Why did this happen to me? What did I do to deserve this? Am I an inferior human being because I think/feel/behave this way? While highly speculative, what this discussion suggests is that self-consciousness must have been an important factor in both the development of what could be called mental disorders and also awareness of it as a concept, both self-reflectively (what is wrong with me?) and as social judgment and cultural concept (what is wrong with him/ her?). While it is common in the field of psychology to think of neurosis as a uniquely modern phenomenon (and obviously has unique modern manifestations), what is proposed here is that various forms of psychological suffering will occur whenever self-conscious individuals find themselves in conflict with their society.

Self-consciousness has profound adaptive benefits, of course. First of all, it should be noted that self-consciousness is an emergent quality that follows from consciousness itself – the capacity to engage in other, increasingly complex and challenging elements of cognition – sensory input, emotional response to that input, analysis, decision making, and subsequent behavioral choice. The progression of this cognitive complex will naturally lead to conscious awareness of the self doing the cognition – thinking about thinking. This has all the advantages of having managerial oversight of a complex organization. One can work with a conscious idea about what one is trying to accomplish (often keeping oneself and one's social group alive) and actively direct the process of gathering pertinent information (while ignoring unimportant information), drawing conclusions from that information (this would be a good day to start planting), and directing behaviors more likely to lead to success (get those bags of seed out of the storage hut and get your whole family out there planting them). Then you can see how that behavior worked (almost none of the seeds sprouted) and reevaluate the whole process for improved outcomes in the future (maybe I picked the wrong day to start planting – what do I need to know to pick a better one next time?).

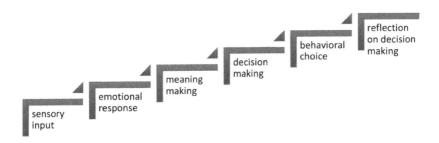

This is based on the evolutionary principle that response flexibility is generally an effective adaptive tool. While it comes at a heavy price in terms of investment in a big brain that burns a lot of energy, the ability to adjust behavior to different circumstances versus relying on preprogrammed response patterns (instinct) is powerful. It is why humans can and do live in almost every part of our planet, in dramatically different conditions, while most animals can only survive within a very narrow range of conditions. Self-consciousness is the ultimate tool for adaptive functioning. Our success (more than 7 billion humans alive on the planet and growing) is proof of the adaptive power of big-brain self-consciousness. It is extremely likely that it developed along with the growing complexity of human society. In other words, the more complex and multifaceted the cultural environment, the more self-consciousness would be *demanded* for individual and group success. So the benefits of self-consciousness (adaptability) would outweigh the costs (neuroses), but it was a double-edged sword. The twin difficulties of psychological suffering through negative self-reflection and negative judgment by others probably emerged alongside the development of consciousness itself.

Another closely related concept is what is typically referred to as *theory of mind*. At some point in time, likely as part of the development of self-consciousness, humans began to understand that other people had a set of beliefs, feelings, and desires separate and different from their own. It is connected to self-consciousness because the conscious awareness of one's own mental states would naturally lead to reflection upon the possible differentness of others. This would lead to thoughts and feelings about that differentness. The result would be judgments about one's own mental state in comparison to others, as noted a few paragraphs ago. This moves beyond the pragmatics of whether one's mental state leads to good outcomes in farming, hunting, etc. It moves human groups toward a cultural situation in which certain thoughts, feelings, attitudes, and behavioral patterns are deemed *normal* or *good*, because the assessment of one's own mental state in comparison with another's mental state requires a separate set of beliefs regarding mental states in general. Whatever authority structure existed in a given place and time would be in a position to reward mental states the group deems normal or optimal and punish those it deems abnormal or problematical. This could well have been the beginning of what we now call abnormal psychology. When it emerged is still a mystery, but there is reason to guess it developed along with art and religion.

The reason is that many of the same cognitive abilities are required for self-consciousness, art, and religion. Steven Mithen (1996) outlines these abilities as they relate to the production of art. They include (1) the use of symbols to represent not only specific things but entire classes of things, (2) the intentional use of symbols to communicate, and (3) the ability to mentally displace time and space (drawing a picture of something that happened before). Similar abilities are necessary for the creation of religion, but we can add the ability to *consciously reflect upon* mortality, the reasons things happen, and possible supernatural forces or entities that make things happen. All these cognitive abilities reflect a core ability to mentally separate oneself from things that are happening in the moment and think *about* them. These would include the problems, mysteries, and challenges of life, including mortality, and imagining solutions or answers for them (Lewis-Williams, 2002).

EVOLUTIONARY PSYCHOLOGY

One question that often arises in regard to evolution and human psychology is, if the two are directly connected, then how could mental illness have developed over the course of our history? Shouldn't it have been generally *selected out*, given the assumption that mental illness would generally reduce adaptive fitness? David Buss refutes this idea. He asserts that there are a lot of psychological phenomena that *present* as problematical but are not really evolutionary dysfunctions because they are not a failure of evolution (2008). In other words, the psychological systems are functioning as they evolved to function. One common problem, though, is that there is such an extreme difference between modern life and the conditions under which the phenomena evolved that they no longer work the way they are supposed to. This is akin to the diet dilemma. It is not a failure of evolution that we have health problems when we eat too much sugar, fat, and salt. Our bodies evolved when these substances were very difficult to attain. They are good for us but now cause problems because we still crave them (evolution) and thus eat too much, since they are easily available.

Some types of depression and anxiety could well be seen in this light. Many if not most humans today deal with very different stressors than our ancestors did. We may live more sedentary (in the bad sense of the word) lives, experience less kin support, work longer hours doing less directly fulfilling work, experience endless exposure to guilt/envy/lust/shame-inducing mass media, deal with much larger groups of fellow humans in smoggy, noisy, fast-moving cities, etc. While many of us are fortunate and don't have to experience as much acute stress as our ancestors did (such as being attacked by a lion or a neighboring tribe), we likely experience more chronic stress and unhealthy lifestyle choices, leading to a variety of health problems, including psychological distress and impairment. While there are many ways that modern life represents a vast improvement on the past (please don't take away my television, internet, indoor plumbing, restaurants, and hospitals – I beg you), there are other ways, described by so many, that it causes a lot of suffering.

One source of problems related to evolutionary advances is psychological mechanisms that, on average, are functional, but in *some cases* the *costs* outweigh the *benefits*. Paranoia is the word we use to describe an undue level of concern over possible or misperceived danger. The challenge is that it makes perfect sense for humans to exaggerate danger. False positives for danger don't kill you. False negatives do. It is better to be wrong a hundred times about that rustling in the bushes in the backyard being a prowler than to blissfully ignore it and get killed by an intruder. For most of us, this is not a big deal (although advertisers, politicians, and the internet in general love to prey on this weakness), but for some, the mechanism operates at a much higher rate or intensity than average, and thus the costs end up outweighing the benefits for them.

Another source of difficulty related to functional psychological processes is the experience of subjective suffering or distress that can coexist with a phenomenon that actually is working well. Anxiety, sadness, shame, guilt, and loneliness all *feel* bad. A whole slew of emotions and other psychological states feel bad, but that is how they are *evolutionarily intended* to feel. These (and other) emotions and states evolved to help coordinate mental activity and influence motivation and teleological direction to engage in functional, adaptive behavior (Al-Shawaf, Conroy-Beam, Asao, & Buss, 2015). Anxiety serves to coordinate awareness of threats and motivates us to avoid dangerous situations. Sadness is the natural ancillary to interpersonal loss, which we experience as emotionally rewarding because social cooperation leads to increased survival chances. In other words, we feel the sadness of loss because we are motivated by the *evolutionary need* for emotionally rewarding relationships. Shame and guilt motivate us to stay within the rules of our society and not upset important people in our lives. Loneliness motivates us to get connected with other people. Do you notice how many of these painful emotions and psychological states are social in nature? As humans (and other higher primates) evolved, we grew beyond simple, instinctual, social patterns. We became more flexible, which is vital for success in variable and changing environmental circumstances. That meant that we evolved psychological states that support complex social behavior in coordination with our adaptive success based on that behavior.

Next, there is a situation in which functional psychological mechanisms lead to socially undesirable behavior that is not actually a problem. While altruistic attitudes and behavior are generally good for adaptive fitness, this is not always the case. Sometimes, selfish, aggressive behavior is better for survival and mating. In other words, psychopathy can be useful from an evolutionary perspective but is often frowned upon by the collective. To the extent that mental illness consists of patterns of thought, feeling, and behavior that are negatively judged by a given cultural group, psychopathy would be viewed in just such a negative light. That is why being "antisocial" is generally considered a mental disorder and being "prosocial" is not. This double-edged-sword problem is reflected in the complex and complicated relationship modern societies have with such patterns. On the one hand, there is moral (and legal) condemnation of selfish, aggressive behavior, but on the other hand, we also celebrate and reward such attitudes and behaviors (Ronson, 2011). We may say "nice guys finish last" and look down on selfless individuals as weak and naive. We give high levels of position and power to people who exhibit highly selfish, aggressive behavior. From an evolutionary perspective, it is safe to say that individualistic *aggression displays* on the part of males are often rewarded with sex, coalition building, and overall social/cultural power. The general conclusion here is that both cooperation/altruism and competition/dominance are strategies for success on both the individual and the collective levels. This is true today and was likely true in our distant past.

What all this means is that our early human ancestors faced a daunting situation. Many of the cognitive and behavioral strategies that drove evolutionary success also propagated psychological suffering and conflict between the individual and society. Anxiety, anger, sadness, shame, and guilt are all uncomfortable states to experience but are valuable for social cohesion and subsequent group survival. Selfishness and aggression lead to cultural conflict but also serve individual and group survival. With the increase in self-consciousness, both individually and collectively, these patterns likely drove the development of concepts of mental health and mental illness but in complicated and sometimes conflicting ways. It is also likely that as societies evolved into their more modern structures and dynamics, these concepts of mental illness evolved with them, and in some ways, the resulting pathologies became *worse*, with many of the underlying psychological systems losing at least some of their evolutionary value. The feeling of shame that helped motivate early humans to fit in with the expectations of their small social group and thus ensure group survival eventually became *toxic shame* that causes unnecessary and unhelpful suffering (Bradshaw, 2015). The aggressive displays that communicated strength, health, and assertiveness and thus were very important behaviors for individual and group survival became the bullying, patriarchal domination, victimization of various kinds, and antisocial/psychopathic personality structures of modern life. The greatest irony of our evolutionary history may be that the source of our greatest success as a species has also been the wellspring of our greatest suffering, problems, and the increase in what we think of as mental illness.

TREPANATION

Up to this point in the chapter, we have explored the early development of general cognitive and emotional capabilities that provided the foundation for the human psychological experience of and thus concepts regarding mental health and mental illness. To further this discussion, let's look at two specific issues. The first is the odd case of trepanation. This practice, the purposeful drilling of holes through a person's skull, has persisted for thousands of years in various places (Nolen-Hoeksema, 2016). The earliest evidence for it goes back about 12,000 years ago, to the Neolithic period (Walker, 1967). Because we are dealing with prehistory, the reasons for its practice are somewhat mysterious. It was probably used to address a number of medical problems, including chronic headaches, epilepsy, and various intracranial diseases (Faria, 2013). It has been conjectured that one of the reasons for its use was to deal with problems closely related to what we now call mental illness. People might have been hearing or seeing things that others did not, exhibiting strange or disturbing behavior, and/or experiencing intense intrapsychic distress. This could have led to the belief that a person suffered from some form of demonic possession or metaphysical influence. The exact nature of these beliefs is lost to us and would, of course, differ markedly from place to place and era to era based on local circumstances. Looking at what is known about the prehistoric world, it is likely that people would attribute disturbing behavior by others to possession, displeasure/punishment by a god or gods, eclipses or other astronomical phenomena, curses or other interpersonally directed witchcraft, or personal sin or personality weakness. It is also likely that there would have been little differentiation between psychological and physical phenomena. In most ancient societies, psyche and soma were considered linked, so mental and physical illnesses would have been considered part of the same overall phenomena.

It seems likely that a similar heuristic understanding of these phenomena emerged through a process of cultural parallelism. Various early human cultures could all believe that spiritual entities exist and that those entities could influence, control, or even inhabit a human being. Further, they could all believe that such inhabiting spirits could be released through the head of the individual if a physical opening was provided. It would then make sense that if prayers and rituals failed to expel the spirit, it would require that such an opening be drilled through the skull to allow or compel the spirit to exit. This is all conjecture, of course. We don't know much about what really took place in early humanoid society. The only direct evidence we have regarding Neolithic trephination is the archeological discovery of skulls with one or more holes burred through them.

From a modern, Western perspective, these religious beliefs and their corresponding surgical practices may be deemed at best misguided and at worst cruel, but they could be maintained for very long periods of time based on the wisdom of epistemological authority and the lack of any reasonable or challenging alternatives. Cultural beliefs and practices (traditions) don't have to be *right*, they just have to work in a social context. They need to maintain the functionality and thus the survivability of the culture (Durkheim, 1912). That means they need to meet the challenges of life in (seemingly) logical and effective ways. In doing so, they enhance cohesion, conformity, and control. Thus, the painful and even tragic outcomes of such practices were secondary to the benefits to society.

SCHIZOPHRENIA

The second issue to explore involves the possible origin of the dysfunctional and often disturbing symptoms of schizophrenia and other psychotic disorders. These symptoms carry no immediately apparent evolutionary advantage. How would it increase fitness for people to hear or see things that don't exist, to believe things that don't reflect external reality, or to lose their capacity for adaptive cognitive, emotional, motivational, or social functioning? These are debilitating psychological problems that have no known corollary in other animals and, by all accounts, are primarily biological in origin. Despite the assertions of psychologists and psychiatrists in the early twentieth century, more recent research has established that although environment definitely plays a role, the severe and chronic psychotic symptoms associated with mental disorders such as schizophrenia and bipolar disorder are primarily genetic and thus biological in origin (Gottesman, 1991; Sue, Sue, & Sue, 2015). This is interesting for a couple of reasons relevant to our topic. First of all, more mild or transitory psychotic symptoms can occur in people with no family history in response to a number of stressors, including developmental trauma and drug abuse, and thus may be a relatively common aspect of psychological distress or disorder. Second, although there are descriptions of psychotic symptoms going back to antiquity, it is unclear if schizophrenia, as we recognize it today, was present in prehistory or is a more recent phenomenon (Mittal et al., 2016). Together, these factors suggest that there is a *general and unique* vulnerability to experiencing psychotic symptoms in the human race and that this vulnerability is *neurological/genetic* in origin. This begs the related questions of why and how such a vulnerability would evolve in the first place.

A number of researchers have been investigating the possible connection between neurological evolution and schizophrenia over the last century. Julian Jaynes developed a radical hypothesis that the hominid brain developed separate areas for the production and, conversely, the neurological recognition or "hearing" of language (1976). He argued that these separate locations were in the left and right hemispheres, which operated more independently from each other in our early development than they do now. He called this the bicameral mind. Jaynes's theory was focused generally on the evolution of consciousness. He proposed that language was developing among humans while they were still lacking many important attributes of consciousness, such as metaconsciousness, autobiographical memory, and conscious introspection of mental content. These later attributes developed in response to the integration of the hemispheres. In his model, because language production and recognition took place in separate hemispheres and there was relatively little communication between them, early humans would have experienced their own internally produced speech (our inner voice) as if it was coming from an outside source. Therefore, at least some internally produced language would be experienced in the form of what we would now call auditory hallucinations, providing commentary, advice, or directions. Because the voice was experienced as external, it could easily be attributed to gods, spirits, or dead ancestors. Eventually, the fuller integration of the left and right hemispheres would result in humans recognizing their inner voice as just that: a manifestation of their own thoughts.

One consequence of this development was that later in human history, this capacity, both for increased self-consciousness and for differentiation of internal and external voices, might break down, and people could *regress* to the previous level of neurological functioning and thus experience what we now call symptoms of psychosis or schizophrenia. It is interesting that Jaynes considers not only auditory hallucinations but other symptoms associated with schizophrenia in his theory. The disorder of schizophrenia often includes a breakdown of the sense of self, along with the corresponding time-space orientation and self-integrity, as well as the ability to differentiate subjective thoughts, emotions, desires, and fantasies from external reality. There appears to be a breakdown in the mental barriers between the internal and external worlds of people with this disorder (Saks, 2007). The cognitive attributes associated with it are all connected to the evolution of self-consciousness, and it would make sense that if they are compromised through a disease process, it could easily include disturbances in the differentiation of internal and external dialogue and result in auditory hallucinations.

David Lewis-Williams expressed his doubts about some aspects of Jaynes's theory, especially the latter's assertion that early humans lacked modern control over their thoughts and behavior, but he provided his own evidence for the Upper Paleolithic (starting around 40,000 years ago) capacity for visual "hallucinations," resulting in the explosion of cave art around that time. As noted previously in this chapter, he associated this evolutionary development with the birth of art, religion, and shamanistic culture (2002). Both Jaynes and Lewis-Williams provide insights regarding the likelihood that early humans had auditory and visual "hallucinations" and experienced them as external to their own minds and that the capacity for self-consciousness regarding the source of these phenomena developed slowly and imperfectly over thousands of years.

The idea that modern symptoms related to schizophrenia and other psychotic disorders may be linked to human evolution are not just the province of speculative psychology and archeology. Geneticists are also exploring these connections and are increasingly in agreement that the evolutionary developments that led to language, consciousness, and other higher cognitive abilities are also responsible for the unique human vulnerability for psychotic symptoms (Crow, 2008; Srinivasan et al., 2016, 2017). Crow refers to the period of expansion of these cognitive and behavioral capacities, connected to the transition to language, as the "big bang" that made modern humans what we are. He suggests that the epigenetic diversity connected with this development of language and its related cognitive developments are also the basis for subsequent predispositions for psychosis. In other words, psychosis and language have a common genetic origin, and thus the presence of schizophrenia and other psychotic disorders in the human population is the price we pay for the otherwise amazing cognitive capacities that define our species (2008).

More recent genetic research has been generally supportive of this picture. Srinivasan and his many associates (2016, 2017) found some support for the emergence of genetic markers for schizophrenia that appeared after the divergence of modern humans from earlier humanoids. They conclude that the evolutionary emergence of schizophrenia, along with other neurocognitive disorders such as autism, neurodevelopmental delay, intellectual disability, and epilepsy, was likely influenced by these markers, but the evidence is far from conclusive. It is likely that a number of factors are involved, but there does appear to be an evolutionary linkage.

NATURE VERSUS NURTURE

The preceding discussion begs an overarching question regarding nature (biology) versus nurture (experience) as the source of mental health and mental illness. This has been a very lively debate in the sciences, especially since Charles Darwin and others introduced the concept of evolution. That introduction was obviously a "game changer" in regard to the general question of what *causes* happiness or psychological despair as well as to their roots in human history. The earlier discussion about cognitive archeology reflects how the question of historical roots has changed in the context of the acceptance of evolution as a foundational dynamic in both the natural and social sciences. However, it is important to point out that evolution is not the only competing model in the social sciences. In fact, there is a large sector in academia that takes a different perspective on the cause, or etiology, of human psychological attributes. While they would generally not deny the reality of evolution in terms of biological change over time, they refute the idea that biology is a primary or determining factor in most human behavior and our underlying psychological functioning, including such areas as mental health and mental illness. Instead, they focus on social factors, especially the combined influence of individual development within a family system and a particular culture.

The debate continues to this day, but currently, we are at a point of trying to integrate the nature and nurture perspectives. This can be challenging, especially because the nurture perspective is still strong in the social sciences. Steven Pinker discusses this issue in great detail (2002). He makes the point that the nurturist perspective is grounded in the idea of the *blank slate*. This concept, made famous by John Locke, asserts that the human mind (thus what we call human nature) has no innate traits. We build up everything we know, believe, and do from the experience of our individual development. This is a compelling and attractive philosophy, partly because it argues that many human evils, including violence, racism, and sexism, are *not natural but learned* and thus can be changed through social progress. However, Pinker asserts that this is fundamentally incorrect. Many of the basic dynamics of human thought and thus behavior are biologically based. These traits, including such things as social emotions, aggression, gender differences, and even personality styles, were shaped by natural selection based on their contribution to survivability and reproduction not personal happiness or well-being.

This argument is carried further by Robert Sapolsky, who, as a neurologist, explores the links between human behavior (both good and bad), its neurobiological explanation, and its ultimate evolutionary explanation (2017). He explores the known biological roots of hierarchy, morality, empathy, selfishness, aggression, competition, heroism, and even criminality. These aspects of human nature are central to much of what we think about in regard to mental health as well as illness. And although we typically think of them as deriving largely from our upbringing, it turns out that they are more wired into our brains than people often care to admit and thus are linked to evolution. This is true even in regard to a human attribute as fundamental to our sense of our mental health as self-will. Sapolsky takes on this issue and concludes that self-will is mainly an illusion – a post-facto rationalization. This has vital import regarding our central topic. Did early humans evolve self-consciousness in order to adaptively solve certain cognitive and social challenges and thus inadvertently give people the illusion that they were choosing more of their behavior than they really were? If that is true, then we are wired to be frustrated by our desire to act differently than we do, take more responsibility for our behavior than makes neurological sense to take, and blame others for their behavior more than we should. These are important factors in the conception of mental health and illness and likely at least as much an issue in our deep past as they are now. On a related note, Sapolsky fully acknowledges the importance of environmental influences on behavior and in fact repeatedly makes the point that we cannot distinguish between aspects of behavior that are biological and those that are cultural or psychological. These *drivers* of human behavior are deeply inter-twined, both now and in the past. It is this last point that best reflects the growing concept that nature and nurture are equally important and need to be considered *together* when exploring the past, present, and future of how we conceptualize mental health and mental illness.

THE ARCHETYPAL PERSPECTIVE

One way to explore the integration of various human binaries – physiological/psychological, mental health/mental illness, individual/collective – is to take the archetypal approach. It has its roots in the work of Carl Jung (Jacobi, 1942; Jung, 1964; Samuels, 1985). He accepted Sigmund Freud's idea that every individual has a level of psyche that is not immediately available for conscious reflection and is shaped by that individual's life experiences, but Jung proposed that below the level of the individual unconscious, there is a collective unconscious. He saw this as the repository of collective human instincts and symbolic structures – the organizers of our species' experiential memory, if you will. He called these archetypes. They include such imagos as representations of the masculine (animus) and feminine (anima) qualities, the wise old man and woman, the aspect of ourselves we show to other people (persona), etc. Jung developed this theory because he noted (as did Freud) that his patients often came up with dreams or fantasies that included images and themes that the patient had no direct experience or knowledge of. These themes actually played themselves out in his patients' lives in interesting and dynamic ways.

The reason this line of discussion is relevant here is because there is an ancient image and theme that reflects the emergence of consciousness in the evolutionary history of humanity. The image is called the uroboros, and it is typically depicted as a serpent forming a circle and biting its own tail. Erich Neumann explored this image in great detail (2014). He provided examples from ancient mythological systems around the world and discovered the same basic dynamics operating between them. He concluded that the image reflects a primordial, preconscious experience of life in which there is no separation of self from world. In his conception, the primordial self is embedded in its own experience and thus is in a state of complete myopic dependence. Life happens and the self reacts but cannot reflect upon or choose responses. In such a state, life has a timeless quality – there is only the nev-er-ending moment of immediate awareness. There is no autobiographical memory of yesterday or fantasy of tomorrow – there is only now. Of course, such a being would react to things based on prior experience but not because he or she is consciously thinking about it. Past experience shapes immediate responses without reflection. The image of the serpent is well suited to reflect this state of undifferentiated consciousness. It slithers directly on the ground, with no separation with the benefit of legs and feet. It is reptilian and thus cannot regulate its own temperature, with no separation from its immediate environment. It sheds its skin and thus was believed by the ancients to be immortal, with no separation between the physical and spiritual worlds. The uroboros represents the starting point, the union of all opposites *before* consciousness emerges into the light of day.

In this chapter, we have already discussed some elements of early human psychology that led to both a conception and an experience of psychological wellness (fitting in with society) and suffering (extended sadness over the loss of important relationships). What the archetypal perspective provides is both a different way to understand how the ancients may have experienced their lives before, during, and after the emergence of consciousness and a link to how people experience these issues in the modern day. At the risk of offending some who approach religious texts as literal *history*, it is important to explore such texts for archetypal themes, because they have much to reveal about the psychological roots of the human psyche. For instance, the creation story of Adam and Eve may reflect a nascent understanding of the emergence of consciousness and its inherent problems, leading to psychological suffering.

In the biblical story, Adam and Eve were created and placed by God in the Garden of Eden. In this place, they roamed naked, without shame, and could converse directly with God. They did not know suffering and wanted for nothing. First of all, as a mythological place, the garden can be interpreted not as an actual location but as a psychological state. Their nakedness and lack of shame can be interpreted as reflecting a state of ignorance of the world of good and evil and their communion with God as a lack of separation between the physical and spiritual worlds. In the language of mythology, this state is referred to as *participation mystique* and is recognized psychologically as a projective identification with things outside the self, including the spiritual realm. Human thoughts, feelings, dreams, and desires are experienced as real things that exist in the outside world, giving life a magical, mythical character. In the case of the story of Adam and Eve, this placement in the Garden of Eden embodies the yearning for a return to the safety and support of the mother's womb. This would correspond to the state represented by the uroboros, undifferentiated consciousness. This state of bliss could not maintain itself, however, because human consciousness was emerging. From the perspective of evolution, this was an incredible achievement and had many benefits to offer, but it cannot be overstated, as it is true in almost all creation stories from around the world, that the arrival of consciousness was experienced as a great fall, as humanity found itself separated from heaven and the gods (Heinberg, 1989).

Going back to the biblical story, Yahweh placed two trees in the garden from which Adam and Eve were forbidden to eat. The first tree was that of the knowledge of good and evil. This is a beautiful metaphor for the birth of consciousness because it represented the beginning of conceptual, self-reflective thought.

Consciousness separates the phenomena of the world (including aspects of ourselves) into moral categories and is able to reflect upon them, forcing the psyche to make choices based on free will. The capacity to conceptualize good and evil reflects an empowerment of the human psyche; the individual rises above the nonreflective instincts of the animal world and takes responsible ownership of his or her life. This profound truth was not lost in the story, for it was clear that God did not want Adam and Eve to eat the fruit because it would make them "like God, knowing good and evil." This would raise them closer to the level of God, and for this they were punished. The punishments themselves reflected some of the sufferings brought on by consciousness, including ejection from the participation mystique of undifferentiated consciousness and painful reflection on the difficulties of life. The ultimate suffering of consciousness is, of course, the awareness of mortality (represented by the second tree, the opportunity for eternal life), and thus the psychologically corresponding punishment in the story was expulsion from the Garden of Eden. Separation from the earth-womb-uroboros-God is the most horrible consequence of consciousness and is directly connected to the ultimate desires stemming from consciousness, to return to the womb or achieve eternal life, which are psychologically commensurate.

It is no secret that the story of Adam and Eve has been very problematical for women in Western culture. Patriarchy and subjugation of women in the West have been driven and legitimized by it (Pagels, 1988). Erich Neumann explained how this development flowed from the core issue of the fear of the *terrible feminine* (1994, 2014). The Good Mother is all loving and giving, but the Bad Mother reflects the chthonic, all-devouring swamp of natural existence, which threatens to drag us back to her bosom, destroying the weak and tenuous self-aware ego. The prize of consciousness was hard fought and all too easy to lose. Conflating the negative feminine with the positive and thus assessing the feminine as *generally* negative has been a horrifying mistake in many cultures, as has treating actual, flesh-and-blood women as *embodying* the underlying feminine principle. Masculine and feminine are conceptual categories and not the same as physical men and women. The fear of the negative aspects of *both* the masculine and feminine principles and the projective overliteralizing of those principles within actual groups of people has led to tremendous conflict and suffering.

It should be noted that inflation and overliteralization of the *positive* aspects of the masculine and feminine also have problematical consequences. When we romanticize and idolize feminine beauty or masculine strength, we both honor and objectify, we inflate as we conflate, and thus we unfairly dehumanize the objects of our adoration. Whether people burn witches or venerate movie stars, they demand a great deal from their projections, and the price paid by actual people has always been quite high. We know very little about its impact on the psyches and lives of men and women before recorded history, but this dynamic has been active from the beginning of human consciousness and has impacted the mental health of both men and women ever since. While the lack of detailed evidence from prehistory makes it difficult to assess just what that impact was, the origin stories from various religions tell a psychological story that has its roots deep in that history.

CONCLUSION

This chapter has covered a lot of ground quite quickly. We started with a discussion regarding the legitimacy of different ways of knowing, especially comparing empiricism versus received wisdom, or epistemic authority. We decided to side with empiricism and take evolutionary theory as the guiding *truth* for our exploration of human history. We then explored the idea that there are really two different types of evolution, the first being physiological and the second being sociocultural. It is likely that physiological evolution was the primary developmental factor at the very beginning of our species – up to around 100,000 years ago, and now, more and more, sociocultural evolution is the main engine of change. Sociocultural evolution builds upon physiological evolution. It impacts the specific *forms* of our anger, jealousy, hopes, and goals, but it was not the original source of them. It has to work with the tools that physiological evolution gave it to work with. We started to explore these tools through what we have learned from the work of cognitive archeology. While it has been difficult to learn too much from the scanty evidence available, these researchers have developed some good ideas about the roots of our capacity for language and abstract thought, which led to much of what we recognize today as human cultural forms, such as complex social hierarchies and differentiation of cultural roles. This led naturally to a discussion of evolutionary psychology. Both cognitive archeology and evolutionary psychology are important to understand how various, typically human patterns of thought, feeling, and behavior developed as adaptive advantages but also led to (mostly) uniquely human forms of psychological suffering, including prolonged shame, guilt, anxiety, and resentment, which could lead to complexes we might recognize today as depression and personality disorders. This question of how general psychological suffering might crystalize into specific disorders led to a discussion of two specific issues – the first known treatment of mental disorders (trepanning) and the neurodevelopmental roots of what we now call schizophrenia. Finally, we circled back out to a wider perspective. Archetypal psychology provides the widest lens we have for exploring and understanding the underlying dynamics of the human psyche – one that includes a deep analysis of its historical roots, not just its modern manifestations.

These different perspectives are all related but come from different academic backgrounds, ranging from neurology to archeology to different areas of psychology. Much more will be said about the integration of these perspectives in later chapters, but in regard to the topic of this chapter, it is important to note that the historical roots of both the experienced reality of and the human conception of mental health and mental illness lie in a combination of nature and nurture, with evolution being the primary natural process driving them both. This combination of factors, reflecting both nature and nurture, within a longitudinal lens of evolution is fundamentally systemic – that is, it includes all parts of a phenomenon (the human psyche), acting in relation with each other, within the contextual dynamic of a challenging and changing environment.

This brings us back to our original topic, mental health and mental illness. Having explored some of the earliest roots of both sides of that artificially binary concept, we can outline the main areas that need to be investigated in our journey through the rest of human history. We can do this in the form of questions to pursue at each historical point. What did people believe about what constitutes mental health and mental illness? What did these people seem to experience as mental health and mental illness? What did they think caused mental health and mental illness? And finally, can we say anything useful about the validity and/or meaning of their answers based on what we know about evolution, biology, psychology, and sociology? Obviously, given the scope of the project, we will only have space for a brief review, a cursory glance if you will, at each historical epoch. The good news is that as we move forward into recorded history, there will be an increasing amount of direct information about what people actually experienced and thought about these matters.

CHAPTER 2

THE MYTHOLOGICAL ERA

INTRODUCTION

Having at least glanced at the evolutionary roots of human consciousness, cognition, morality, emotions, and cultural life, we can now explore the early efforts people made to understand the larger world, their place in it, and the subsequent impact on their experience and understanding of mental health and mental illness. It is there, in a period stretching roughly from around 10,000 to the beginning of the Classical era (around 800 BC), that we begin to see a clearer record of what people thought about themselves, their values, their dreams, their nightmares, and the forces they saw shaping the way things are inside themselves, in other people, and in the larger world of which they were a part. We can see the emergence of a direct, written record of these dynamics. We see them emerge, in symbolic form, in the mythological systems that people created. The gods and their characteristics, the stories that were created that embodied those characteristics, and the roles of the humans included in those stories all reflect the psychological dynamics of the people who created them and believed in them.

The acclaimed scholar of mythology, Joseph Campbell, spoke of the drive of human beings to create myths. He saw that myth making goes back as far as there is a record of our species. He asserted that myths were not just silly fables or fantasies but instead reflected universal symbols and themes connected with the deepest, most essential aspects of being human (Campbell, 1972). Lying underneath the literal aspects of these stories are clues to the human soul and the answers it seeks to the deepest questions about life, death, and the world around us. This was true for ancient peoples and was no less true in regard to questions of mental health and mental illness. What did these people see as *normal or healthy?* a life of richness, purpose, and fulfillment? What led to joy or sorrow? What behavior or attitudes did they recognize as being crazy? What caused people or even gods to go crazy? These questions find answers in the mythologies of early human cultures.

The challenge here is that different groups of people, in various parts of the world, facing different local challenges and conditions, developed a wide variety of mythologies. It is far beyond the scope of this book to explore all or even a significant number of them. Instead, what we will do is look at some of the common features of these mythologies as they reflect on our topic, citing a limited number of specific examples to elucidate the process. The good news is that, as many have pointed out, the primary issues of human existence are universal. There is the challenge of being a singular person with individual desires, fears, and limitations, within a society of others. There is the challenge of success, finding a way to survive, procreate, and even prosper in a harsh and unforgiving environment. There is the challenge of development, moving from childhood through adulthood to old age with its different demands and opportunities. There is the ultimate challenge of being conscious of mortality, with the horror of a time-limited existence making all the other challenges more profound and immediate. It drives people to reflect on their lives and ask basic questions. Am I living a good life? What do I want to accomplish? What is the ultimate meaning and impact of my life? The horror of mortality also drives fantasies of life beyond this one. Is there an afterlife or reincarnation? If so, how do I live my current life so the next will be better? These are some of the common human concerns that have driven the creation of religious systems from the beginning. They are also the concerns that directly impact a sense of psychological well-being or, conversely, madness.

THE HERO'S JOURNEY

As just noted, universal aspects of the human experience and its challenges have led to a certain commonality of mythological themes and resulting ritualistic practices throughout history (Campbell, 1972; Eliade, 1954; Otto, 1923). One of those common themes is what Joseph Campbell referred to as the hero's journey (2008/1949). This journey, in Campbell's conception, is primarily developmental in nature. Every person is born in a state of profound biological and psychological dependency, is compelled to individuate (to use the Jungian terminology), and then reconnects to the world at a higher level of mature, conscious integration. This universal developmental challenge is symbolized within the storyline of an individual making a dangerous journey, beset with temptations and challenges, often through the underworld. He or she must survive, succeed in the quest, and return with a boon for society. In other words, the cultural journey parallels the needs of individual development.

The idea here, as introduced in the previous chapter, is that every psyche is originally deeply imbedded in the womb, both actual and metaphorical, of the natural world. This state of preconsciousness experiences no separation of the self from its material existence. This state is, at one level, one of ultimate bliss. Untroubled by conscious reflection on such fundamental problems as good and evil or mortality, the preconscious psyche suffers no guilt, no shame, no resentment, and no existential fears. This state of primitive immersion is tragically terminated with the onset of consciousness. The original blissful – or at least nonreflective – experience of nondifferentiation is transformed into the challenge of psychological alienation, reflection, and thus suffering.

Throughout history, the bliss of nondifferentiation has been imagined through dreams of a Golden Age, a mythological time when humans lived in joyful, untroubled unity with the divine (Heinberg, 1989; Jacoby, 1985). In this mythological fantasy, humans live much longer lives and typically do not suffer the many trials and travails of everyday earthly life, but something happens. Sometimes it is the fault of the gods, and sometimes it is the fault of humanity, but humanity is expelled from paradise. There is a Fall. Human life is suddenly shorter, harsher, beset with problems, and alienated from the gods, and the deepest human desire is to get back to paradise. There are three main ways to do this. The first is personal. Each individual is responsible to live his or her life in accordance with the moral and ethical dictates of the gods and thus can attain salvation, if not in their earthly life, then upon death. The second is cultural. If the group can do likewise, it can win the affirmation and support of the deities. Again, reward may come on the earthly plane, with cultural success (victory over enemies, successful hunts or harvests, the attainment of a promised homeland) or eventual entry to heaven as a *chosen* group. The third way is historical. After passing through a long period of suffering, the world itself will be redeemed. The third way is often still flexible, in that humanity can still hasten or extend the eventual redemption through its virtuosity or wickedness (Eliade, 1954).

In regard to the second and third ways, people can participate in the beliefs, practices, rites, and rituals of their culture to align with the will of the gods and return to paradise. This can be as simple as following the rules for the preparation and consumption of the right foods. It can be as difficult as submitting to painful and even life-threatening rites of passage. In this case, mental health is likely to result from correct practice. Knowing and following the rules and completing culturally assigned tasks mark the path to well-being and to feeling accepted and esteemed, a valued member of the group. But on the mythological level, it runs much deeper. The successful followers of the rules feel that they are aligned with the will of the god/s. As a group, they feel ennobled, emboldened, on the side of Good, and ultimately on track to win the ultimate prize of a return to paradise. This is a powerful force, especially within the social context of group support and pressure, reward and punishment. It is hard to resist the lure of being one of "God's chosen people," and it can unleash bursts of collective energy, which can build pyramids or kill millions. Conversely, it can lead large groups of people to believe they are cursed by God, wandering the earth in punishment, or visited by calamity for the group's failure to live up to its spiritual responsibilities, with profound ramifications for an individual's sense of psychological well-being.

On the individual level, the inflationary feeling of being in alignment with the will of the gods may be combined with various fears and resentments. Self-doubt creeps in – "am I doing well enough?" "Why won't everyone else go along with me?" There is also the challenge of hypocrisy. People may feel that they are *doing* the right things, but deep in their hearts, they know that they are still sinners. This is particularly true when (as always happens) the real-world results do not match the promise. "I prayed and prayed, but my son still died; my prayers must not have been worthy." This form of religious neurosis, with its guilt, shame, and (often) projection onto others will be covered in more detail in later chapters. That is because, in more ancient societies, this was probably less of an issue. There was much more focus on outward behavior and less on inward thoughts, feelings, and hidden desires. This conclusion follows from the fact that, as noted earlier, very few ancient texts explore the interior life of the authors. Some historians see this as a reflection that most of these texts started as stories, passed down from generation to generation through oral tradition, and thus lack the personal voice of an original author. Some, like Erich Neumann and Julian Jaynes, have postulated that it reflects the early developmental quality of the emerging ego-consciousness. Just as young children do not exhibit the highly developed ego consciousness that they will exhibit later in their development, the people in these ancient times simply did not reflect on their internal life to the extent that would become the norm later in history.

This leads us back to the hero's journey. The hero is an individual who is driven to break out of the bonds and limitations of his or her current existence to attain a higher level of individuated consciousness. The hero has to travel through a dark, dangerous place and come through to the other side, back into the light. It is important to remember that the original, undifferentiated state is not just blissful. The dark side of the eternal feminine – the uroboric serpent – represents a horrifying, depersonalized embeddedness in the world. It is not just the all-loving mother but the destroyer that cares nothing for the individual in the endless cycle of life and death of natural existence. This reality often comes through in images and themes of being stuck in swamps, eaten alive by insects, chained and tortured by demons, etc. This primal, existential fear is likely at the heart of the fear of the feminine, which represents, at a fundamental level, a conflation of the positive and negative mother (Neumann, 1994).

Part of what this means is that the patriarchal demonization and repression of women has deep mytho-cultural roots. This has important ramifications for our topic here. It suggests that the challenge of developing a healthy psychological attitude about oneself, relatively free of depression, anxiety, and poor self-concept, would have been more difficult for women than for men in all cultures where this core mythological dynamic was (and continues to be) in effect. It suggests that this dynamic is more or less universal and reflects an existential reality of the challenges of consciousness and human life. It does not suggest that women are incapable of happiness or have not enjoyed *some* of the power and honors within various societies but rather that they have been put at a cultural disadvantage in many cultures, for a very long time, based in part on the mythological dynamics of those cultures. This, of course, does not come as news to many people, but it is important to remember that patriarchal dominance has deep mytho-cultural roots, and its resolution requires an honest look at those roots and a reconstruction of the vision of healthy psychological development for modern society, a theme we will return to later in the text.

Returning to our story, the hero has to enter the underworld to slay this uroboric dragon. Only then can he or she attain the "pearl of great price" and return to the everyday world of culture with a boon for society. However, the journey does not start there. It starts with what Campbell referred to as a *call to adventure*. There are signs of danger, a problem, a challenge that needs to be faced. For many, this leads to a *refusal of the call*. Not everyone is up to the challenge, and as Jesus said in the Book of Matthew, "many are called, but few are chosen" (Matthew 22:14, New International Version). It is easier to stay within the relative safety of the known, the accepted, the less risky. This is a psychological dynamic that is probably as old as consciousness itself. Should I hide? Can I stay safe? What is the cost to my soul for not taking up the challenge in front of me? What about shame and self-derision? The bitter irony here is that refusing the call can include staying within the confines of the existing group identity.

So far, we have described mental health in terms of conforming to group norms, and this is true. The hero's journey introduces a new element in which breaking the norms is an essential part of growth, both individual and collective. What this entails is the strength of character to voluntarily experience great discomfort and possible disaster to achieve something greater. What is important then is help.

The next stage of the journey is *supernatural aid*. The heroes in these mythical stories almost always have assistance, a helper, a guide, who teaches, trains, corrects, chastises, and supports along the way. With help, the hero *crosses the threshold* and enters *the belly of the whale*, often conceived as a literal underworld or psychological "dark night of the soul." In this place, the hero must endure terrible trials, risk death, insanity, or worse. There are temptations, sidetracks, and opportunities to give up the quest and return to a safe, peaceful life.

If the hero endures and succeeds in his or her quest, the reward is a *great boon*. This boon is sometimes of a worldly, material nature, such as riches or romantic love, and sometimes it is of a spiritual type – enlightenment, nirvana, heaven. Whatever the boon, the hero then has to *return and reintegrate* with his or her normal, everyday world. There are many ways this can occur, including offering the boon to society and helping others to attain it (Buddha) or providing the boon and leaving again for good (Christ). Sometimes the hero is so changed by the journey that he or she does not fit in any more (Frodo Baggins), while others have grown so much from their adventures that they become leaders in the community, and others have matured from adolescence to normal adult responsibilities of marriage and parenthood with wisdom and self-assurance (Samwise).

The point here is that the hero's journey is where the stories and gods of ancient societies come into contact with the lives of everyday people. Religion is not just what happens on festival day. It provides the themes, the exemplars, and the roadmap that people use to navigate and provide meaning for their lives. From this perspective, every individual's life is a hero's journey, with many different types of challenge. The ultimate boon, however, is universal in terms of achieving a higher state of integrated consciousness. By definition, this represents a better state of mental health and, in fact, provides both an imago of what such a desired state would look like and a roadmap for how to get there.

Let's move on now to explore some specific examples of religion in action from ancient mytho-cultural systems connected to this idea of personal development and how they effected the emerging concept of mental health and illness in the ancient world.

RITES OF PASSAGE

Joseph Campbell came to the conclusion, through his extraordinary lifetime of work on the subject, that the purpose and effect of mythology is to help people deal with the challenges of human life (2008). Rites of passage, designed in accordance with a culture's mythological system, are particularly concrete manifestations of this ideational dynamic. In a way, the collection of rites in a society can be considered a culturally sanctioned hero's journey. For many thousands of years, people of both genders and all ages have been guided through such processes of initiation and transformation to help them negotiate the developmental stages of their lives (Van Gennep, 2010). Around the world, for as long as we have recorded history, there is evidence of rituals and ceremonies around birth, naming, puberty, entrance to adulthood, marriage, war, old age, death, burial, etc. These cultural activities are shaped by the groups' mythological themes and thus imbue these experiences with particular meanings and importance, but they universally center around the idea of successfully moving through life's stages and transforming the self into a higher level of consciousness (Eliade, 1958). The level of importance given these practices and their underlying purposes is reflected in how much time, effort, and often severity and danger they entailed.

Some of the best known involve bodily mutilation (circumcision, piercing, or tattooing), isolation (Aboriginal "walkabouts"), or drug ingestion (Algonquin rite of passage). The Algonquin practice was a particularly harrowing one. It involved taking adolescent boys and isolating them in cages in the wilderness. They were given a powerful drug called wysoccan, which can cause severe memory loss. The purpose of the ritual was to cleanse the boys of their memories of childhood, thus preparing them for adulthood. This pattern was not unusual. Many cultures have utilized similar rituals that include a very challenging experience that was designed to shift the person's entire perspective from that of a child to that required of an adult in the community. In order for it to be effective, it required a profound level of intensity, involving an experience of psychological death and rebirth. In most cultures, it was a particularly difficult and physically dangerous one for the boys. This likely stemmed from two sources. First of all, in cultures with a high level of conflict with other groups, boys needed to be psychologically prepared to become warriors, with a corresponding high level of physical courage. The second source was the perception that girls experienced a *natural* rite of passage to adulthood through first menses and then through pregnancy and childbearing. That being said, many cultures have developed separate and sometimes difficult adulthood initiation rites for girls as well as boys.

Another example of a ritualized rite that is pertinent to our topic involves an interesting practice called "land-jumping." It originated on Pentecost Island (but surely has many similar precursors going back thousands of years) and involves tribal members climbing a tall platform, tying vines to their ankles, and jumping off (Attenborough, 1966). The vines, which are attached to the top of the platform, need to be just the right length to stop the plummeting jumper inches from the ground. The practice is designed to be a test of courage, a way to ward off evil spirits and even to assure a good harvest. All three of these purposes are very important and thus justify the risk involved.

These examples were chosen, first, because they reflect or are similar to ancient practices but are still in place today, and thus we know a great deal about them and, second, because they both have inspired "modern" people to develop similar activities. In the modern versions, there is little cultural or religious value connected to the activity. Modern technology has removed almost all personal risk from it, which has relegated it to the level of sport. The impulse, to test oneself, to take on an adventure, is still there deep in the psyche, but the method to manifest it has been stripped of its original meaning and gravitas. A homogenized trial is no trial – it is a fun and harmless weekend adventure with friends. This issue of the demythologizing of modern life – its divesture from deeper investment, meaning, and spiritual engagement – will be an important theme in later chapters of this book. What is important here is that in their original forms, rites like these were essential to the psychological well-being of the practitioners as they moved through the various challenges in their lives.

In regard to the issue of mental health, one can only imagine the feeling of shame and failure that would result if one did not succeed in the initiation process. And what of the consequences for the rest of his or her life for such a fundamental, individual failure? On the other hand, if the child succeeded, imagine the joy, pride, and honor resulting from the group welcoming one into the brotherhood or sisterhood of adulthood that would result. Such an outcome could propel him or her to future success and a deep sense of well-being and interconnectedness. An interesting source of support for the idea of the deep historical roots of this dynamic comes from research on social status and sense of well-being. It turns out that overall socioeconomic status in large, modern cultures does little to impact people's sense of well-being; however, comparisons with one's immediate peers does (Boyce, Brown, & Moore, 2010). Sometimes called the "local ladder effect" or, more popularly, "keeping up with the Joneses," it would make sense that this dynamic would have evolved in and been particularly strong in the small group settings of early human history. As civilizations emerged, along with more complex hierarchies and job stratification, people who were struggling to succeed may not have suffered when comparing themselves to individuals or groups at the very top of the ladder but would still have suffered when comparing themselves to friends, relatives, and neighbors who seemed to be doing better. Rites of initiation provide a structured process for personal development or promotion within a given culture, thus enhancing self-esteem and mental health or, conversely, a sense of failure and shame and possible mental illness.

MENTAL ILLNESS IN THE ANCIENT WORLD

Moving from general principles of psychological wellness and suffering back to mental illness, let's take a look at a few examples of documented insanity in the ancient world. Starting around 5000 BC, we begin to find written records of ancient peoples. They typically do not involve everyday private citizens. Rather, they are stories of gods, prophets, and kings. We can only guess that these stories reflect realities that "struck home" with everyday people, representing troubles, triumphs, and challenges that they understood and, at some level, had experienced or seen in others. As Emil Durkheim asserts, in his seminal book on religious systems, all religions are true (1912/2008). They cannot rest on basic errors or falsehoods about the world, or they could not survive. At the same time, as previously noted, the range of common human concerns and lived experiences in the real world lead to *standard* patterns in religious systems. So, as civilizations developed, increasing in complexity, hierarchal institutions, and contact with the outside world, so did their religious systems. These systems typically included little differentiation between religion, medicine, and mental illness, as they all reflected the integrated human experience.

For example, the earliest Babylonian doctors were priests who dealt with both physical and mental diseases. These diseases were typically attributed to demonic possession and treated with religious methods (Alexander & Selesnick, 1966). The Babylonians had many demons, and every disease had its own demonic representative. Insanity was caused by Idta, but the belief in demonic possession was combined with more animistic conceptions, as well as astrologic and oracular practices, leading to a variety of related beliefs and treatments. These would have included incantations, prayers, and the use of various medicines. The faith of the afflicted in these beliefs and remedies would certainly have accorded them great power of suggestion, and although we moderns may not take much stock in the Babylonians' ideas about mental illness, it was still a significant achievement that they developed a sophisticated institutional approach to medicine that included what we might today call psychiatry, with officially recognized diagnoses and treatments.

It is important to remember that on the practical, everyday level, these "treatment" practices were probably directed by a priest, shaman, or medicine man, a person who was able to form a point of connection between the people and the gods (Alexander & Selesnick, 1966). A bridge or conduit, this person would typically either inherit the position from a parent, or have had experiences early in life that led to the conclusion that he or she (usually he) had a special ability. It is quite likely that such experiences would include hearing and seeing things that others did not. Today, we might call these psychotic symptoms. However, it is likely that in the past, such experiences would be interpreted as indicating the person could easily move from the earthly plane to the spiritual plane, communicating the people's thoughts and feelings to the gods and returning with messages and directives from the spiritual plane back to the people (Lewis-Williams, 2002). This was a very important and venerated position in society. Depending on the society in question, such a position may have required extensive training and internship, where we can assume (partly based on what we know from how such things are handled in current tribal societies) that the inherent abilities of the individual would be developed and honed to fit the specific belief system of the group. This provision of a highly complex conceptual and institutional structure for these experiences could well have helped maintain the overall functionality of the individual in a way that is much more difficult in the modern day for people hearing voices or seeing visions, with a limited support system for their unusual experiences outside the conceptual and practical context of mental illness. It is also quite different from the modern conception of a psychological healer, who is expected to maintain a position *outside* the experience of the client who has the troubling symptoms. They are supposed to empathize but not sympathize – that is, understand but not feel with their clients. The doctor gives treatment *to* but does not share the journey *with* the sufferer. This separation of doctor and patient reflects how modernity has separated the realms of psychology, medicine, and spirituality in a way that would likely have been unimaginable to the ancient psyche.

Another example that highlights the integrated model of biopsychospiritual in the ancient world is how insanity presents itself in the Bible. Perhaps the most famous example was King Saul. The first major king of the Hebrews, he was an unsurpassed military commander, but he also experienced a tumultuous series of failures, leading to his ultimate decline and fall. His intense highs and lows have led many to wonder if his was the first historical representation of mental illness

(Vartejanu-Jourbert, 2017; Cook, 2012; Stein, 2011; Ben-Noun, 2003). The troubles of King Saul, as presented in the Hebrew Bible, stem from his own misunderstandings and bad judgment. He was driven by God's spirit (*ruah*) but often in ways that were disastrous, leading to questions regarding possible demonic possession or more modern concepts of depression, bipolar disorder, or even psychosis. One aspect of his story centers around how his tragic failures follow from his transgressions against the will of God. For instance, his poor judgment in disobeying a divine commandment regarding carrying out a sacrifice leads to punishment and failure (1 Samuel 13:14, New International Version). This reflects the common idea among the Hebrews (as well as many other groups at the time, including Persians, Indians, and Chinese) that madness was caused by divine forces and typically involved punishment for sins or failures (Alexander & Selesnick, 1966). Putting oneself above the rules and norms of societal and religious authority would leave one vulnerable to affliction by demons and subsequent madness. Thus, the concept of hubris again plays out in the Judeo-Christian tradition. Like Adam and Eve before him, Saul puts his own interests and desires above the law and pays a very high price. There is the way *things are supposed to be* and *the way people are supposed to act*. When individuals go their own way, trouble follows, and there is a thin line between heroism and meshuga (the Yiddish and originally Biblical Hebrew word for madness).

Another aspect of the story of Saul was his disconnection from reality. His way of thinking, of seeing how things are, was flawed. He did not see things accurately but rather through the lens of his own thoughts and feelings. This naturally led to poor results. Modern psychology would call this a failure of "reality testing" and think of it in terms of mental illness. To the extent that people process external reality through the distorting lens of their own psychological biases, neuroses, and preconceptions, they will make decisions that have a low chance of success. This can, as in the case of Saul, spiral out of control, with each failure reinforcing a distorting process, leading to more dramatic failures and ultimately disaster or, in more professional terms, "poor functionality." Far in the future, postmodernists would question the legitimacy of objective truth, but in the time of Saul, few would question the idea that there was a single truth to be known. Alignment with that truth, in close connection with the previous point about socioreligious law or direction, brought you closer to sanity; misalignment could result in or be a manifestation of madness.

Still another part of the story of Saul is how he is tormented by an evil spirit (1 Samuel, 16:14). This is a theme that was introduced in the first chapter of this text and would remain central to the concept of mental illness up to the present day in various parts of the world. Madness as caused by an external entity either influencing or inhabiting the sufferer is a belief extending back to the earliest traces of human history and continues wherever there remains a belief in such entities. It invites us to reflect on the experience of madness as *feeling* like an invasion of psychological disturbance to the sufferer, and *appearing* as such to outside observers. This is particularly true if the *change* is profound, sudden, and unwanted. Interestingly, Saul's torments by an evil spirit followed directly upon his abandonment by the spirit of God, who switched allegiance to David and rejected Saul as king because he had failed to fulfill his commandments. Again, in the ancient world, there wasn't the separation of factors (politics, religion, biology, sociology) that we take (somewhat) for granted in the modern world. In Saul's world, his psyche, his political actions, his relationship with God, and his relationship with his society are all closely linked in a holistic experience of life and its consequences.

On a more mundane level, there is also the question of whether King Saul actually had a specific mental disorder (Cook, 2012; Stein, 2011; Ben-Noun, 2003). From what we know of his childhood, Saul was very impressive, with no signs of mental illness. He was tall, strong, and so generally impressive that the people declared him their king. At first, his reign was equally impressive, with one military victory after another. But then there appeared times when "an evil spirit from God" would afflict him, and he would either fall into despair or enter a "prophetic frenzy." For the former, soothing music would help. For the latter, it just had to run its course, which could include King Saul stripping off his clothes and lying naked all day and night (1 Samuel 19:24). He was also prone to fits of jealous rage against David, who was otherwise his favorite and could soothe Saul when he was in despair. Thus, it appears that Saul's mood, energy, and rationality would shift dramatically over time, with periods of remission and periods of severe dysfunction. Later in life, Saul's overall functionality appears to have deteriorated; he became paranoid and committed suicide. This pattern of mood swings, combined with paranoid ideation, may fit best the modern diagnosis of bipolar disorder with psychotic features (American Psychiatric Association, 2013).

This leaves open the question of etiology. From a modern perspective, we might explore genetic factors, medical or drug-induced symptoms, and developmental problems such as abuse or neglect. None of these are considered in the story of Saul. As noted before, according to the Bible, the primary cause of Saul's psychological sufferings was his repeated failure to carry out the commandments of God. It started with his not following the proper protocol regarding a sacrifice, but the major problem was when God ordered him to destroy the Amalekites utterly, men, women, children, and even their cattle and sheep. When Saul kept the best animals alive to offer as a sacrifice, God was "grieved," rejected him as king of Israel, chose David to eventually replace him, and began to afflict him with evil spirits. Again, from a modern perspective, we may wonder about the influence of a sense of guilt, shame, and failure, leading to resentment, depression, and paranoia. From the perspective of his time, however, Saul's sufferings stemmed from disobedience, leading to his jealousy of a rival and his despair at losing the direct support of God. Although his eventual suicide was after being critically wounded by the Philistines and not wanting to be "abused" by his enemies, it is generally considered the tragic end of a long process of self-destruction.

Of course, Saul is not the only example of signs of mental illness appearing in the Old Testament. Cook (2012) lists a number of symptoms that make their appearance in various places in scripture, including anxiety, depressed mood, substance abuse, impulsivity, aggression, jealousy, elation, and failure to conform to social norms. Even signs of psychosis are evident, such as hallucinations, thought insertion, delusions, catatonia, and paranoid ideation. Ezekiel is noted as a particularly extreme example of someone from the Old Testament who may have experienced symptoms of what we now call schizophrenia. He heard the voice of God, in the form of what psychiatrists today would call command hallucinations. At the time, his status as a priest, from a priestly family, gave him social legitimacy for his experiences and proclamations. He was considered a prophet not a madman. There is no evidence in the Bible of his contemporaries doubting his sanity, but that was not true for all the Old Testament prophets. Hosea, Elisha, and Jeremiah, for instance, were all accused of madness in their own time. It appears that reported experiences outside the norm, including hearing the voice of God, were not automatically accepted as legitimate but were considered in the context of other factors to assess the possibility of insanity. Cook noted that cultural context is vital to consider when addressing the question of mental illness in sacred texts. This refers both to the issue of the process of writing these texts, which may not accurately reflect the historical facts regarding any individual's personal experiences, and to the interpretation of those texts, which religious believers view as reflecting real, spiritual experiences. This second issue not only reflects a respect for the beliefs of others but also raises the question of ontological and epistemological humility. On what basis can anyone say that there is no God, or if there is, God does not speak directly to people? In other words, on what authority can one say that these experiences were not real but rather the result of mental illness?

CULTURAL HOMEOSTASIS

While there is no simple answer to those questions, and to some extent, they lie outside the bounds of what we moderns call psychology, there is at least a rational way to approach them. If we take a wider view of human functioning, beyond the socioreligious, we can consider the multiple levels of functional human life. The most basic is biological. How physiologically healthy is the organism? This involves a number of components or factors. The organism must exist within a safe temperature range; it must have enough hydration; it must have regular, nutritious food. What are the prospects for long-term survival beyond maintaining minimal health? This typically involves environmental threats, such as animal predators, disease, and warfare or human predation. Another level of functionality is social/cultural. How well does the organism function within its social/cultural environment? Like biology, this involves a number of components or factors. The organism must be able to form and maintain supportive relationships, typically at the family, friendship, work, and wider cultural levels. This is vital because humans are collective by nature. People need each other for survival because no one individual makes or does everything necessary for that survival. Even at the relatively simple clan level, someone needs to take care of the young children when a parent is off hunting, and that person needs to still be able to obtain meat from the hunters in return for taking care of the children. As society became more complex, people become more dependent on ever-widening circles of other people doing the things they didn't but needed done, and vice versa. For human beings, expulsion from a community to live "in the wild" is a huge problem, so getting along with others is not just the Golden Rule, it is a core requirement for survival. Part of getting along with others is maintaining fundamental areas of cognitive agreement – shared truths. It also requires maintaining culturally established patterns of behavior. Thinking and acting differently than expected by others in the social group is a recipe for disaster.

All of this is an introduction to the idea of human homeostasis. This term refers to the processes used to maintain stable conditions for survival. While typically utilized to explore and understand physiological (biological) processes, it can be used to comprehend the psychological and sociological processes that "maintain stable conditions" for human group survival as well. This dovetails with the concept of systems theory. According to that model, understanding human functioning requires that we consider the *relationships* between subparts of any whole, whether it be parts of the brain, parts of the body, individuals in a family, families in a subculture, subcultures in a society, or different societies in a geographic area. Every unit, at each level, *both* exists as a separate thing (holon) and is connected in a transactional relationship with other units and levels, which together constitute a holarchy (Huitt, 2012; Koestler, 1990 [1967]). Therefore, the transactional relationship is, in practical effect, more important than the separate units in and of themselves. While the separate units are real and their attributes do matter, largely because they effect the relationships involved, it is ultimately the relationships themselves that are primary.

This is important to our topic in a number of ways. One has to do with religious faith. In a systems model, it hardly matters whether God is an ontological reality or not. What matters is the *relationship* between a *belief in God* (a subjective holon) and other holons and levels of a holarchy (the cultural system). In a society with a strong, unifying religion, individual faith and participation in collective ritual behavior are important in forming and maintaining effective bonds between individuals, between individuals and groups, and between groups. As long as the religious beliefs conform to experienced realities in the world (for instance, God only talks to selected individuals privately or through dreams rather than expecting God to talk out loud to entire groups of people in assembly), they can be maintained over long periods of time and meet the needs of society by providing shared purpose and meaning, societal cohesion, and addressing the existential challenges of human life. That is, religion generally promotes the stability of both holons (individuals) and the holarchy (nested groups), and thus homeostasis.

On the other hand, there are also many ways that religion can upset homeostasis; for instance, when individual beliefs conflict with other individuals or one's group/society, or when accepted religious belief exacerbates emotional suffering in regard to anxiety, guilt, or shame. That means that religion/mythology is directly related to the concept of mental health, as well as illness, but the connection is anything but simple or unidirectional. Based on what we know from modern research, religion can be an important coping mechanism and lower the risk for depression, anxiety, substance abuse, and antisocial behavior, but it can also increase neurotic fears and guilt and primitive defense mechanisms that restrict flexible responses to situational challenges (Koenig, 2009). Although it is always tricky to apply current psychological findings to ancient societies, if we look at the story of King Saul in a very general way, it is easy to see how his faith was both a source of his original *mental well-being* as a great leader when he believed he was supported by God and then his *mental disorder* when he believed he had been rejected by God.

CONCLUSION

The chapter reviewed some of what we know about mental health and mental illness in the ancient world. It focused on the roles of mythology, religion, and related aspects of the increasingly complex, hierarchal societies of the time to promote or disrupt mental health. It also touched on the question of specific psychological disorders. Did they exist? And how were they conceptualized at the time? Finally, it returned to our intention of increasing our understanding of mental health and mental illness by approaching it through a systems theory perspective. By taking this perspective, we can begin to integrate multiple factors in any phenomenon by thinking of it in terms of relationships and nested holarchies. How does an individual's biology relate to their psychological functioning and potential mental disorders? How does people's mental health or illness relate to their relationships with immediate peers and family? How does this relate to the larger community or society? These questions have different answers at various times and places in history. They do not fit well with simplistic notions about fixed nosologies of mental illness, even when they make some small, grudging allowance for cultural differences. What does become clear is that in the ancient world, there were emerging concepts of mental illness. However, they did not include anything regarding biological processes or individual development (with a brief nod to the Egyptians, who correctly identified the brain as the site of mental functions). Instead, they were dominated by the religious beliefs of the time, including demonology, animism, magic, and sensory experiences associated with communication from spiritual entities.

In the next chapter, we will start to explore the Classical era, when the dominance of religious explanations began to give way to more secular, humanistic conceptions regarding our topic.

CHAPTER 3

THE CLASSICAL ERA

The Classical era represents a period of history stretching roughly between the eighth century BC and the sixth century AD. The cultural and intellectual contributions of the era centered around the civilizations of ancient Greece and ancient Rome, sometimes referred to as the Greco-Roman world, which dominated life in the Mediterranean world at the time. Its influence was powerful throughout Europe, North Africa, and Western Asia, and the ripple effects of its influence continued to be felt long after its decline. As is well known, the rubble of the Greco-Roman World laid the foundation for what we now call the Western world, and it continues to have powerful impacts around the globe, in nearly every society on Earth. How many humans came to think about themselves and their place in the natural world was fundamentally altered. Modern concepts related to our topic, including humanism, the medical model, and empiricism, all have their roots in this era. The gods themselves began to shift from being unquestioned ontological entities to being regarded more as *ideas*, reflecting psychological realities more than external ones. Man became the measure of all things. Mental health and mental illness started to become human concerns rather than religious ones.

MENTAL ILLNESS IN THE CLASSICAL ERA

That, of course, is not how things started out. At the beginning of the Classical era, insanity was still considered a form of divine punishment (Alexander & Selesnick, 1966; Scull, 2015). Priests and other cultural authorities were in charge of identifying, interpreting, and treating mental illness. Mental health was generally associated with proper alignment with the will of the gods and society. The gods were, of course, always meddling in the lives of people and sometimes even striking them with madness. The modern word "panic" derives from the hysterical fear that Pan could induce with a scream in wild places. Followers of Dionysus could expect to be swept away in ritualistic ecstasy, driven to murderous rage or orgiastic lust. It was a madness designed to liberate the follower from the strictures of rigid authorities and unleash passions typically associated with the chthonic underworld.

Thus, in the Ancient Greek world, there was already a shift away from being possessed by demons toward being driven mad by the gods. A classic example was Oedipus, who famously became the unwitting pawn of the gods, fulfilling his fate despite all human attempts to avoid it. He was prophesied to end up killing his father and marrying his mother. As we all know, he unknowingly fulfilled his destiny, and the awareness of it drove him mad. Sigmund Freud saw this as an example of unconscious wishes driving the psyche despite conscious intentions. The Greeks saw it as an example of the hubris of the human personality to try and shape its own fate in opposition to or ignoring the fate assigned by the gods. In the end, the gods will win, even if it breaks the sanity of the human pawns in their game.

Over time, this would change. Greek philosophers and physicians moved toward a more rational, naturalistic understanding of mental illness. Their conception of mental health moved toward an individualized ideal of optimal human functioning in a variety of areas, including morality, ethics, physical health, human relationships, and the importance of the individual making meaningful contributions to society (Alexander & Selesnick, 1966; Millon, 2004; Scull, 2015). This meant that people were called upon to look deep inside themselves, take stock of their lives and their psyches, and set upon a project of personal self-improvement. The details regarding such things as morality, ethics, relationships, etc. were all up for debate. The answers were no longer assumed to come simply from religious texts. They had to come from a rational exploration of each area, trying to figure out a logical basis for each in turn. This shifted the cultural focus from the priests to the philosophers and the doctors.

Perhaps the best place to start in briefly describing this massive shift is the vital contribution of Pythagoras (582–510 BC) to the Greek understanding of nature and reality. He may, without too much overstatement, be credited with the foundation of science itself (Koestler, 1990 [1967]). He did this primarily by establishing that the phenomena of the world can and should be understood through the conceptual lens of numbers. In other words, there is underlying form and structure to all that exists, and rather than looking to the gods for understanding, it can be approached through the universal language of mathematics. For instance, he established this foundational truth in the field of music, identifying that the pitch of a note was directly connected to the length of the instrument's string and that the related scales are connected to a simple set of mathematical ratios. This established that a matter of human quality or experience (music) could be understood through an objective, measurable quantity (mathematics). Thus was science born. Many centuries later, the postmodernists would decry such mathematical objectification as a misleading, limiting, and reductionistic *misunderstanding* of reality. However, at the time of Pythagoras, this move represented a step away from relying on cultural authority for proclamations of truth and toward a more impersonal and intellectually freeing interpretation of reality. It also ennobled nature through the disembodied and ethereal nature of mathematics, which competed directly with the cultural and religious epistemologies of the time. It should also be noted that the Pythagorean focus on form and structure over substance and direct experience helped establish an epistemological dynamic that remains in effect to this day, in which we dichotomize between the material and the metaphysical. From atoms to atomic forces, from photons to light waves, from the brain to the mind, the pendulum of history swings back and forth between an emphasis on one versus the other, with a far greater emphasis on the delineation of these binaries of various phenomena than existed previously.

MENTAL ILLNESS

For the first time in human history, the Classical era established an increasingly clear demarcation between mental illness and mental health, or "a life well lived."

They began to be separate topics of study, one increasingly dominated by the philosophers and the other increasingly the purview of doctors and the medical establishment. Let's explore the second topic first, that of mental illness. As noted before, at the beginning of the era, Greek ideas about mental illness were not dissimilar to those of the Mythological era. Madness was typically seen as a punishment by the gods. It was visited upon someone in response to errant attitudes or behavior. We can see this in the world of Greek theatre, particularly its tragedies. Characters such as Orestes and Ajax were stricken with madness by divine entities, and the entire genre was dominated by this model of insanity (Thumiger, 2017). However, that was not the whole story. Greek tragedy developed a view of human life that was much more complex, where inter- and intrapersonal forces clashed to create suffering, chaos, and often disaster. Erotic love becomes a source of madness in the poems of Sappho. There were even suggestions that some forms of madness were "a gift from the gods." This weakening of the previous link between insanity and external punishment opened the door to a more nuanced, natural, and even medical understanding (Millon, 2004).

The Ancient Greeks increasingly supported the Egyptian idea that the brain was the source of mental activity. They also accepted the idea that hysteria in women was caused by a "wandering uterus" that had moved from its proper location (Alexander & Selesnick, 1966). This set the stage for more naturalistic if not more accurate conceptions of mental illness. One of the fundamental notions in the Greek approach to natural philosophy was the theory of the four elements – earth, air, fire, and water. All of creation was thought to be comprised of these elements, and they each had differing qualities, with both physical and psychological attributes and effects. The elements corresponded with their biological theory of the four humors – yellow bile (fire), black bile (earth), blood (air), and phlegm (water). Mental illness in various forms was thought to be caused by an imbalance in the humors. Too much or too little of any one was associated with certain psychological problems. An excess of yellow bile was associated with anger and aggression, blood with mania, black bile with depression, and phlegm with apathy or lethargy. Health was connected to the proper balance of the humors.

This sense of balance or harmony as a prime factor in mental health was developed by Pythagoras, who thought about mental life as consisting of opposing forces such as love–hate, good–bad, single–plural, sleep–wake, etc. In his view, mental disorders reflected an imbalance between these forces and was mediated by the humors. This idea of balance or harmony of biological (elements and humors) and psychological (hate–love, etc.) attributes was developed further by Alcmaeon (557–491 BC), who conducted careful dissections to map structural anatomy and tracked the nervous system from sensory nerves to the brain, which he recognized as the organ of thought. His concept of metabolic harmony, called isonomy, could easily be extended to mental health and its connection to physical health.

A major character in our story is Hippocrates (460–367 BC). Working with his associates at the Cos College of Medicine in Athens, he started with the humoral and homeostasis principles of Pythagoras and added the practice of detailed clinical observation and inductive reasoning. The physicians at the college saw the patient him- or herself and not religious phenomena as the source of all mental disorder. In other words, it wasn't the gods that cause mental illness but a bio-logically based disease process. Hippocrates was an early empiricist, relying on case history, observable symptoms, and treatment outcome to guide his thinking. An interesting side-note is that Hippocrates also relied on dream interpretation to understand the cause of his patients' maladies, especially when they reflected a conflict between the contents of the dream and the patient's recent activities. This foray into psychomedical dream interpretation was a forerunner to Sigmund Freud's famous reliance on dreams to understand the unconscious psyches of his patients.

Another contribution of Hippocrates and his associates was his development of a classification system for mental illness. Building on the foundation of the humoral theory, they proposed four basic temperaments: the choleric (an excess of yellow bile), the melancholic (an excess of black bile), the sanguine (an excess of blood), and the phlegmatic (an excess of phlegm). They also identified other clinical syndromes we would now call delirium, phobias, hysteria, and mania. They proposed various etiological sources for these problems, but mainly they adhered to the humoral system. This appears to roughly parallel both the modern conception of personality disorders and our ongoing difficulty clearly differentiating relatively healthy character types from personality disorders and acute clinical syndromes such as major depression.

One consequence of the more naturalistic approach to mental illness was a more empathetic attitude toward and treatment of the mentally ill. Although we are focusing on identification rather than treatment of mental illness in this text, it is important to point out where treatment practices *reflect* changes in the underlying understanding of mental illness. In this case, moving toward a conceptualization of mental illness as a disease process led to a more sympathetic attitude, combined with treatments designed to address the imagined disease process. The focus was on a return to health. In the older mythological model, mental illness was seen as a punishment by the gods, and thus the logical response was often condemnation, ridicule, rejection, and further punishment. In the newer model, an identification of symptoms, combined with conjecture about their naturalistic source, led to the prescription of medications and other medical treatments under the caring and sympathetic eye of a physician.

It is important to point out that this change of thinking, attitude, and sub-sequent practice was not complete or universal under the Ancient Greeks. For instance, public attitudes and practices did not typically reflect the beliefs of the intellectual elites. The public had a tendency to lag behind intellectual prog-ress and hold onto older paradigms. Also, how much cultural change occurred depended a great deal on what city-state one lived in, with Athens being at the forefront of progress. In addition, almost all of the great thinkers in the Greek era continued to at least *feign* an ongoing belief in the gods and their influence on the human psyche and behavior, and many still actually believed in it. The result of these conflicting influences was what many would term a fundamental *tension* in the Greek worldview between the divine and the naturalistic (Tarnas, 1991). The level and dynamic results of this tension were unique in the Greek situation, given their position in history as a "crossroads" of the world. There was a great deal of trade and movement of people throughout the Greek world, making them unusually influential in the wider world. As a result, this tension between science and tradition became the norm in many areas and continues to this day as an ongoing dynamic in our modern world. What is important here is that in many ways, Ancient Greece was the *birthplace* of this tension. We can see, in the Greek experience, the many elements that result, including (1) the process of change in a culture's fundamental beliefs, (2) the growing coexistence of different and conflicting worldviews within the same culture, and (3) the resulting need to *justify* a worldview in ways that at least attempts to sway those who disagree with it through logic and facts.

Returning to the changing beliefs about mental illness in the Classical era, we need to take a look at the contributions of Ancient Rome. An interesting dynamic of that culture was its emphasis on the practical application of technology and practice rather than the Greek preoccupation with philosophy and theory (Millon, 2004). Subjects like engineering, architecture, and applied medicine were their forte, not the development of theories of mental illness. On the other hand, this practical-mindedness of the Romans actually moved the era's conceptualization of mental illness toward the rational and naturalistic and further away from the religious or mythological. The intellectual elite of Rome wanted to leave behind the myth, magic, and superstition of the Greeks while building upon the Hippocratic movement toward the empirical, rational, and naturalistic explanations for mental phenomena.

For instance, Asclepiades (171–110 BC) focused on direct observation to differentiate acute from chronic mental disorders, as well as identifying more specific symptoms such as hallucinations and delusions. He also stressed environmental impacts on mental health, which increased the perceived importance of the complex interplay of organistic and environmental factors in mental illness. Finally, he proposed a systematic approach to the newly emerging "corpuscular theory" of his day. That model rejected the Greek humoral theory of mental functioning and instead embraced the idea that the nervous system, including the brain, had pores or small passageways (*canalicula*), which became enlarged or tightened as they were impacted by various factors. Overenlargement or overrestriction led to the symptoms of mental illness. Overenlargement led to apathy, anxiety, and depression (*laxum* state), while overrestriction led to excitement, delirium, and aggression (*strictum* state). If the two sets of symptoms co-occurred, it was referred to as a *mixtum* state. Mental health could be restored by returning the canalicula to their optimal openness. This could be achieved through a combination of biological, chemical, and lifestyle oriented treatments, thus foreshadowing modern, multimodal, or integrated treatment planning. This multifactoral model was developed by thinkers like Cicero (103–43) and Celsus (15 BC–30 AD), who explored the impact of the psyche on physical disorders (psychosomatic illness) as well as lifestyle choices such as city living versus rural living – with an agrarian lifestyle being seen as healthier and promoting biological and psychological homeostasis.

Galen (131–201) was probably the best-known Roman physician, both then and now. His brilliance, knowledge, expertise, polemic attitude, and ambition led him to produce the most extensive, forward-thinking, and influential medical books in ancient history. He sought to incorporate everything that was already known with his own observations and research. He studied the most advanced anatomy and neurophysiology of his time. As a result, his conclusions about mental illness included both the humoral system and the corpuscular model of mental functioning. He also considered environmental, lifestyle, and emotional influences. In addition, he proposed a general life force (spiritus anima) to explain the difference between organic and inorganic matter. In combination with more specific animal spirits (pneuma), these forces regulated a variety of physiological and psychological processes and were complicit with mental illness. This eclectic approach to etiology extended to his taxonomy of mental disorders. Galen differentiated multiple types of depression, anxiety, hysteria, and psychoses, based in part on their various causes and presentations.

Later Roman writers reinforced and extended some of Galen's ideas. They expanded the biological models, getting no closer to what we now know about how the body and brain actually work but reinforcing the naturalistic approach and moving further away from the older mythological model. By the third century AD, the Western world had reached the fullest extent of this shift of thought and practice. The changes included a naturalistic approach to mental illness, a rational, observational approach to assessment and diagnosis, a focus on specific symptoms and direct linkage to clearly differentiated disorders, and finally a humane, empathetic, and medically oriented approach to treatment. The divergence from a mytho-cultural system was profound. By the end of the Roman period, at least among the moneyed and learned classes, mental illness was no longer viewed as punishment of the gods, calling for an equally punitive response, but a naturally occurring disease process, calling for a rational, professional treatment program.

MENTAL HEALTH IN THE CLASSICAL ERA

The previous section focused on the changing conception of mental illness in the Classical era. This section focuses on the concept of mental health. The first point to make is how necessary it is to separate these sections. In the Mythological era, as discussed previously, all areas of life – the religious, the political, the social, the medical, and the psychological – were closely linked. One of the hallmarks of cultural evolution is increasing differentiation between various spheres of life. More extensive hierarchies develop, along with skill and knowledge specialization, into professionalization, social and physical separation of different groups, and the appearance and tolerance of different worldviews within the same overarching culture. These changes naturally bring about new challenges, such as intracultural doubt and angst, individual alienation, intergroup conflicts and resentments, and an increased need to justify one's beliefs and practices. These dynamics were exacerbated by the *weakening* of the unifying and meaning-making power of religion in the Greco-Roman world over the course of the thousand-year stretch of time dominated (in the West) by this cultural system. This new reality created a profound new field of human thought and practice – a human potential movement.

Yes, I used the controversial phrase associated with the New Age self-help movement of the 1970s and 1980s. Who is a better historical model for a '70s style New Age "guru" than Socrates? He was an eccentric man who snubbed his nose at the intellectual and cultural elites of his time, proclaimed a new wisdom for the people, lived his philosophical beliefs as a lifestyle, promoted total honesty and authenticity whatever the consequences, and thus inspired a cadre of disaffected youth (mostly from the upper classes) to follow him, causing resentment and repudiation from their elders. If I hadn't mentioned Socrates' name, you might have thought I was writing about Fritz Perls, the founder of Gestalt therapy and leader of workshops at Esalen Institute (CA, USA) in the 1960s. Of course, many of these similarities break down when you explore the deeper aspects of their respective teachings, but the core parallel is there. They each led a "counterculture" movement that emphasized individuals figuring out for themselves what they believed, what their core values were, and how they wanted to live to manifest those beliefs and values. Happiness was not pursued by following the given cultural rules and doing what the gods tell you to do. It is found by living an honest, authentic life – being true to yourself and what wisdom you can carve out from your own self-exploration, wisdom about the world, and personal experience.

Of course, like the more naturalistic understanding of mental illness by the end of the Roman period, this approach to mental health (wellness) was not there at the very beginning of the Classical era. In Homer's epic poetry, written around 1000 BC, insanity was still depicted as a form of punishment by the gods. By 500 BC, this focus was shifting toward the anthropological. Mental health was just beginning to be explored at the human level. What constitutes a "good life"? This was increasingly based on discourse regarding possible universal moral values and the improvement of human life through diet, exercise, social relationships, medicine, sport, relaxation/sleep, sex practices, and civic engagement. By the time we get to the Stoic and Epicurean systems of Rome, the enterprise of improving psychological well-being was primarily a humanistic affair (Alexander & Selesnick, 1966).

We mentioned Hippocrates earlier in reference to mental illness, but he was also important in regard to our current discussion regarding mental health. He proposed a naturalistic etiology not only for mental illness but for mental health as well (Millon, 2004). Like others at the time, Hippocrates emphasized the principles of balance, harmony, alignment with nature, and self-healing. He was quite humble about the ability of physicians to administer "cures" that were effective and thus developed the motto that medical students to this day are reminded of: "If you can do no good, at least do no harm." This leaves the physician in the position of trusting in the power of nature, the patient's own good wisdom, and the limited professional interventions that were available to produce healing. This idea was reinforced through another Hippocratic idiom, "It is nature that heals the patient." Doctors are seen as "nature's assistant," helping the sufferer to realign (harmonize) their life with health-giving nature. Again, sleep, exercise, good diet, being surrounded by peace and beauty, as well as by caring, supportive people, were all considered vital elements in pursuit of psychological wellness. This was also true in the treatment of mental illness, and because of these factors' generic connection to overall health, they dovetailed with an overall understanding and practice regarding both physical and psychological wellness.

It is this general idea of individual psychological wellness that occupies us here. There is little indication that the pre–Greco-Roman world cared much about this. What material is available points to the priority of the well-being of large groups of people, which was seen as secondary to and dependent upon fulfilling the will of the gods. The decreasing priority of religion in the Greco-Roman world created the space for the ascendency of a more human psychology. This demanded a new philosophy that sought to establish values and principles of human life separate from or at least primary to religious faith. The two philosophers most closely associated with early efforts in that direction were Plato and Socrates. Given that little is known of Socrates' actual discourse, since he wrote nothing himself, and much of what is known about his thought was written by his student Plato, we will discuss their ideas together as Platonism.

Platonism centers on a core belief that there are fundamental ideas or forms that support all that is true about the world, both physically and metaphysically (Durant, 1926; Russell, 1945). The visible world of objects and behavior are but the manifestation of these forms, or archetypes, reflecting their foundational reality. This is a vital concept because while this model may be embraced in conjunction with religious faith, it can also be understood, discussed, and acted upon with little to no reference to any particular divinity or religious belief. In the Platonistic view, the forms are fundamental to all reality – not contingent upon particular deities, although their existence assumes a transcendent divine reality behind the physical world. They are pure, changeless, and universal. They include not just the physical universe (which is not our concern in this text) but also concepts of justice, goodness, evil, beauty, and health. Platonism invites us, even insists, that we look beyond the ever-shifting cacophony of manifest phenomena to their underlying essence.

In regard to the human personality, Plato saw its fundamental characteristics as based on three primary sources: emotion, desire, and cognition. He connected these sources or functions as centered in the loins (desire), heart (emotion), and brain (cognition). He saw human strife and suffering arising from conflicts within the psyche between these three main functions. One of the primary conflicts that caused problems was between our animalistic desires and those values and insights gained by the intellect. Goodness and peace arose from aligning oneself with the mind over the loins. The better one was able to master one's passions and instead align with pure knowledge, the more wise and calm one would be. To achieve this, it was important to look past the superficial aspects of reality, including oneself, and investigate deeper truths. After all, like Socrates, he promoted the idea that one could use rational analysis to cut through the superficial manifestations of reality to reveal a truth that was objective and universal.

This means one cannot trust the received "truths" of his or her given culture or even their immediate sense experience but must look deeper, with their intellect, to discover truth. This idea that what is immediately apparent cannot be trusted as real or true and could in fact be a self-deception or at least only a superficial representation of something much more fundamental was a radical concept. It placed the individual human intellect in a new position, as the only path to wisdom. We have to figure it out for ourselves, the world does not self-evidently reveal itself to us, or be revealed by the historical beliefs of our culture. Not only that, but it will take a great deal of effort, skill, and discipline to get closer to truth. The phenomena of the world, including the culture one is living within, are powerful forces, distracting and deceiving us. They are directly powerful, in that the given truths of our cultures carry worldly authority, so defying them has many consequences, from social censure to torture and even death. Seeking truth is not just an act of will; it often takes profound courage. It is, in the spirit of Joseph Campbell, a hero's journey.

One of the important aspects of this new approach to truth was its aforementioned relation to mathematics. It didn't take long for Greek philosophers to realize that if the truth about the natural world extended to human psychology, and that truth consisted of universal constants, then those constants must correspond to the fundamental constants of mathematics. They discovered such constants in the areas of art and music, so they must be there in all areas of science. Although they were not able to take this idea very far in the area of psychology, they did develop a sense of the importance of balance, harmony, logic, and structure over confusion and randomness, which relates to mathematics. Geometry in particular seemed to reflect this emerging sense of mathematical order underlying the apparent flux of the natural world. Dovetailing with this belief was an awareness that understanding mathematics did not follow from studying religious texts or following the dictates of society. It was the human intellect, seeking truth beyond the historical givens of those sources, that moved understanding forward. This reinforced the idea that seeking wisdom about the human condition was a rational exercise of human reason. We are the source of self-knowledge, the seeker of deeper wisdom about optimal human functioning, the discoverers of the values and meaning that should produce and support a "good life." This was the birthplace of the dictum "the unexamined life is not worth living."

Of course, this was also the birthplace of skepticism and sophistry (Tarnas, 1991). If the human intellect is the source of all wisdom, then the door is wide open for relativity in the form of competing personal opinions. It becomes a marketplace of ideas that can be bought and sold like any other commodity, made popular by classic forces of salesmanship – superficial attraction, the charisma of the salesman, appeal to vanity, overpromising results, and ease of purchase. The sophists realized that it is possible and relatively easy to refute other beliefs. There is always a chink, a weakness that can be exploited to discredit an opposing idea. While they freed people from the chains of traditional belief, the replacement was the shifting sands of pragmatism and good (sophisticated) argumentation. This was the birthplace of distrust in the manipulations of smart, educated people (elites and charlatans) as they promoted their pet ideas for their own ends. Manipulating gullible followers, the history that followed would overflow with a succession of Svengalis, offering easy bliss for those who would take their advice and pay them handsomely. It is important to note that not all these characters and trends were lying charlatans. Many, if not most, have been honest players. Having developed a system for human wisdom and happiness that they truly believed in, they wanted to offer that great gift to others. But how is one to separate the wheat from the chaff? What is the universal truth by which to judge these gifts? Judging them by their results is not adequate, because pragmatism in human affairs is problematical. Ideas can work in the human world because they are attractive, easy to digest, and appeal to our vanity – not because they hold a deeper wisdom or truth. Nazism worked – authoritarianism works – hate, prejudice, and brutality all work, in their own ways, at least for a time. And if "man is the measure of all things," then on what basis can we even say these things are bad if the people say they are good and their leaders have provided sophisticated rationales for their value and truth?

With this in mind, we can return to the Greek and later Roman ideas about what constitutes the good life, as revealed by their philosophical explorations regarding what is good and healthy in human psychology and subsequent behavior. The first principle that Plato espoused was alignment with the universal forms of truth, beauty, and goodness (Alexander & Selesnick, 1966). He saw the human mind as a creation of nature and thus having the capacity to access to its deeper truths. This could happen through either an effortful, slow process or a sudden awakening, a moment of intuitive insight. As such, this view foreshadowed the Buddhist idea of enlightenment and reflected a similar process of reconnecting a lost union with eternal truths of existence. It should be noted that in the Platonic tradition, this awakening was not just philosophical or humanistic but included a belief in the divine. People were thought to be able to assimilate with the divine and share in its immorality. This elevated humanity closer to the level of the gods but also reflected a depersonalization of the gods. This included a concept of the divine as reflecting a single god, which was closer to a pure spirit of *nous* or *logos* and directly accessible to humanity rather than separate, anthropomorphized gods, which were not. One consequence of this belief was that psychological suffering was seen partly as the result of ignorance or self-deception. Psychological wellness resulted from insight not just into psychological phenomena but into the divine nature of our souls and experiencing the reconnection with that nature and thus the *cosmos*.

According to Plato, the cosmos (order of the universe) reflects the logos (divine wisdom) (Durant, 1926). Therefore, one could attain knowledge of the logos through an understanding of the cosmos and could participate in that universal order by aligning with the logos. Thus, geometry, astrology, and mental health are intimately linked. Geometry was the language of the universe, astrology its communication to us through the heavens, and our mental health could be improved by knowing the language, receiving the communication, and living according to the wisdom received. All of this was pursued through logic and spontaneous insight. Direct observation, measurement, and deductive reasoning were highly suspect, as they would at best reflect temporary manifestations of reality and not the underlying, fundamental forms themselves. Platonic idealism was certainly a compelling approach to truth and continues to influence us today, as people not only seek for universal forms (personality types, depth psychology archetypes) and values (equality, individual rights, democracy, love, freedom, tolerance/acceptance of difference), but they are happy to do so with little to no demand for epistemological proof of their reality. In Plato's time, as today, it was enough to "feel" that one had found a system of truth to base one's life upon.

Not everyone agreed with this, even during Plato's era. The idea that more was needed than faith in a new mythology, based more on observable facts than previous ones, was developed by Aristotle and his followers. Aristotle believed that true reality was to be found in the concrete world of observable phenomena, not eternal *ideas*. He replaced these ideas with categories, based on common characteristics, to organize and understand reality. For instance, a dog can be understood by measuring its weight, its color, its disposition, and other qualities. One does not have to refer to a universal ideal of "dog-ness." There has to be a real substance-object to be described. That is not to say there are not forms in the world (acorns from oak trees don't spontaneously grow into other kinds of trees), but in Aristotle's conception, form was another inherent quality, a potentiality of the substance. We know the truth of things by observing their qualities not just at one point but over time. Therefore, birth, development, decay, and death were important dynamics to consider in the reality of existence. If mathematics was the favorite science for Plato, for Aristotle, it was biology (Millon, 2004; Russell, 1945).

This shift in thinking had the effect of both increasing the primacy of the objective, observable world and calling into ontological question various human values like love, equality, and democracy. Values lose their fundamental legitimacy and start to sound more like transitory personal opinions. This shift was not lost on Aristotle, who recognized that with his approach, it was impossible to attain perfect knowledge of ethics and morality. In this view, these areas are, by their nature, ambiguous, contingent, and ultimately derived from human experience. He saw the goal of life as happiness deriving from virtue, but virtue was situational and typically required some form of balance between two extremes, both of which would be misguided to pursue exclusively. For instance, temperance is the balance between austerity and indulgence. Pride reflects the balance between arrogance and self-abasement, and so on. The proper balance of the extremes can only be derived from human reflection on the unique and ever-changing factors in each situation. Divine geometry cannot help you. The good is not a transcendent, singular idea, but an equivocal, subjective decision, that ultimately can only be judged by its practical results. This signaled the birth of humanistic pragmatism, in many ways the opposite of idealism, and established what Richard Tarnas elegantly described as the, "balance and tension between empirical analysis and spiritual intuition" that has driven the Western world ever since (1991, p. 68).

As noted before, this tension between different approaches to psychological wellness was a unique characteristic of the Classical era. It started because the Greek religious system was an amalgamation of multiple sources, including the Minoan, the Mycenaean, and later, those of invading tribes from the north. There was also the fact that what we call Ancient Greece was not a single nation or empire but actually a loose affiliation of different city-states without a strong, central authority that could take a side on these matters and enforce it as a single orthodoxy. This made it easier for the primacy of Greek mythology to fade over time and be influenced by a multitude of cultural forces both within Greece itself, as well as from other cultures, through the various colonies it established, as well as international trade.

This situation was exacerbated by the conquests of Alexander the Great. He conquered immense areas, bringing them under the influence of Greek thought, but that influence would not be consolidated or extended after his early death.

Rather, it quickly faded, leaving only an "afterglow" of Greek thought and practice, with the original cultural beliefs remaining intact and in conflict with the Greek system. The situation was then further complicated by the transfer of power from Greece to Rome. Rome had its own history and early influences but famously absorbed Greek mythology and philosophy wholesale. This meant that the cultural power of Greece both endured and expanded its reach but also was forced to adjust, reflecting the realities of the Roman world. These realities included a much more pragmatic mindset, a more massive and homogeneous political world of its own design under its sway, and a fundamental lack of cultural allegiance to the Greek religious system.

As a result of these factors, the Roman approach to mental health moved away from its deep philosophical roots and connection to Greek mythology and took on more of the characteristics of modern "self-help" movements. On the one hand, there was a continuation of the Greek concern with healthy lifestyle regarding food, exercise, family, relationships, spiritual practice, useful work, and contribution to society. On the other hand, there was competition between two main philosophical schools of thought, the Stoic and the Epicurean (Alexander & Selesnick, 1966; Tarnas, 1991). While their roots were in the Greek Platonic and Aristotelian traditions, they were both more pragmatic in nature, seeking to help people deal with the vicissitudes of life in uncertain and troubled times. There was no need to align with a particular religious system or deep beliefs about the nature of the universe.

The ultimate goal of the Stoic and Epicurean systems was the attainment of lived experience of peace and happiness. By their time in history, there was far less reliance on cosmology or metaphysics, at least in the Greco-Roman world. The Stoic and Epicurean approaches were practical and materialistic. Stoic philosophy asserted that human happiness can only follow from a radical acceptance of the realities of life and death. There are extreme limits on what humans can control or even influence (certainly not the ultimate reality of one's eventual death). Fighting against those limits only causes stress, anxiety, bitterness, and misery. Psychological stress is the inevitable response to lack of acceptance of what is. We can take actions that may affect our situation, but we should not be emotionally invested in the results. If this sounds familiar to some readers, it can be seen as a forerunner to Buddhism's four noble truths (life is painful; this suffering is caused by desire; suffering/desire can be ended; there is a recipe for ending it). The Stoic view first emerged in Athens in the third century BC but became increasingly influential in the Roman world through the writings of Cicero and Seneca. Being rooted in the older Greek tradition, it saw reality as embedded in an intelligent, divine force that ordered everything. Therefore, peace could be achieved by aligning oneself with the inherent order of the cosmos. This alignment was essentially ethical and virtuous in nature. It required a great deal of discipline and self-denial. Fulfillment of duties to others and the larger community was highly valued. The temptation to give in to selfish, short-term desires was to be overcome.

By contrast, although the Epicureans agreed that freedom from stress was the source of happiness, their prescription for lowering stress was not to accept a higher logos of the cosmos but to pursue personal pleasure in all our affairs. This philosophy represented a clear break from its Greek roots, rejecting a belief in anthropomorphic gods or transcendent ideals of goodness. Instead, it asserted that beliefs in such things were a powerful *source* of human suffering, creating unnecessary guilt, shame, stress, and self-denial (Russell, 1945). Happiness is best pursued through a withdrawal from the tumult and vicissitudes of worldly life and retirement to a quiet, peaceful enjoyment of life's pleasures in the company of friends. This may have been the first formal adoption of the idea of freedom *from* religion rather than freedom *through* religion. At its most extreme, this approach led to Skepticism.

Thinkers like Sextus Empiricus and Pyrrho of Elis asserted that since there was no basis for absolute certainty about any basic truths, the only rational position was to suspend all judgment. Nothing was certain, not even the assertion that nothing was certain. If the Epicurean position laid the foundation for modern humanism, the Skeptics can be seen as the first postmodernists. Like their modern counterparts, they noted that any conflict between competing truths required some outside criterion, but that in turn required justification about another criterion, which leads either to an endless regression of postulates – a groundless circular argument. Since finding ultimate truth was impossible, the only source of peace was to remain radically open-minded, practical, and humble about life.

Of course, the limitations of these models are many. The Stoic approach was rather dry, serious, and entailed hard work. It had the advantage of being both practical and idealistic, but its execution was difficult and therefore not very appealing to the masses. The Epicurean approach certainly sounded more fun, but it's philosophical foundation was thin and uninspiring. It's hard to get too excited about a belief that nothing is true, including the argument that nothing is true! As a result, not too many rank-and-file Greeks or Romans pursued these lifestyles. Instead, like many in our own postmodern world, most remained inspired by the spiritual path. Not only does it offer a foundation for truth about the world, it asserts there is an escape from its sufferings and provides a variety of practices (combined with the advantages of group membership) to achieve that escape.

The last philosophical development in the Roman world that impacts our thesis was the advent of what became known as Neoplatonism. This movement sought to bridge the world of rational philosophy and the mystery religions. Its high point came with the work of Plotinus in the third century AD. He espoused the idea that it was legitimate to develop a rational understanding of the natural world, but this was only a prelude to a deeper and ultimately transcendent reality and spiritual life beyond reason and nature (Russell, 1945). This reality was conceptualized as emanating from a singular, nonanthropomorphic entity called the One or the Good. Clearly a precursor for the later Roman acceptance of Christianity, this belief saw the material world as the most distant and flawed level of reality. It was transitory and atomized, prone to disintegration and decay. Therefore, any true peace or freedom had to be sought beyond the natural, mundane world, including mainstream religion and culture. What was needed was a deep, personal relationship with a transcendent, spiritual force to transform one's life beyond that experienced by the masses and thus actively participate in a spiritual life that offered a special and exclusive path to happiness and peace to the initiated.

If Neoplatonism was the last philosophical development of the Classical era, then the rise of the mystery cults was the last spiritual development, just before the emergence of Christianity as the new dominant religious force in the Western world. The basic idea of a cult is that it is a relatively small group of people who are tightly aligned with a religious system that is outside the mainstream for their culture. Sometimes they are affiliated with a particular leader, but this is not necessary. More often, the affiliation is with a set of unusual religious beliefs. Partly in order to protect themselves from outsiders, they tend to be highly secretive not only about their membership but about their beliefs and practices. Another dynamic of mystery cults is that they emerge from religious pluralism (Johnson, 2007). They develop in situations in which there are a variety of religious alternatives available to people, stemming from the influx of different, often foreign cultural influences. They offer an alternative to the mainstream, so this requires that the dominant cultural forces do not or cannot stop them. Like other developments in the Classical era, this prefigures our modern situation, in which in an increasing number of places, people can choose their religion in a marketplace of faiths.

There were many of these cults in the Classical world, so we will discuss only one. The Eleusinian Mysteries were associated with the god Dionysus (Bacchus to the Romans). According to most stories, Dionysus was the son of Zeus and Persephone (Evans, 1988). When he was a child, he was taken and killed by the Titans. His heart was rescued by Athena, who gave it to Zeus, who then fed it to his human lover Semele in order that Dionysus might be reborn. Zeus also destroyed the Titans, and humanity arose from their remains, thus imbuing human nature with a core of sin. According to the beliefs of the Eleusinian Mysteries, humans must strive to overcome this "original sin" through their initiation to achieve a form of salvation, both in this world and, more importantly, in the next. If this story sounds familiar, it has been noted as prefiguring Christian religious themes. Humans are born into sin. A savior is born through the union of God and a human. The savior is killed by his enemies but is reborn. Salvation is found through a rejection of traditional religious and civil arrangements and "following" the savior through a purifying transformation of heart and soul.

Of course, there were also significant differences between Christianity and the Eleusinian Mysteries. For one thing, Christian piety typically entails a rejection of bodily instincts, interests, and desires, reflected in the traditional vows of poverty, chastity, and obedience. The Mysteries, on the other hand, appear to have served as a channeled release for what later Christians would think of as baser, more material and self-centered energies. Dionysian rituals, although by definition cloaked in mystery, appear to have included violence (tearing animals apart), orgiastic behavior, and great consumption of food, drink, and perhaps other drugs (Evans, 1988). They reflected a ritualized release of bodily passions – ecstasy – rather than their consecrated censure and control. The existence of such practices, within the context of a larger religious system, signaled that such energies or passions were not necessarily evil, although they did need to be released in a controlled setting. These Mysteries prefigured later pageants, festivals, spontaneous ecstatic social eruptions, and even entire social movements such as the "hippy" movement in the 1960s. Free love, rock-n-roll music, and mild-altering drugs were supposed to transform the world, but it can be argued that a lack of ritualized control of these elements doomed the movement from the start. Like an out-of-control nuclear reaction, it naively thought the power it was unleashing would naturally lead only to good results, but without the limits and channeling of energy required, it quickly exploded and burned out. Whatever the failings of the counterculture movements of the West, their regular reemergence throughout history suggests that these earthy, material, bodily energies are powerful, embedded in our very being, and cry out for some kind of release. Much of our Western history regarding spirituality and mental health can be understood in the context of a conflict between those who feel that such energies are sinful and must be repressed and those that feel they are natural and should be released, at least within reasonable limits (Eliade, 1957; Evans, 1988; Pagels, 1988; Reik, 1970). The demonization or sacralization of the body and its needs and desires has continued to be a central point of contention in the ongoing history of the West.

A closely related element of all the Mysteries was the power of group identification and experience. As noted earlier, initiates in these cults enjoyed a sense of being special or chosen, standing apart from the mass of humanity still wandering in error, darkness, and the mundane existence of everyday life. This has been a powerful force, deeply embedded in human psychology, throughout history. This force is amplified exponentially when it includes profound, life-changing experiences (Eliade, 1958). These experiences, shared in a group format, reinforce the beliefs of the group, solidify the group bond, and have a transformative effect on the individual's psyche. Fear, loneliness, dread, alienation, and despair give way through ecstatic experiences to an afterglow of peace, love, affiliation, hope, and faith. Whatever the ontological validity of the specific beliefs associated with the Eleusinian and other Mysteries, nobody can doubt the allure of such an initiation and the likely positive psychological effects for many of its adherents. Released from at least some of the concerns and strictures of everyday life and promised preferential treatment in the afterlife, devout members must have experienced a tremendous benefit to their emotional and cognitive well-being.

An important connection needs to be made here. The combination of religious and cultural beliefs, group identification, and initiatory practices designed to elicit profound change in the participants' lives have all the hallmarks of what we have called "rites of passage." Sarah Johnson (2007) makes the point that the Eleusinian mysteries, in particular, may have developed out of clan-based adolescent initiation rites. This means that such activities were not just for group identification or an expression of religious belief but were supposed to be transformational. The people participating in them were experiencing something very intense and changing as a result. This was important in a society from which rites of passage were increasingly missing. It suggests that such rites and the changes they produce are a deeply felt need in the human psyche. Something profound is missing for people if there is no collective, ceremonial process to undergo and emerge from one developmental or status level and into another. These status areas include such things as stage of life (child, adult, elder), religious affiliation and level of commitment, professional affiliation, political power, relational commitment (marriage, divorce), etc. The initiatory process helps provide meaning for the different status states, produces group affirmation of the initiate's new status, and sets forth the rules, obligations, and rights accorded people in their new status. This would naturally be a source of pride, accomplishment, empowerment, and sense of stability in what one could do and expect from others, based on one's status in the culture.

CONCLUSION

While this similarity with traditional initiation rites was true in relation to the mystery religions, there were a number of things that set them apart. For instance, they were not mutually exclusive and were usually not condoned by mainstream society. People were allowed to be members of different mystery cults, and they were vulnerable to occasional attempts to weed them out. However, these attempts were generally sporadic and ineffective. This followed from a number of factors, including the fact that the Greco-Roman world was highly fractionalized. Ancient Greece was famously a loose affiliation of different city-states, and while Ancient Rome may have had a stronger central authority, it ruled over an immense empire that included widely differing cultures and native religions. In both cases, the central authority had a generally relaxed attitude about other people's religions. This meant that there was little expectation that all people, in all places should be practicing the same religion.

This plurality made it a precursor to the modern situation in which people can literally shop for a religion of their choice, build their own religion from various sources, or even choose no religion at all. In fact, the complex, heterogeneous, and increasingly secular nature of the Classical era made it a profound transition point between the ancient and modern worlds. The ancient world was dominated by cultures that were homogenous, rigidly hierarchal, and dominated by a seamless integration of the religious, the political, and the personal. Mental illness was defined within the religious and cultural idioms of the day, and mental health was primarily a product of personal alignment with those idioms. The Classical era shifted that foundation. As time went on, the Greco-Roman became increasingly secular, atomized, and individualized. More and more, it became the responsibility of individuals to decide what they wanted to believe about religion, what their role should be in the world, and how they should live their lives to feel happy and fulfilled. Mental illness was increasingly seen as a medical problem, which could be diagnosed by physicians and treated through medical interventions. There was still a great deal of overlap between the concepts of mental health and mental illness, of course, and much of the attention paid to achieving mental health was aligned with the alleviation of mental illness, but that was changing as well. The key to understanding the Greco-Roman world is recognizing that the weakening of a single, religious-political force to shape people's lives opened the door to a medical and more personalized approach to both mental health and mental illness. Of course, this weakening or a centralized cultural authority also set the conditions for Rome to be able to switch to an entirely different religion – one with no roots in its unique history or traditions. That religion was Christianity, and the impact of that historical change on ideas regarding mental illness and mental health is the topic of the next chapter.

CHAPTER 4

THE MIDDLE AGES

The Middle Ages was a period of history ranging roughly from the sixth to the fifteenth century AD. The contributions of the era we will explore centered around the civilizations of Western Europe and the Middle East, which extended from North Africa through Northern Europe and from the Atlantic Ocean to the Arabian Sea. Two religions, Christianity and Islam, dominated this part of the world with their competing religious and cultural views. These views greatly impacted the developing conceptualizations of mental health and illness in the West. We will explore the transition from the Classical perspective through the medieval to the dawning of the Renaissance. We will also look at the views and practices developing in China and India at the time. Most of the rest of the world was dominated by more local, mythologically oriented ideas about mental illness and thus was not changing much in fundamental approaches from the mythological era, although specific beliefs were different from place to place. Thus our focus in this chapter will be on geographical areas and cultures that represented *fundamental changes* to the concepts regarding mental health and illness and directly impacted what would become the dominant views of the West in modern times. This is not because of an assumption that the West has it *right* but rather that for almost everyone likely to be reading this book, *this* is the world they live in, and besides, it is the Western view of these issues that is expanding its influence around the world, specifically through the DSM and more generally through the expansive influence of Western culture in the modern world. Many decry this development, and criticisms of the Western approach to mental illness will continue to be explored in this text, but the basic truth of its importance is hard to deny. The influence of non-Western cultures is important. However, these various influences must be considered in relation to each other and in historical context. For the period of time explored in this chapter, these developments were happening mostly in isolation from each other. They would only come into powerful contact around the nineteenth century and start to be integrated toward the end of the twentieth century and beginning of the twenty-first. For now, we will consider them in isolation.

MENTAL ILLNESS IN THE MIDDLE AGES – EUROPE

The Middle Ages was a time of radical transition for Europe. The Roman Empire collapsed, and its power and influence were supplanted by a number of different nation-states and cultural regions, each with its own history and traditions (Clark, 1969; McNeill, 1999). Roman civilization did not simply disappear, however; it lived on through the Holy Roman Empire, which exerted an authority over many of the developing countries of Europe but found it increasingly difficult to manage as the Middle Ages gave way to the Renaissance. One thing the Holy Roman Empire was able to do, however, was guarantee that Christianity would remain the state religion and develop as the primary religion throughout Europe, replacing local, more ancient, mythologically oriented religious traditions. It was this change, combined with the rise of the various competing European nation-states, that set the tone for coming centuries. What we know of their approach to mental illness and mental health resulted from this transition, with much of their medical understanding of mental illness continuing from the Greco-Roman tradition, but to the extent it began to diverge from that tradition, the cause was the shift to a Christian-based perspective on psychology.

The medical texts of the time, including perhaps the most famous, the *Canon of Medicine*, by the Persian physician known in Europe as Avicenna, followed the humoral model of biological and mental functioning. The Canon was translated into Latin and, by the end of the twelfth century, had become a standard text for teaching medicine in universities throughout Europe (Alexander & Selesnick, 1966; Millon, 2004; Scull, 2015). The rise of both academic universities in Europe and scientific scholarship in the Islamic world were powerful factors in the field of medicine at the time. Despite this, there was no fundamental challenge to the humoral system developed by Greek and Roman physicians and philosophers. In fact, prior to the establishment of empiricism and the scientific method in the sixteenth and seventeenth centuries, the basic conclusions of the Classical period were held sacrosanct. Religious doctrine (both Christian and Islamic) generally denied researchers the freedom to dissect corpses to learn more about anatomy, conduct experiments to learn more regarding physiology, or speculate along humanistic lines about the causes of mental problems. Particularly in the Christian West, knowledge was generally thought of as *given or revealed* rather than developed slowly through research. Scholars looked to the past for wisdom rather than to the present and future for objective facts. It was these limitations in Europe that led to the rise of the Islamic world as a source for new information, as there was less of a stricture on such research and scholarship in the Islamic worldview (McNeill, 1999).

Overall, insanity was not often explored in much detail in the European medical texts of the Middle Ages. Instead, it was usually described as a symptom of other medical problems or was approached in a generic way, with limited insight into various types, etiology, or treatment outside its connection to humoral medicine as developed in Ancient Greece and Rome (Trenery & Horden, 2017). The Greco-Roman world had asserted that what differentiated the healthy psyche from the insane was reason and intellect, so the question of insanity in the Middle Ages continued to be focused on how, why, and in what ways this capacity might break down.

There were two main ways this was conceptualized: the biological model and demonology. The first way, a medical explanation, was the primary approach. As noted in the last chapter, psychological and physical well-being were reliant on the healthy balance of the humors. The humors had essential qualities (blood was hot and wet, yellow bile was hot and dry, black bile was cold and dry, phlegm was cold and wet). Because balance was the key, patients who exhibited too much of one quality would be treated to increase the opposite quality. Too much blood (hot and wet) called for an increase in black bile (cold and dry). The brain was typically believed to be naturally cold and moist, so it could be destabilized by an excess of any influence that was hot and dry. The nature of the illness was determined, in part, by what part of the brain was thought to be damaged. The brain was typically divided into three areas. The front of the brain was believed to be the seat of information processing, since it was located nearer to the main sense organs (eyes, nose, mouth) and was associated with imagination and emotion. The middle of the brain received the sensory information and was the seat of logic and rational thought. The back of the brain was the repository of memory, directly imprinted on the cold, wet tissue. Thus, an excess of hot, dry vapors in the back of the brain could damage a person's memory functioning. A similar problem in the midbrain could cause the person to become irrational.

There were three main clinical conditions linked to this humoral model: frenzy, mania, and melancholy. Frenzy was thought to be caused by an excess of yellow bile, leading to a hot abscess in the brain. The condition was characterized by night terrors, sleep disturbance, and inappropriate bouts of laughing, crying, or rage. Because the cause was an excess of heat, treatment consisted of efforts to cool the brain. This was attempted through techniques such as cold baths and bloodletting (to draw the hot blood away from the brain). Mania was similar to frenzy and was associated with a confusing group of symptoms. It was sometimes differentiated from frenzy by either its chronic nature and/or its lack of associated fever. It was also commonly associated with poor diet, and thus treatment often focused on purgatives, sweating, and dietary controls. Melancholy was often associated with an excess of black bile. This condition was believed to cause sadness, suspicious/negativistic thinking, poor reality testing, hallucinations, delusions, and odd, irrational behavior. Humoral balance could be restored through decreasing the level of blood (hot and wet) in the body. This was attempted through purging. It should be noted that various environmental treatments were also prescribed, including listening to soothing music, vacationing from stressful influences, and attempts to talk the person into a better, more positive state of mind.

Of course, during the Middle Ages, the medical model was not the only approach to mental illness. There were various theories regarding the nature of insanity (Alexander & Selesnick, 1966; Porter, 2013; Scull, 2015). The second-most-important etiology that was commonly asserted was demon possession. Bouts of insanity were often attributed to the interference of demons – sometimes the singular devil in Christian theology and sometimes the multiple Jinn in Islamic lands. It should be noted that belief in Jinn came from pre-Islamic tradition, where they were believed to be spirits, some of which were evil and some good. The Quran refers to Satan, typically in alignment with the Judeo-Christian idea of a fallen angel who opposes God and leads humans into wickedness. However, in some passages in the Quran, Satan is implied to be the leader of a group of evil Jinn. Either way, all three of the Abrahamic faiths believed in the devil and thought it possible that it could either possess or directly influence people in ways that would produce a form of insanity. Most of the faithful did not believe that the devil could enter a human soul, but it could enter the body and control the person's mind. Purely biological insanity was believed to be differentiated from demonic possession by the presence or absence of such phenomena as having convulsions, using blasphemous language, a fear or abhorrence of religious objects, and having special powers.

The differentiation of humoral and demonic/religious explanations for insanity was not absolute; they could co-occur. Also, the precise etiology was often difficult to assess and was seen differently from place to place, time to time, and practitioner to practitioner. Part of the complication was that the human soul was thought to be incorporeal – that is, nonphysical. It could be influenced by both physical and spiritual phenomena. For instance, there was the condition of *acedia*, which was considered a spiritual malady but was related to melancholy. It was a diagnosable condition affecting mostly monks or nuns. It was characterized by amotivation, sadness or dejection, restlessness, aversion to the ascetic life, and a yearning for having a family or a "normal" life. While it was primarily considered a spiritual or psychological condition, it could also be attributed to an excess of black bile or phlegm.

Although there was a slow shift toward naturalism toward the end of the Middle Ages, it is impossible to ignore the initially regressive intellectual tenor of the times. It has been called the Dark Ages for good reason. At best, there was little advancement in knowledge about mental illness, and in many places, the situation grew worse, with ideas about sin and demonology prevailing over anything resembling medical science. It appears there was a trajectory to this change. At the beginning of the Middle Ages, there was still a strong influence from the Greco-Roman rationalism, which balanced the emerging Christian worldview. However, with the collapse of what was left of the Roman Empire, the catastrophic waves of disease that traumatized and decimated the population of Europe, and the resulting rise of virulent anti-intellectualism, scientific exploration of mental illness collapsed into religious dogma and fear of satanism. Europe was held in thrall to its baser fears.

Despite this, although beliefs about insanity became more regressive at first, it appears that as the centuries passed, they then grew increasingly naturalistic. Belief in possession or demonic influence as a cause of madness began to wane by the late Middle Ages. That is not to say that belief in Satan or satanic influence went away but rather that the belief in it being a primary cause of insanity weakened (Kroll & Bachrach, 1984). Evidence for this shift comes from such areas as the law, where medieval juries and judges increasingly saw madness as an illness, made no reference to demonology, and treated such cases as worthy of leniency and protection rather than punishment for sin. During this time, there was also the establishment of the first mental hospitals. At the beginning of the Middle Ages, there were virtually no medical facilities available for the mentally ill. By the end (fifteenth century) there was at least some provision of institutional care in places like Santa Maria Nova in Florence and Bethlem Royal Hospital outside London. While their "services" were horrific by modern standards (patients were often kept in chains, provided almost no treatment per se, and lived in grossly substandard conditions), they were still considered patients with a mental illness and not sinful or possessed (Trenery & Horden, 2017). Their awful conditions were more a result of neglect and lack of funding than a sensed need to punish patients for sin or "treat" demonic influence.

This naturalistic progression in the concept of mental illness was driven by a number of factors. One was the reemergence of Greco-Roman philosophy and rationalism, which had maintained itself in the Middle East. Thinkers and writers, such as Rhazes (860–930), Unhammad (870–925), Avicenna (980–1037), and the Jewish Maimonides (1135–1204), were not subject to the direct power of the Roman Catholic church and thus were able to explore the rational, secular aspects of Greco-Roman philosophy. They were also able to maintain a more naturalistic approach to mental illness. While the Muslim faith decreed that they had to support preestablished authority and could not dissect cadavers, see unclothed women, or conduct surgery, there was still a tradition of separating religion from science, and they did not automatically connect madness with demonology. As a result, although they did little to advance the state of knowledge of mental illness, they kept it alive until Europe was ready to come back from darkness. They also took a more humanistic approach to mental illness and established a number of hospitals throughout the caliphate that treated the mentally ill with much more kindness and support than was typical in Europe at the time.

A second factor was the development of technologies that provided evidence of a reality at odds with religious dogma and aided the dissemination of that knowledge. Two of the most important technologies in this regard were the telescope and the printing press. Throughout the Middle Ages, the Roman Catholic Church espoused the Ptolemaic, geocentric view of the universe. As early as the tenth century, however, Islamic astronomers such as Abu Said al-Sijzi were beginning to doubt this conception, but it took direct observation of the moons of Jupiter by Galileo through a telescope in 1609 to produce direct evidence that not all heavenly bodies circled the Earth. For some historians, that moment marked the end of the Middle Ages. Of course, it can be argued that the invention of the printing press by Johannes Gutenberg in 1439 was even more important. That invention vastly increased the general availability of people's efforts to increase knowledge. It made possible the quick dissemination of Galileo's evidence of heliocentrism in his treatise, *Sidereus Nuncius* (*Starry Messenger*). Within one year of its writing, *Starry Messenger* had sparked a profound debate about the relationship between faith and science.

The spread of new knowledge began to break the spell of medieval scholasticism. This approach to knowledge had developed in the Middle Ages as a way to rectify Christian faith and the pagan philosophies of Ancient Greece and Rome (Russell, 1945). To the extent the texts of Aristotle and the Neoplatonists still existed and were considered valid and sacrosanct, they had to be harmonized with Christian dogma. This meant that scholasticism was not focused on an objective search for what was real or true. It was not interested in gathering facts and drawing conclusions based on those facts (empiricism). Instead, it started with established truths and used logic and dialectics to overcome contradictions and reach consensus. Through this method, ancient texts could be analyzed and reinterpreted to support Christian beliefs. Ironically, given the dominance of received authority as the arbiter of truth, these interpretations of classical philosophy were then treated as unquestionable in a way that directly contradicted the spirit in which they were written. Greek and Roman science became the "last word" on the natural world, and classical philosophy was twisted to fit Christian theology and ethics. Further research was unnecessary and dangerous, as the truth had been *revealed* by God to these ancients, and to question it was to question God. However, despite the protests and punishments meted out by the church and its supporting political allies, curious, intelligent, and brave rebels throughout Europe were gathering evidence of realities that starkly contradicted those espoused by the Church.

By the end of the Middle Ages, a trickle had become a flood, and the church could not stop the presses. The universities began to assert themselves not just as repositories for religiously approved dogma but as centers for free thought and experimentation. Many of the universities of Europe had begun as extensions of the Roman Catholic Church. Its students were seen and protected as important members of the church. At first, this guaranteed that universities would serve as bastions of the faith. However, over time, the ironic truth was that ecclesiastical protection allowed students and instructors to take stands at odds with local authorities, both political and religious. Students and instructors began to gain strength and independence even from their own university administrations. This did not happen quickly or without struggles – even deadly ones – but the result was an increasingly strong and independent faculty and student body, which could challenge the dogma of its day and assert that true knowledge followed a process of free exploration and experimentation rather than the ingestion of authoritatively approved interpretations of received wisdom and logic through the scholastic model.

MENTAL HEALTH IN THE MIDDLE AGES

Of course, before the emergence of free exploration and experimentation led to differentiation of different academic topics (thus the various schools and departments within modern universities), the medieval concept of psychology included a confluence of such concepts as mental illness, sin, demonology, and medical science. This relates directly to the central topic in our discussion. Just what is meant by the terms "mental illness" or "mental health"? It is important to remember that both the writer and the reader of this text are operating from the position of modernity, living within a reality that has already experienced the Enlightenment, the industrial revolution, the rise of modern medicine, the developments of modern psychology and psychiatry, and the evolution of epistemology toward postmodern relativism. It is not possible to transport our minds back to a time before those developments, and we need to tread very lightly when using modern concepts to try and understand the past. Leigh Ann Craig (2014) makes this point strongly, reminding us that the people of the past, who we may call "mad," had their own complex circumstances and understandings of their own situations, quite separate from those we assign them from a modern, historical perspective. This is quite true and highlights the shocking reality, from the modern perspective, that in the Middle Ages, there was no clear or consistent differentiation between mind and brain, body and soul, sinful temptation and self-agency, madness and demonic possession, or even different types of madness as the people of the time defined them.

The previous point about the confluence of religion and mental health and illness during the Middle Ages was amplified further by Michel Foucault (1965).

He described the transition from the medieval experience and understanding of madness to a more modern one in the Renaissance as one of beginning to "confine" insanity within the concept of mental illness. He offered an interpretation of mental illness during the Middle Ages that focused on spiritual powers, the Fall of Man, the will of God, the influence of the devil, and secret knowledge. He described this as a "dramatic debate" and emphasized its subjective, holistic, and shared experiential qualities rather than the objective, atomistic, and scientifically understood qualities that would reemerge in the Renaissance and come to typify the Modern Age.

What this means is that during the Middle Ages, what was understood as pertaining to mental health was not meaningfully separate from what pertained to mental illness, or spirituality for that matter. A good example of this confluence can be found in the writing of St. Augustine. Aurelius Augustinus was born in Tagaste (North Africa) in 354 AD. The future St. Augustine grew up with a father who was a pagan and encouraged his son to follow the life of free expression of his appetites and pursuit of worldly ambition. His mother was a pious Christian who wanted her son to follow her example of spiritual self-discipline. Much of St. Augustine's life revolved around his internal conflicts regarding these opposing values (Alexander & Selesnick, 1966). As a young man, his carnal desires apparently held sway, but after he was baptized at the age of 31, his desire for a life of Christian virtue increasingly ruled his life. As a result of his own internal struggles, St. Augustine believed that humanity was so weak and corruptible that redemption was only possible through divine grace. He believed strongly in the opposition of material, worldly desires and the spirit. The temptations of sin are so strong that they must be fought with ongoing, tremendous effort, and they can never be completely vanquished; thus the need for grace. This position, that humanity is, by its nature, hopelessly sinful and corrupt, was in opposition to the much more nuanced Greco-Roman approach, which tended to seek internal and external balance and did not see material desires themselves as representing pure sin but rather the overindulgence of those desires.

One element of St. Augustine's personal journey and resulting influence in Medieval Europe that is important here was his exercise of introspection in his highly influential book, *Confessions*. In this seminal work, he explored his own personal struggles with sin, desire, guilt, sorrow, shame, and sexual desire (Alexander & Selesnick, 1966; Millon, 2004). Moving beyond the philosophical abstractions of the Ancient Greeks, St. Augustine's approach was profoundly personal. He painstakingly explored his own childhood, adolescence, and early adulthood to understand the psychological roots of his subsequent conflicts and sufferings. Even his drives and attempts to communicate them in infancy were explored as the roots of his human selfishness. The process he used to address the pain in his soul set the foundation for what would later become psychoanalysis. The conclusions he reached set the tone for the rest of the Middle Ages and continue to reverberate throughout Western culture. Human desires are the source of sin and suffering – disciplined rejection of these desires is required to be free from them – God's grace is also required, and without it, we are ultimately helpless against our own failings. These extreme dichotomies (body/desires/sin vs. spirit/grace/freedom from sin) reinforced the idea that everything naturally or materially human is corrupt and must be aggressively rejected.

Another element of this position was St. Augustine's aggressive attacks upon others who he saw as failing to think or behave correctly. Taking on heretics of all sorts, he was able to externalize his internal conflicts and thus free himself of self-doubt, shame, or guilt (Alexander & Selesnick, 1966). Today, we call this projection – a defense mechanism that serves the individual (or group) by removing or at least lessoning the level of internal conflict or self-judgment by focusing on its presence in others. The intensity of the projected judgment and desire for punishment and ultimately destruction is in direct relation to the level of internal disturbance. Rather than approach others' shortcomings with compassion and mercy, they are attacked with unreflective rage. If I can destroy the evil in you – most effectively and permanently by destroying you in total – then I can be free of the evil in me. Of course, I am not aware that this is what I am really thinking and instead wallow in the pleasure of self-righteous indignation and retribution.

Two groups that were quite vulnerable to this dynamic in the Middle Ages were religious heretics (including non-Christians such as Jews and Muslims) and women. Since our purpose here is to explore the development of ideas about mental health and illness (versus more specifically religious persecution), we will focus on the demonization of women. At the beginning of the Middle Ages, the communal, egalitarian, and peace-loving aspects of Christianity were still influential, and the perception and treatment of women was relatively positive compared to what would emerge later. When Christianity was embraced by Constantine I and became officially accepted in the Roman Empire through the Edict of Milan in 313 AD, it took on the authoritarian aspect of the Empire it now represented. Later, as the Roman Empire collapsed, chaos, disease, and violence increased. Christianity moved even further toward authoritarianism, with its emphasis on hierarchal, patriarchal control. Men were seen as superior to women. With very few exceptions, men were the head of the family, the churches, and the governments. Women were vulnerable to become the receptive vesicle of all projections of sin and weakness. For instance, since women could tempt men with their beauty, thus sparking sexual desire, they were seen as the *source* of that desire and the embodiment of lust itself.

This projection of the materialistic, the human, the lustful, and all body-based drives and desires onto women has deep roots (Eisler, 1987; Eliade, 1957; Evans, 1988; Pagels, 1988). In the Judeo-Christian world, it goes back to the story of Adam and Eve, in which Eve was all too easily tempted by the Devil and then passed that temptation onto Adam. Taking a wider perspective, as an archetypal force, the feminine was seen as carrying the essence of materiality, while the masculine carried that of spirit. He was the leader and she the follower. He had the right of control; she had to submit. He could carry the "burden" of worldly power because his spiritual core was stronger and could maintain itself through the flux of worldly distractions, temptations, and threats. The reason for this ancient, archetypal gender differentiation is likely the collective observation that it was the female who bled every month in connection with the lunar cycle. She developed within her the next generation of physical, human life through pregnancy and raised it through the production of milk. The contribution of men to the biological lifecycle was more mysterious and thus seen as more spiritual than material. He was the spark of life, while she was the carrier of physical life itself.

As long as a given culture's relation to the material world was fundamentally positive and balanced with the spiritual world, then her role was honored. This was true in many parts of Africa during the Middle Ages, where many tribal cultures were led by and/or maintained the empowerment of women. They could own property, control the upbringing of children, and hold positions of power in the tribe. However, if a culture rejected the material world as fundamentally sinful and corrupt, then so were all women seen as sinful and corrupt. If man was tempted to engage in the material world or gave in to temptations related to the natural appetites, then it was because woman had tempted or otherwise influenced him. From a modern perspective, this is grossly unfair and inaccurate. In biological terms, males are no more naturally spiritual than females, no more free from worldly temptations, and certainly no more moral. Modern feminism is still working to free women, and thus men as well, from these patriarchal projections. The point here is that the Middle Ages took a cultural complex that was already active in many ways in various parts of the world and gave it a particularly powerful form that established a pattern of male and female psychology that continues to impact us to this day.

Given this cultural complex, it is likely that many women, during the Middle Ages of Europe and the Middle East, as well as most of Asia, suffered psychologically. They would have, as people of all times do, absorbed the projections of their society and taken them as truth. Most women must have seen themselves as inferior to men and more vulnerable to the sins of the flesh. Many of these women would have simply accepted this "reality" as a given. Some would have felt shame or guilt over their inferiority. Some would have felt anger and resentment, sensing an unfairness in this state of affairs. Many, of course, would have simply accepted the status of their gender as the "natural state of things" and not suffered psychologically. What there was not was any kind of large-scale, public organizing or political-social action along the lines of the modern feminist movement. Any resentments or rebellions were a private affair, perhaps joined quietly by supportive friends or relatives. There was sure to be private talk within women's social groups or between sisters working together in the kitchen, but this talk could not go public. There were also, of course, exceptions to the rule – strong women who were successful in the public sphere despite the efforts to stop them.

Whether in China, India, the Middle East, South America, or Europe, the vast majority of societies around the world during the Middle Ages were male dominated. Women were generally honored for the receptive qualities of humility, chasteness, quietness, loyalty, and obedience. Even the veneration of Mary, which gained great popularity in the Middle Ages, focused on the idea that she was not only impregnated through Immaculate Conception but retained her virginal purity throughout her life. This was hardly an example a normal, everyday woman could emulate, especially when part of the cultural expectation for her was to bear children, presumably in the traditional way. This meant that women in the Middle Ages were in a no-win situation. If they maintained their purity, they failed to fulfill the cultural demand of motherhood. If they became mothers, then they were seen as defiled and having failed to fulfill their culture's spiritual expectations for respect and admiration.

One way out of this conflict for women of the Middle Ages was to voluntarily reject the secular world and become nuns. In fact, this became the choice of many women. Obviously, it can be assumed that many chose this path out of a true spiritual calling, but one must wonder how many were driven by a desire to escape the demands of womanhood in their cultural setting. How many were fleeing the fate of patriarchal marriage, including (but not limited to) unwanted heterosexual relationships, unwanted sex with a family-chosen partner, unwanted motherhood, unwanted servitude to a man and his family, and the almost complete lack of any other options? After all, for women, the priesthood and its relative prestige and authority was not an option either. Shakespeare wrote, "Get thee to a nunnery!" as an admonition reflecting the sense of a "shamed" woman who must flee from "decent society" to hide herself away. This means that taking the orders was not only an honored spiritual option but could, in many cases, be experienced as an escape, or worse, a punishment or disgrace – an imprisonment for women who had failed, in one way or another, to live up to the cultural demands placed on her gender by her society.

This state of affairs for women was explored by Rosalind Miles (2001). She reviewed the history of women and noted that during what we call prehistory, the lives and roles of men and women were much more equal than in later, more "developed" societies. The demands of tribal or small-village life typically required full participation of all members and thus a basic acknowledgment and respect for the relative contributions of both men and women. As noted before, in societies that honored the natural world – which would occur in societies that live much closer to an everyday reliance on its vicissitudes – the archetypal feminine would, in both its positive and negative aspects, have equality, if not outright superiority to the masculine. This was reflected in the now well-known worship of the Goddess, which was widespread throughout the ancient world (Eisler, 1987). The rise of more complex societies marked the end of this period and the transition to more patriarchal societies in the Classical era. The emergence of the Judeo/Christian/Islamic world of the Middle Ages pushed this patriarchal shift to the next level. Worship of the Goddess was forbidden, God became singular and exclusively male, and the imagery, principles, and specific lives of women became an archetype of weakness, sin, and inferiority to men. Women had to either submit to the males around them or, as noted before, escape to the relative safety of the nunnery. However, even this escape was not without problems. There were allegations of sexual abuse from some of these institutions. They could be seen through modern eyes as simply another expression of male dominance and control of women, and over time, the projective conflation of women with sinful sexuality led to the use of the term "nunnery" to mean brothel.

Miles (2001) presents extensive evidence that the subordination of women was driven by the fact that all five of the main spiritual belief systems of the time (Confucianism, Buddhism, Christianity, Judaism, and Islam) were clear and adamant about the inferiority of women to men and the requirement that men be dominant in all aspects of life. This was not the case in some tribal societies of the time, especially in Africa, where, as noted before, there was still a place of power and respect for women. However, many other societies, despite being "closer to nature" than those represented by the five belief systems noted above, engaged in what most today would consider the grossly oppressive and abusive treatment of women. This included a number of practices, including forced marriage, child brides, bride sales, the use of "chastity belts," female genital mutilation, female infanticide, witch hunting, culturally approved rape, and others. This dramatic shift in beliefs and behaviors appears to reflect a number of dynamics. One possibility is what is typically referred to as "womb envy." It is likely that in the early years of human culture, men reacted to the special connection of women with the natural world (menstruation, pregnancy, lactation) first with a sense of awe and respect but later with envy and rage. Envy could emerge from an ongoing sense that women represented something that was valuable and honored in a nature-based spirituality. Rage and condemnation could follow the shift toward a rejection of the natural world in favor of the spirit-based one (Eisler, 1987; Evans, 1988). This rejection would make sense given the desire to escape the sufferings, limitations, and ultimate mortality of physical existence (Eliade, 1954, 1958; Neumann, 1994).

Thus, envy of the feminine developed into outright rejection of the feminine, as culture "evolved" and people sought to escape or transcend their material existence. This shift resulted in various practices (mortification of the flesh, self-denial, asceticism, etc.) and corresponding virtues (modesty, spirituality, etc.) and sins (gluttony, lust, greed, avarice, pride, etc.) that had ramifications for the real lives of both men and women. In general, as we have discussed, women bore the brunt of being burdened with the negative aspects of material existence. However, men were physical creatures as well and had to deal with the self-condemnation of this moral branding of the "sins of the flesh." This meant that the focus on spiritual transcendence was a complicated matter in the Middle Ages. Many men and women pursued religious practices along these lines. This was true within the Abrahamic religions (Judaism, Christianity, and Islam) as well as Indian religions (Buddhism, Hinduism, and Jainism) and others, including the Incas, Taoism, and Zoroastrianism. Many voluntarily removed themselves from the material concerns of their given cultures to join monastic communities. Free from the day-to-day struggles involving making a living, engaging in sexual relationships, raising children, participating in politics, etc., they could dedicate their time and energy to spiritual escape from the material world. Where the Classical world sought balance and integration of the worldly and spiritual, this new movement saw the material world as hopelessly corrupt, and thus disengagement was the way to peace, happiness, goodness, and ultimately salvation.

In a particularly thorough and fascinating study of this phenomenon, Kroll and Bachrach (2005) explore the lives of medieval mystics and ascetics, illuminating the psychology of these practices to see how they could obtain mystical states of altered consciousness. They examined a database of more than 1,400 aspirants in the Middle Ages, looking at how they engaged in such practices as self-laceration, sleep deprivation, and starvation, among others as a pathway to holiness. They note that historically, humans are always trying to escape ordinary states of consciousness, that virtually all societies recognize this and develop both sanctified and illicit methods for doing so, but that the Middle Ages was marked by an increase in religious belief that emphasized the individual's relationship with God. This set the conditions for extreme asceticism and mysticism to become popular, as more individuals sought to escape the implicit sufferings of ordinary life and consciousness to become one with the divine.

One of the more profound examples that Kroll and Bachrach (2005) explore was Beatrice of Nazareth. She was born in 1200 to a lower-middle-class family in the town of Tienen, in what is now Belgium. She was the youngest of six children. Her mother died when she was quite young, and after a single year of school, at the age of about eight, she was sent by her father to a monastery with the goal that she would become a nun. After seven years of study, she asked to be accepted as a novitiate, or novice, and became a nun at the age of sixteen, quite young even for that time. She was quite successful and eventually became the prioress (deputy administrator) of her religious community, a position she held for many years, up to her death in 1268. This personal history establishes her ability to function at a high level in the "regular world" of social, business, and administrative responsibilities. However, while she was engaging in this work, she was also dealing with intense internal struggles that led to a regular practice of extreme ascetics and self-immolation. By her preteens, Beatrice was already engaging in severe fasting and self-flagellation, exposure to cold air, and excessive prayer/genuflection. These practices led to her being reprimanded by her superiors in the order, but this only caused her to carry on in secret. She would fill her bed and clothes with sharp yew leaves to cut and scrape her body throughout the day and night. She tied ropes around various parts of her body with knots to cause more pain. She slept on the cold, hard floor rather than the in bed she was provided. She wore torn and soiled clothes to denigrate herself. By her mid-teens, it became clear that in order to be allowed to become a nun, she had to scale back her behavior. She did so and earned the support and acceptance of the community. As she got older, she was influenced to adjust her beliefs and practices to reflect a more "positive" type of relationship to Christ, including prayer and meditation that would lead to ecstatic experiences. However, this did not seem to work for her. She tried to restrain her impulse to engage in the more extreme practices of her early youth but continued to feel a sense of separation from God, along with unwanted carnal desires and other blasphemous thoughts. This apparently supported chronic feelings of guilt, unworthiness, sinfulness, and what we would now term depression. She evidently continued to engage in some of the extreme ascetic practices throughout her life but increasingly sought a gentler path of prayer and contemplation as she got older and did not return to the severe self-injurious behavior of her youth.

There are many important elements in this story. One regards the response of those within her order. Some supported her behavior as reflective of a deep and legitimate spiritual dedication, while others saw it as excessive and evidence of a disturbed mind. Apparently, this dichotomy of thought was typical at the time, and many extreme ascetics were condemned both in the public and even within the monastic community as "crazy," suggesting that despite the cultural shift toward spiritual rejection of the natural world, there was still a strong sense of the need for moderation or balance. Perhaps, given its near-universal appeal, human psychology leans toward a conceptualization of mental health as reflecting balance between the emotional and the rational, the sensual and the ascetic, the worldly and the spiritual, the social and the isolated, and maybe even the sane and the crazy.

Another important element is the question of whether she really was "mentally disturbed." This question is fraught with difficulties, as the concept of mental disturbance and mental wellness is obviously inexorably entwined with cultural beliefs. One can wonder if the loss of her mother at such a young age and being sent by her father to a nunnery at the age of eight led to a deep-set sense of her own unworthiness. Children often internalize such losses and treatment by parents as "their fault" and more or less consciously seek out punishment to atone for their "sins." Modern-day therapists often work with clients to overcome the internalized messages of such life experiences, especially when they occur at too young an age to be processed through the more logical cognitive processes of an older person. Is it fair, however, to assess Beatrice of Nazareth using such modern psychological concepts? How could we know, looking backward in time, with very limited evidence, if they are valid for her? She kept a diary, which is how we know about many of her spiritual practices and thoughts, but she did not divulge them in a way that could answer these modern clinical questions. We do know, as noted previously, that such behavioral extremes were considered by many, even within monastic communities, to be "crazy." But they also inspired respect and admiration for someone so dedicated to their spiritual practice. It reflected a norm of the time that supported religious martyrdom and material self-denial as a legitimate and honored pathway to salvation.

MENTAL HEALTH AND SPIRITUALITY IN NON-WESTERN CULTURE

Another, more famous religious figure of the time reflected these difficulties inherent in the approach to psychological wellness, and that was the Buddha. Siddhartha Gautama lived sometime between the fourth and sixth centuries in the northeastern part of what is now called India (Skilton, 1994). The historical details of his life are unclear and conflicting, but legend has it that he was the son of a nobleman who wanted to protect his son from the sufferings of life and thus tried to cloister him in the palace, providing every pleasure imaginable. Of course, this was destined to fail. The young Siddhartha eventually ventured out and saw an old man on the road – he became aware of the sufferings of illness, old age, and death. He recognized that pursuing sensual pleasure and worldly power could not protect him from these difficulties. This led him to explore the nature of suffering. His initial conclusion was that in order to be freed from it, one must reject all worldly, material existence. Thus, he spurned his birthright of power and wealth, left his father's palace, and became a religious seeker of truth and enlightenment. He evidently studied and practiced many of the religious paths available to him at the time, including becoming an extreme ascetic, eating as little as possible to survive, and rejecting any form of physical comfort, including clothes and shelter. The problem was that this did not lead to enlightenment for the young man. He continued to suffer, but he did find that meditation was helpful, although complete rejection of the material world was not, so he decided to sit in silence under a Bodhi tree until enlightenment came to him. Again, according to legend, after 49 days of quiet contemplation, he became enlightened. He also came to a realization of the Four Noble Truths of human suffering and liberation. They include the ideas that (1) life is painful, it is unavoidable, (2) suffering is the result of being attached to things, including the wish to not experience pain, (3) it is possible to overcome attachment and thus end suffering, and (4) there is a path to achieve this. He conceptualized this path in eight parts – right view, right aspiration, right speech, right action, right livelihood, right effort, right mindfulness, and right concentration.

Together, this plan of action is often referred to as the Middle Way. The basic idea is to avoid the extremes of self-indulgence and self-mortification. The Buddha (as Siddhartha became known – the Enlightened One) recognized that extreme asceticism reflected as much an attachment to the material world as self-indulgence. It was the other side of the same coin. Therefore, to avoid these equally unsatisfying extremes, one should set upon a dedicated journey to focus on the deeper truths of human existence, detach from the sources of suffering, and practice those principles in all of one's affairs. In some ways, this reflects Beatrice's journey, as she backed away from extreme asceticism later in her life, but it is unknown and frankly unlikely that this resulted from insights similar to those of the Buddha. The path of the Buddha was more in alignment with the Neoplatonists of Ancient Rome, who sought to balance the material with the spiritual. By the Middle Ages, in the West, the material world had become so demonized that a religious philosophy that sought to balance the two would meet great resistance. The best they could do was, like Beatrice's superiors, condemn her extremism and demand that she *moderate* her approach.

In China, during this same period of time, there were a number of religious/ ethical systems in practice that influenced their concept of psychological wellness or health (Keay, 2009). From ancient times, the Chinese had developed folk religions that included veneration of ancestors, forces of nature, and various gods and goddesses. The specific forms were highly variable from place to place and time to time, so a single description is nearly impossible and would be misleading. By the Western Middle Ages time period, a number of newer influences were in play, including Buddhism, Confucianism, Taoism, and even Christianity (in the late period). Because we have already discussed Buddhism and Christianity (and these were outside influences), we will discuss the two endemic trends.

The Chinese philosopher Confucius probably lived during the fourth or fifth century BCE. More a philosophy or way of social/public life than a religion, Confucianism emphasizes the importance of family and social harmony. It seeks to transcend the dichotomy between the religious and the secular and views the everyday activities of life as having a sacred nature and thus potentially an expression of a spiritually transcendent moral foundation. It believes that human beings are essentially good, teachable, and improvable. It focuses on the cultivation of virtue both individually, through self-discipline, and collectively through the virtuous organization of society. The primary virtues are compassion and the desire to do good.

Confucianism led to the development of ritual norms of behavior and social/ political organization that reflected the Law of Heaven, however that was interpreted by the authorities at a given time and place. Individual practices could include a contemplation of this law but, more importantly, focuses on practical, everyday behavior, which should include such virtues as benevolence, justice, filial piety, knowledge, integrity, loyalty, cleanliness, bravery, gentleness, respect, frugality, and modesty. It is important that everyone know their place in the natural order and play their part well. Thus, obedience within a sanctified social structure is a form of high virtue and leads to harmony and peace. While on the one hand, this entrenches hierarchies that many find disturbing (rulers over ruled, parents over children, men over women, old over young), it is also true that fealty runs both ways, and the person or organization in the position of authority has a responsibility to practice benevolence, justice, and respect toward those below them and risk losing their sanctified place of authority if they fail. Of course, human beings being what they are, this vitally important element has often been ignored by those who find themselves in positions of power over others and seek to exert that power for their own ends.

The second endemic movement in China we will look at is Taoism. First developed in the fourth century BC, it complements but is separate from Confucianism. Rather than focusing on ethics, rituals, and social order, it establishes the source, pattern, and substance of *all* existence. As such, it is closer to a religion and incorporated aspects of the older folk religions, in reaction to the growing popularity of Buddhism. It is similar to Confucianism in that it teaches that wellness stems from aligning with the patterns and rhythms of the universe. In that way, one can lead a "natural" life that is simple, spontaneous, and attuned to the way things are. The Tao, or the way, suggests that the universe has a natural rhythm, flow, or intention, and thus alignment with the universe should result in an effortless "letting go." To some extent, this corresponds with Confucianism's belief in a Law of Heaven, but rather than prescribe very specific behaviors and institutional forms, Taoism recommends a relaxation of moralistic "shoulds" in favor of a more spontaneous, simple, and humble approach to life. For instance, while Confucianists might support a political leader's right to wage war and the people's responsibility to obey that leader, the Taoist is more likely to oppose such autocratic dictates and support a peaceful resolution to the political problem. This lack of support for rigid hierarchies and obedience to authority made Taoism less popular with the ruling class of China but has made it more popular in modern times, with Westerners seeking a philosophical alternative to traditional Western religions that is supportive of individual freedom and alignment with nature.

What we see in China, during the Western Middle Ages, was the coexistence of a number of major religious and philosophical streams, including ancient folk religions, Buddhism, Confucianism, and Taoism. Given that China is a very large place with a long history of different cultures, political systems, and even languages, often disconnected or in open conflict with each other, it is not surprising that different religious philosophies could coexist, in various places, in various forms, and with varying levels of influence. There is not one simple, clear story of this development. What does emerge is a combination of currents. First, there was a strong interest in maintaining cultural order and clear rules of social behavior. Second, there was the development of philosophies and practices to align oneself with the natural patterns and forces of nature. Third, there was a thirst for individual spiritual fulfillment or transcendence. Interestingly, and in contrast to the West, these three paths were *not* seen as mutually exclusive. Although they had their differences and debates, the three paths were not experienced in Chinese culture as being in direct conflict with each other the way they often were (and still are) in the West. It may be a unique characteristic of Chinese history that the extreme chaos and violence in its early days led to the attitude that seeking order and conformity in society and politics could and should correspond with peaceful alignment with nature, individual spirituality, and psychological wellness.

CONCLUSION

Not surprisingly, the Middle Ages refuses to be "pigeonholed" into simple definitions. For the most part, it was a time of stultification and even regression regarding mental illness. By the end of the middle ages, there had been shockingly little progress from the end of the Classical era in the medical understanding and treatment of insanity. In some circles, insanity had become conflated with spiritual issues and was assessed in terms of possession, demonology, sin, and witchcraft. However, this was not universal. In some places, and within some important social circles, such as the law, there had been substantial change, conceptualizing the mentally ill as sick, not sinful, and deserving of empathy and care, not condemnation and punishment. In regard to mental health, or wellness, there is a distinct lack of clear information from that period in history. Obviously, there would be *some* overlap with the Classical era in regard to the good life stemming from balance, worldly success, physical health, self-awareness, and a philosophical approach to life. However, this overlap appears to have been superseded, for the most part, with the religious and correlated cultural changes in many parts of the world at the time. Both the Indian and Abrahamic religions that were on the rise emphasized the spiritual over the material, the individual relationship with God over alignment with one's culture, and demonized the feminine versus the masculine archetype. As a result, the concept of personal wellness shifted away from valuing balance and moved toward a rejection of material comfort and pleasure, or worldly success. But this was not universal, and there was some movement toward a more balanced approach to life, especially in the Asiatic philosophies.

In regard to the epistemological question of truth in these matters, we are faced with a historical period that begins to look more familiar to the modern Western reader. The religious beliefs and cultural groupings and patterns that developed in the Middle Ages are the roots of our own. These roots in the West include not only the religious and cultural forms endemic to the Western world but, over the years, have been increasingly influenced by those that were growing in India and the Far East. In many ways, this complicates the picture for Westerners. Everyone is at least partly bound by a sense of what is true about mental illness and health that is based on the beliefs they are born and raised with. If one is a Christian, to what extent does one see psychological health and well-being as reflecting an attitude of humility, selflessness, sacrifice, and hope for a better world to come after death? Such truths cannot be analyzed in an objective way, from an "outside" perspective, because they are self-fulfilling prophecies. To the extent that one believes them, they *do* create a sense of peace and happiness. If one believes them but fails to live up to those values, like Beatrice of Nazareth, he or she will suffer emotionally, feeling guilt, shame, and profound need to atone. The point here is that these truths of human happiness, which are still a profound part of a Westerners cultural DNA, were established in the Middle Ages, differing markedly from those that came before. As we will explore in upcoming chapters, they come into direct conflict with the truths that developed later, creating a foundational psychological conflict in Westerners that is our psychological inheritance from this period of history.

CHAPTER 5

THE RENAISSANCE

One of the best-known periods of human history, the Renaissance, took place in Europe roughly between the fifteenth and seventeenth centuries. It involved dramatic changes in a wide range of human endeavors and ultimately how people saw themselves and their place in the world. The advances of this age impacted Western knowledge, beliefs, and practices in areas as wide-ranging as politics, economics, philosophy, religion, medicine, art, and literature. Of course, it is beyond the scope of this book to review all the achievements and consequences of this era. Instead, we will focus on two particular movements that directly impacted our subject matter, the changing concepts of mental health and mental illness.

These two movements were the development of empiricism as the primary, authentic road to truth or reality and the rise of the concept of humanism and how it changed how people thought and experienced themselves in the social and natural worlds (Durant, 1926; Tarnas, 1991). In some ways, these movements complimented each other, seeking authenticity unbound by the truisms offered and even demanded by various preordained authorities. In other ways, they were at odds, with empiricism providing a rational, objective view of reality, no matter how "ugly" it might be, while humanism was aspirational, inviting people to think about and experience themselves in ascendant ways based on the very best characteristics that could be imagined, sometimes ignoring or denying their "uglier" qualities. Together, these movements set the stage for the subsequent unleashing of human potential for the scientific knowledge, technological advancement, and economic development that would emerge in the following centuries. Of course, it also unleashed many of the problems of the modern age, including the wholesale diminution and abuse of supposedly "inferior" peoples around the world, the economic mistreatment of workers in the industrial age, and the devaluation, rape, and general trashing of the natural world. In other words, both the wonders and the horrors of the modern world have their roots in the Renaissance.

THE RISE OF EMPIRICISM

With that heady (or windy if you prefer) introduction, let's look at the development of empiricism and its impact on how people viewed mental illness. At the beginning of the Renaissance, in the early fifteenth century, the search for truth was dominated by two epistemological approaches, reliance on authority and deductive reasoning. The first, reliance on authority, is just what it sounds like – church, political, and other cultural leaders had the right to proclaim and enforce what they saw as true. It was not just that they had the power to do so, but they were justified through various cultural traditions and beliefs. For instance, within a particular cultural mindset, the pope was chosen by God, and therefore his dictates reflected the wisdom and wishes of God. The layperson was chosen by God to be on a lower rung of the ladder of authority, and thus it was God's will that he or she submit to the higher authority. Of course, if that layperson was lucky enough to be born a male, he could still exert authority over his wife and children, so he was not without some power in the system.

The second epistemological approach popular at the end of the Middle Ages was deductive reasoning. This approach starts with a premise that is assumed to be true then links other premises that are conceptually connected to a logical conclusion. A classic example of this, offered in all undergraduate courses in logic is as follows: Men are mortal > Socrates was a man > Socrates was mortal. This makes sense and can often be a good way to discover logical truths, but it has a profound limitation. The premises have to be valid or true themselves, or the conclusions drawn from them are spurious and tautological. Few would have a problem with the idea that Socrates was a man or all men are mortal. However, what if the premise is that people are immortal? Then the deductive reasoning could be as follows: Men are immortal > Socrates was a man > Socrates was (is) immortal. Thus, deductive reasoning can be used to justify nearly any belief or action that people want to take, as long as they start with a presumed premise, meaning a shared belief. This was an important part of the Scholastic movement in the Middle Ages because the search for truth was pursued through a dialectic based on logic, which was embedded in the deductive approach, and did not require an empirically based foundation for any particular premise (Alexander & Selesnick, 1966). This meant that authority figures of the time could dictate what were acceptable premises and then encourage an endless dialectic based on them. This led to, for instance, twisting the meaning of ancient Greek philosophical texts to fit Christian theology. As the centuries went on, it became increasingly clear that this process was creating amazingly dense commentaries on various ideas and texts, but little progress toward and actual obfuscation of objective truths about the world. This gave the appearance of an intellectual pursuit of the truth, but in reality, one could have endless logical, rational debate about how many angels could dance on the head of a pin and make no progress toward the fundamental question regarding the existence of angels.

A number of factors led to a change of epistemological focus. As the Middle Ages moved toward the Renaissance, (1) the West rediscovered Ancient Greek texts, (2) it experienced increased contact between Europe and ideas/beliefs from other parts of the world, (3) there was the invention of the printing press, which dramatically accelerated the dissemination of knowledge, (4) there was the rise of an increasingly educated and powerful middle class, (5) the Reformation not only fractured the authority of the Roman Catholic Church but promoted the right of the individual to read and interpret scripture for him or herself, (6) there was the discovery of whole new continents through oceanic exploration, which greatly expanded the known world, and (7) there was a flood of objective information from new technologies such as a the telescope and the mechanical clock which provided the means to see and measure the "real world" far more precisely and increasingly contradicted religious doctrine in ways that could not be discounted through dialectical analysis. Together, these (and more) forces pushed Europeans toward a questioning of authoritatively established truths and a need to find a more legitimate way of establishing just what was true and real.

That new way would reveal itself in the development of two complementary ideas, empiricism and inductive reasoning. Empiricism is a theory that asserts that true knowledge comes primarily from sensory experience. As a direct rebuke to the validity of innate or "received" ideas, empiricism demands that there be direct, measurable data to support an idea. While many like to ascribe the birth of this theory to John Locke, its roots go back in the West to Aristotle (Tarnas, 1991), who first postulated the infant mind as basically empty, waiting to have the experiences of life imprint upon it. This was in opposition to Plato, with his belief in preexisting forms that human beings had the potential to access. Religious authorities in the Middle Ages naturally preferred the Platonic approach, although there was still an active debate, led by such figures as Thomas Aquinas (who took the Aristotelian position) and Bonaventure (who took the Platonic). Overall, the Neoplatonics ruled the day until the late-medieval forces listed above dramatically weakened the idea that truth about the world could, in all cases, be intuited spontaneously or derived from ancient authorities. A series of thinkers, from Al Farabi, Avicenna, Ibn Tufail, and Abu Bakr in the Islamic world to Leonardo da Vinci, Bernardino Telesio, Francis Bacon, Galileo, John Locke, George Berkeley, and David Hume in the West developed the theory and insisted that abstract concepts (ideas or beliefs) should follow from direct consideration of the phenomena of the world (Russell, 1945). The listing of these names is important not only to establish that this intellectual movement was active in both Europe and the Middle East but also that it was just that, a movement, and not the singular inspiration of John Locke. Its influence rose steadily throughout the Renaissance and the Enlightenment periods, spurring the development of what we now call the scientific method.

Complementing the theory of empiricism and establishing a basis for the scientific method, inductive reasoning starts with hypothesis (a *possible* premise, in contrast to deductive reasoning, which starts with an *established* premise) and then calls for evidence that can support or, very importantly, refute the premise. If enough evidence supports the premise then it can be concluded that it is valid, but that validity is always in the form of a probability rather than an absolute certainty. There is always the possibility that more evidence will become available that will refute the premise. Truth, through this method, is always contextual and uncertain. This can feel unsatisfying to many, but it reflects the humility of accepting that there is always more to know, and it is fundamentally impossible to ever be in a state of perfect, complete knowledge about anything. For many, this is not unsatisfying or destabilizing but actually rather exciting. From this perspective, truth is always a developmental process, and participating in it, through either one's own research or the exploration of others' work, one is expressing an openness to change and a belief in human progress. But of course, not everyone feels this way, and there have been and likely will continue to be many who yearn for eternal and absolute truths.

The scientific method is a process of formalizing empiricism and (typically) inductive reasoning. The researcher starts with an interest in a particular area of human knowledge, learns what is currently known about it, develops a hypothesis about what *might* be true, and then carefully designs a way (research design) to gather information that will support or reject the hypothesis. It is both an aspirational and a fundamentally humble process. The investigator should be just as open to being wrong as hopeful or confident of being right. Previous beliefs and established authority should have no bearing on the hypothesis, methods, or outcomes of the work. In reality, there are many influences that affect scientific work, including the limits of current knowledge, the bravery of the researcher to resist existing biases, the quality of his or her design, the influence of funding sources, and limitations on the inherent ability to gather the appropriate data. Over the centuries, these and other problems have led to profound errors (think cold fusion or the entire field of phrenology), vicious infighting in various fields of study, and even fundamental doubts about its validity from the public (the debate over global warming). However, at its core, the scientific method has established itself as the best way to develop knowledge that ultimately transcends individual and collective beliefs to approach universal truths. At this point in history, hardly anyone believes the earth is flat or is orbited on a daily basis by the sun.

EMPIRICISM AND MENTAL ILLNESS

Perhaps the first real assertion of empiricism against established beliefs regarding mental illness was the fight to show that those accused of witchcraft were mentally ill rather than actual witches. This fight was taken up by Agrippa and Paracelsus but most effectively and professionally by Johann Weyer (Alexander & Selesnick, 1966). He was born in 1515, in what is now Holland. He never became as famous as either Agrippa or Paracelsus, but he was a brilliant scholar who was methodical and conscientious in his approach to various medical subjects. He studied under Agrippa and later became the private physician to Duke William of Cleves. The duke had chronic psychological problems and had relatives who had become insane. Both he and Weyer noted that those accused of witchcraft often manifested similar symptoms. While in the duke's service, Weyer travelled extensively, investigating reports of witchcraft, gathering data, and using it to challenge the accusations with naturalistic explanations for what he found. His carefully developed case studies contained detailed descriptions of various psychological disturbances and asserted strongly that cases of witchcraft should be reevaluated as cases of mental illness and treated accordingly. While Weyer did not develop a comprehensive theory of mental illness or create a nosology, he did help reestablish a medical interest in mental illness as a naturalistic disease and approached the work through a process of careful observation and case study, like his Ancient Greek forebears.

The following two centuries, the sixteenth and seventeenth, were awash in various representations of insanity (Foucault, 1965; Mellyn, 2017). Literature, paintings, sculptures, theology, philosophy, and even medical science explored the stories and meaning of brooding, melancholy, suicidal, obsessive, hallucinating, and supposedly demonically possessed individuals. Debates raged about the apparent predisposition of artists to be melancholy if not outright mad. People questioned whether the whole world was mad. And of course, there was the famous trope regarding the "ship of fools." This idea was first introduced in Plato's *Republic* as an allegory representing the dangers of letting society be led by foolish and irrational people. It was taken up by Sebastian Brant in his late-fifteenth-century book of the same name, to lampoon both the church and various weaknesses and vices of his time. The most famous example of this trope was Hieronymus Bosch's painting of the same name, which he completed sometime around 1490–1500. The painting depicts a motley group of travelers, eating, drinking, climbing the tree-like mast, vomiting over the side of the boat, and all ignoring two men who have (presumably) fallen overboard. They are clearly "adrift," without morals or reason, despite the presence of a churchman, who is as mad or foolish as the rest.

Foucault (1965) reminds us that the ship of fools was not just a cultural allegory but that it really existed, in the sense that during the Middle Ages and the Renaissance, the insane were often expelled from families, towns, and cities, and set adrift on the roads and rivers of Europe. While there were a few places of detention for the mad, care for the insane was typically the responsibility of the sufferer's family, and one can imagine how often that responsibility would become an overwhelming burden, leading to expulsion of the mad from the care of their families and local communities. Of course, such circumstances would also lead to escape and flight from abusive and/or neglectful caregivers and communities. Either way, there was very little medical understanding or care being provided. This reflected the general state of medicine at the time but was a particular concern regarding mental illness. For those suffering insanity, who were thus identified and sent to one of the few institutions available, the "care" had almost nothing to do with medicine, and these patients were generally treated the same as if not worse than common criminals. In fact, some of the first asylums for the insane in Europe were utilized to ease the suffering of criminals who complained about being forced to be confined with the insane.

The trope of the ship of fools and its very real invocations in cultural practice are presented here not as a review of treatment (specifically not covered in this book) but rather to elucidate the state of knowledge and beliefs at the time. The problem of insanity was still highly conflated with issues of morality, religion, and cognitive incapacity (Alexander & Selesnick,1966; Porter, 2013; Scull, 2015). It was not yet consistently seen as a purely medical issue. Despite the efforts of individuals like Weyer, up until the seventeenth century, madness was still typically conceptualized through the lens of culture, morality, and theology. To the extent it was considered in medical terms, it would still have focused on the humoral system inherited from the Romans. As discussed previously, this system focused on the integrated confluence of physical, psychological, and spiritual/cosmological factors. The bodily aspects (black bile, yellow bile, phlegm, and blood) were influenced by emotional states, often connected to life stressors, as well as lifestyle practices, such as diet and exercise. These, in turn, were impacted by religious factors (faith and prayer) and other cosmological factors associated with astrology. This meant there continued to be no significant differentiation between the fields we now identify as medicine, psychiatry, psychology, health/nutrition, religion, and self-help. Doctors of the time, dealing with mental illness, were expected to be conversant in all these related areas.

This made for a rather confusing and confused historical situation. Medical doctors still focused on the humoral system, which was considered scientific and biological, but they also had to account for a variety of spiritual and cultural factors involved in mental illness. Clinicians like Girolamo Mercuriale (1530–1606) believed that demons worked *through* the humoral system to create noxious internal environments that compelled the patient to exhibit signs of madness. This kind of complication led to the emergence of two types of doctors: bodily physicians (*medici corporali*) and spiritual physicians (*medici spirituali*). Often, people seeking help would first go to a bodily physician, who would provide treatment, then refer them to a spiritual doctor, especially in cases of madness. Given the beliefs of the time, many sufferers would attribute their problems to spiritual sources and were supported in this by their doctors. Paracelsus (1493–1541) refuted the humoral model and believed that most diseases were caused by poisons, but he continued to assert the importance of such influences as witchcraft, astrology, and sinfulness. A century later, things had not changed much. Richard Napier (1607–1676) was a physician who was also a devout Anglican and believed he communicated directly with the archangel Michael. Of the 2,039 mentally disturbed patients he saw, nearly 300 complained of religious problems either complicating or causing their mental problems. As a result, he often conceptualized and treated their afflictions based on this belief.

Further complicating the situation in Europe, the Reformation led to a bifurcation of beliefs. The rejection by many of the authority of the Catholic Church in the sixteenth century led to a splintering of beliefs. In much of the still-Catholic southern Europe, the historical beliefs about mental illness of the Middle Ages held sway. In the Protestant north, things began to change. Although a belief in witchcraft remained, and in some areas even increased, the belief in possession waned, along with the belief in the power of the religious authorities to directly access the power of God to heal. There was an increased sense that individuals could learn about their psychological problems themselves and seek help through a variety of practitioners, which drove a market for alternative medicine, led by astrologers, occultists, and charlatans of all stripes. This situation was exacerbated by the increased availability of texts made possible by the invention of the printing press. An increasing number of people could read and had access to a wide variety of professional books. These included Timothy Bright's *Treatise of Melancholie* (1586) and Robert Burton's famous *Anatomy of Melancholy* (1612), as well as a new genre of "self-help" books such as the *Secrets of Alessio of Piedmont* (1555), which provided recipes to address a wide variety of personal problems, ranging from improving bad breath to restoring mental health.

In 1521, Berengarius of Carpi published detailed anatomical drawings of the human body and thus introduced medicine to a more realistic and fact-based view of the human body. It was a direct rebuke of the age-old restriction on direct study of the human body. These drawings included cross sections of the brain, so he was accused of vivisection, and it was known that when he was a student at the University of Paris (where dissection was forbidden), he robbed graves to continue his study of anatomy. This shows the lengths that some people were willing to go to in order to further human knowledge in the medical sciences. Ambroise Paré

(1510–1590) was the first advocate of a truly experimental approach to medicine. A simple barber-surgeon in the French army, he noticed that when he treated wounds in the traditional way (dousing them in boiling oil), they typically became severely infected, while those simply cleaned and bandaged healed better. He also conducted a study of treatment in which he systematically utilized a proposed healing agent on some wounds and not on others and tracked the results. These observations and experiments helped establish the role of controlled research in medicine and provided evidence that many of the traditional beliefs and practices not only were wrong but often made matters worse.

These developments led to a picture of mental illness during the Renaissance that continued to be dominated by nonempirical forces and beliefs but was slowly moving toward empiricism. Empiricism was making strong inroads in areas such as the development of mechanical technologies and sciences like astronomy, which lent themselves easily to direct observation and measurement. However, it lagged in its impact on the field of mental illness. There were various reasons for this. For one thing, very few people ever went to medical professionals for care; the large majority of people could not afford doctors or hospitals and thus relied on the lower-cost options of home remedies and the alternative healers mentioned earlier. Interestingly, these healers, or "empirics," were often sued by doctors' guilds or medical boards, who tried to ban them from the practice of medicine. Some cities passed laws to restrict certain types of practice or require that empirics obtain a license for their work. Then as now, these efforts were typically unsuccessful, and the population flocked to practitioners whose ideas reflected the beliefs of the time in their local areas and were less expensive than those of more learned and professional caregivers.

Another reason for the lack of impact of empiricism in the area of mental illness at the time was the relative difficulty of utilizing this method for the topic. Unlike subjects such as astronomy, mental illness was hard to study or even measure with empirical methods. The mind, up to the current day, is notoriously hard to "see." Behavior can be observed, but that is secondary to the underlying workings of the psyche, which can only be understood by self-report or interpretations of outward behavior. If someone says they hear voices of people who are not physically present, does this reflect hallucinations, clairvoyance, or a culturally sanctioned religious experience? A person can even be lying about their experience, faking mental illness for secondary gain. If the experience is real, and a given culture does not believe in either clairvoyance or that type of religious experience, then it would be easy to assume that the person is experiencing the psychotic symptom of hallucinations. But what if the person's culture does believe in these things? How would someone assess the given experience and conclude it is normal and legitimate or instead a sign of mental illness? One can look at other behavior to assess. For instance, the person may be engaging in actions that are abnormal or dysfunctional, but that still requires a reference to accepted or functional behavior within a cultural context. In the case of astronomy, stars and planets exist in the external world and are fundamentally separate from human culture. Observing their existence, position, and movement in objective ways is possible. Drawing conclusions based on those observations can be done empirically. The results of these observations and the conclusions drawn during the Renaissance rocked the world. The inability to see inside the "black box" of the mind, however, and the culturally confounding nature of interpreting human behavior meant that little scientific progress was made during the Renaissance regarding the nature and causes of mental illness.

MENTAL HEALTH IN THE RENAISSANCE

While the academic study of mental illness made relatively little progress at that time, there was profound movement in the area of mental health. This occurred not as an outgrowth of the study of mental illness or even as a field unto itself, as happens now with such areas as positive psychology and the wide-ranging interests and publications within the self-help movement. Instead, it came as a result of a confluence of historical, cultural, and intellectual factors, largely contained within what is typically referred to as Renaissance humanism. This movement, stretching from the fourteenth through the sixteenth centuries, was centered in Italy but had contributions from various places throughout Europe.

One of the primary contributors, in regard to historical factors, was the Reformation. It was mentioned in the previous section but deserves a somewhat longer explanation. This was a period of profound challenge to the authority of the Roman Catholic Church that began in the sixteenth century (Clark, 1969; McNeill, 1979). A number of factors drove it, including problems with immoral and unethical behavior on the part of priests, the increasing "worldliness" of Church authorities, and the insistence of the Church that it was both the exclusive source of spiritual salvation and the sole arbiter of religious doctrine. The sale of indulgences was a particular problem and one that reflected many of the other factors. Through indulgences, the Church had developed a system of forgiving sins and even guaranteeing escape from purgatory after death in return for a monetary "contributions." This reflected (1) the need to raise large sums of money to purchase art, buy land, construct very expensive buildings, and support the increasingly extravagant lifestyles of its leadership, (2) the belief that the Church could intervene directly with God to forgive sins, and (3) that it could create a doctrine, purgatory, which was not contained in scripture. Together, these factors led to a Catholic Church that had become very powerful but seemed to have lost its spiritual and moral bearings.

The rebellion against the Catholic Church was famously personified by Martin Luther, when he sent his *Ninety-Five Theses on the Power and Efficacy of Indulgences* to his bishop in 1517. In contrast to Church teaching and practice, Luther believed that people could only be saved through God's grace and not through either individual good works or the intervention of any church authority. This had two important ramifications for humanism. First of all, it asserted that people were, by their nature, too weak and sinful to attain salvation on their own. Only faith and subsequent grace could achieve what people by themselves could not. Not only did this constitute a rather negative view of human nature, it also meant that extreme spiritual practices involving self-immolation and others discussed in the previous chapter were mostly useless. It established, however, that salvation was based on an individual's relationship with God, not membership in an authoritative religious organization. Second, it asserted that what was true about Christianity could be found directly and exclusively in the Bible and thus was accessible to anyone who had a Bible and could read. This reinforced the previous point as well regarding the importance of the invention of the printing press, which made Bibles, along with other religious texts, available to a far wider audience than existed previously.

These theological challenges were joined with a political rebellion, which led to various wars, culminating in the Thirty Years' War (1618–1648), which devastated Europe and fundamentally changed the power structure of the region. It weakened the political power of the Catholic Church, especially in Northern Europe, and established the basis for modern, more secular nation-states. The political chaos of the period, followed by the rise of more secular nations, created the conditions for an increase in the honoring and empowerment of the individual, the right to choose his or her own faith, and the freedom to develop a set of beliefs, values, and lifestyle of his or her own choosing. From this historical beginning, it was increasingly seen as the purpose of the state to provide a safeguard for individual freedom, an idea that would become much more fully developed in the Enlightenment.

The final factor we will look at here regarding the Renaissance was the fall of Constantinople to the Ottoman Turks in 1453. This event, following the long, painful decline of Constantinople and the Byzantine Empire, has been marked by many as the end of the Middle Ages. It had powerful symbolic and practical implications for the hegemony of Christendom in the West. Constantinople had stood for centuries as a bulwark of defense for Europe, and with its fall, the mainland was open to invasions from the east. This had profound military and political ramifications that are outside the purview of this text to explore, but it also had important cultural, intellectual, and religious effects, which are within our area of interest. On a fundamental level, it raised the question of the primacy of the Christian worldview. If God would allow such a "catastrophe," what did it say about the Christian God's power or motivation? Was he unable to stop the event? Or perhaps he allowed it as a punishment for the failings of the Roman Catholic and Eastern Orthodox Churches. It became more difficult for the Catholic Churches to say that God was on their side, supporting their authority, not just in regard to political and religious power itself, but also in how it defined human nature and required that people subject themselves to religious and political authority.

This situation helped create the cultural and philosophical conditions for the rise of the idea that human beings have an inherent intelligence, dignity, and autonomy that are not based on religious or political authority but should be protected by them. This happened partly because the fall of Constantinople created a migration of Greek scholars into Europe, helping spark a revival of Greek and Roman philosophy in the West. This factor, along with the relative autonomy of many city-states in Italy and elsewhere and the world travels of the great explorers, dramatically increased the influence of ideas from the Classical era, as well as from other cultures around the world.

This confluence of factors inspired the idea that people should be free to seek wisdom wherever they can find it and develop their own visions of truth. This basic idea was encapsulated in work of Giovanni Pico della Mirandola. His most famous work was the *Oration on the Dignity of Man* (1486), which has been called the "manifesto of the Renaissance" and included a *synthesis* of various sources, including Medieval scholasticism, Platonism, Neoplatonism, Aristotelianism, Hermeticism, and Kabbalah. This odd mix of influences reflected an awareness of and openness to a wide variety of beliefs, as well as an insistence on the right of the individual to draw inspiration from whatever sources were available, from anywhere. It also inspired strong resistance from the Catholic Church, which made it the first printed book to be officially banned by the Church.

This banning reflected a deep division within the Church that emerged during the Renaissance. The Catholic Church was actually a secular leader in the beginning, embracing a return of the Greek and Roman philosophers, a focus on human interpretations of scripture and church doctrine, more worldly church leaders who were highly involved in politics and even military action, and, of course, its materialistic interests. The Church sponsored artists and architects to create highly aesthetic, realistic, and very expensive products, paid for by wealthy donors and through indulgences. The center of influence of the Church, Italy, was ironically a collection of semi-independent city-states that led the way in establishing the principles and practices of the modern, secular nation-state while at the same time guaranteeing that Italy as a whole remained weak enough to be politically dominated by the Church. These changes in the Church and its influences led to the Reformation but also to the Counterreformation. This later movement was an attempt by the Church to return to a truer spiritual path and to reassert its power. It included apologies, more devotional spiritual submovements, anticorruption efforts, and ecclesiastical reconfiguration. In other words, it was spiritually conservative rather than progressive. As a result, although the Church had supported humanistic projects at the beginning of the Renaissance, it was summarily opposed to them by the end (Clark, 1969).

At the same time, the Protestant movement was also opposed to humanism. Luther and his followers were deeply distrustful not only of the Scholastics' attempts to bridge reason and faith but of any human attempts to use the intellect to better understand the world. The irony was that in the Reformation's efforts to break the power of the Catholic Church, it helped establish the beginning of the modern, secular Western world. By decrying the Catholic Church's hegemony on spiritual power, it called into question the legitimacy of *any* institutional religious authority. By asserting the validity of truth as read and experienced by the individual, it inadvertently opened the door to all philosophical and spiritual criticism, which would lead eventually to existentialism and postmodernism in the nineteenth and twentieth centuries.

At the same time that these religious debates were developing, an artistic movement was emerging, with a wide variety of writers, painters, philosophers, and sculptors representing nature and humans in glaringly more realistic terms. Giotto dared to paint Jesus appearing as a normal rather than idealized human figure. Philosophers ranging from Ockham to Eckhart elevated the reality of inner, psychological experience as well as the idea that human feelings and desires are primary and the intellect should be their servant rather than the other way around. Writers like Boccaccio represented people in a more natural light, with emotions and impulses in a real world. Together, Renaissance artists and philosophers helped break the Medieval bonds to an idealized, spiritualized, and highly structured view of human beings in a sacralized world.

Thus, the Renaissance was a period of tremendous conflict and change, rife with contradictions, ironies, and paradoxes. It spawned the modern age of individual autonomy (and rights), with its freedom to decide what to believe about the self and the universe, as well as its subsequent myriad paths to happiness, peace, and spirituality. At the same time, it was deeply conservative, clinging tightly to tradition, spawning the Inquisition and many other attempts to reassert a fundamental set of truths about people, society, and religion. If the Renaissance radically realigned personal loyalties throughout Europe, it also set in motion the modern tendency to regularly question truths and shift loyalties, along with proclaiming the *human right* to choose one's truths and loyalties. The man or woman of the tenth century in Europe did not question whether they should be a Catholic – it was a given, and they *knew* their immortal soul depended on it. By the sixteenth century, this had significantly changed. The explosion of different *truths* coming from the radically shifting political, cultural, and religious powers made it psychologically and practically possible to make more choices about one's life.

This is radically important and a double-edged sword. In a world without choices, there are no alternatives to the beliefs, values, and lifestyle a person lives. The positive side of this, from a psychological perspective, is that it provides a secure, consistent worldview. People are relatively free from doubt. "I *know* how things are." Obviously, many people yearn for this kind of surety and join organizations, groups, and societies that offer such a closed system, even when other choices are open to them. Doubt is uncomfortable. Choices are difficult. Each has different costs and benefits, strengths and weaknesses. Finding truth for oneself takes effort. It is so much easier to have truth handed to one in a complete package, presented with complete confidence.

Despite this temptation, the Renaissance made it difficult for the West to return to such a situation. It founded the modern mind and sense of self. It confronted and undermined entrenched ideology and made all beliefs subject to criticism and the subsequent need for direct testing or logical defense. It pushed people to directly face reality, stripping away traditional preconceptions provided by authorities. This rebellious attitude would, for the most part, triumph, but it met great resistance, as it always does. The quest for truth is in many ways a battle. On the individual level, it is a battle for one's very soul. The Renaissance was the birthplace of the *heroic culture rebel*, who rejects the truths of the past for his or her own truths, hotly won and often dearly paid for. A few centuries later, Freud would conceptualize individual human maturity in terms of hard-fought autonomy, successfully won only through separation from and then difficult rapprochement with the mother and other cultural authorities.

The dynamic interplay of forces unleashed in the Renaissance had important implications for the mental health of those who lived through it. On the one hand, there is the example of the House of Medici. Considered the wealthiest family in Europe at the time, they built their fortune on banking, and although they were strong patrons of the Catholic Church, they were fundamentally secular and humanist in temperament. They supported the work of many artists and scientists of the time, including Leonardo de Vinci, Michelangelo, Machiavelli, and Galileo. They used their wealth to influence local governments and even put multiple people on the throne of the papacy (Leo X, Clement VII, Pius IV, and Leo XI). Interestingly, and reflecting the paradoxical nature of the times, they supported the Counterreformation. It was likely their financial and political links to papal power rather than conservative religious ideology that drove their support of the Church. The family was amazingly secular for the time, flaunting its wealth and exerting its power in an ironically Machiavellian way, apparently seeking pleasure, comfort, and self-interest for their own rewards.

What you had in the House of Medici was a strong example of seeking wealth and power for personal happiness and fulfilment. One could remain aligned with a religious institution but still live in a deeply secular, humanist, and even hedonistic way. The materialist or worldly path to happiness was certainly not something new, but its reemergence in the Renaissance was powerful and unique. The Medicis were not royal or ecclesiastical. They had originally been farmers but rose to great worldly success. They retained the trappings of morality, civic-mindedness, and religiosity, at least partly to maintain popularity with the masses. The foundation of their wealth and power was in the business world, not in agriculture or trade. They were people of the city, not the country, savvy in politics, and urbane. The modern dream of going from "rags to riches" through capitalism and thus achieving feelings of success and happiness could find no better inspiration than the Medicis of the fifteenth and sixteenth centuries.

This dream was not in direct conflict with the emerging values of the Reformation. While the theologians of the time were deeply uncomfortable with self-centeredness and hedonism, they valued hard work. Moral discipline, thrift, honesty, integrity, and the personal dignity of a vocation combined to align capitalism with religion. One was providing for one's family and the overall community. Success within this area of life could, within reason, be a sign of both individual righteousness and the grace of God. This was particularly true in light of the Calvinist belief in predestination. Material success could only be achieved if God wanted it, and thus success was a sign of God's favor. Conversely, being poor, destitute, unemployed, or afflicted with ailments or injuries that made one unable to work could be seen as a sign of moral failing or worse, God's disfavor. What had one done to deserve such misfortune? Thus, the poor were not to be pitied but judged and exhorted (or forced) to change their lazy, sinful ways.

This development of beliefs and values had to have an effect on the collective concept and experience of mental health. Previously, the wealthy probably experienced a strong dose of guilt with their success and gave heavily to the church to atone for their sins of avarice and greed. Now, they could smile peacefully with a sense that God was on their side. On the other hand, the poor would previously have suffered but still felt "justified" in the eyes of God and, in fact, more so than the rich. Did the Bible not say that a rich man has as much a chance of getting into heaven as a camel through the eye of a needle? There was moral dignity in poverty. Not being morally encumbered with worldly, material success, the poor and needy were truly God's children. Now they had to wonder if they had been cursed by God, stricken with failure and/or poor health for their perceived failings. They became a blight on the city. Rather than an opportunity to express generosity of spirit and donation, they became an outrage and an embarrassment. How can one think about oneself in this situation? We can only imagine that some must have found it a motivation to change in some ways, while others would simply sink into a depressive morass of self-loathing, accepting their fate as failures in the eyes of God and man.

This period of transition, conflict, and paradox was embodied in the life and work of Francis Bacon (1561–1626). Born into royalty and wealth, he failed to receive an inheritance from his father and ended up penniless and sued for unpaid debts at one point in his life (Sargent, 1999). He was educated at home, in the medieval style, but went on to be dramatically critical of scholasticism and reliance on authority for true knowledge. He was very well read and a first-rate philosopher, yet he was a firm believer that the life of an intellect should be active and engaged with the world. As such, he pursued a life in politics and rose to the level of attorney general and Lord Chancellor of England. He strongly supported the idea that knowledge *should* be gained by empirical observation and inductive reasoning, and yet his political ideology was deeply conservative, supporting the English monarchy and its claim to authority and power.

Francis Bacon was an extraordinarily intelligent and capable man. While he engaged in a busy and very successful professional and public life, he found the time to pursue a variety of other intellectual interests. He was familiar with the conflict between the Stoics and the Epicureans (see Chapter 3) and took the side of the Epicureans. Both practical and worldly, he decided the Stoic prescription of disconnection from the problems of life was an impossibility and ultimately ineffective in producing happiness or well-being. It was impossible because human sufferings arise from nature (illness, loss, hunger, lust, and ultimately death) and thus cannot be completely ignored or disregarded as long as they are alive. It is ineffective because passively accepting the travails of life leaves one vulnerable and disarmed to deal with them. This position, accepting one's natural desires and seeking at least some fulfillment of them, with an eye toward succeeding in the secular world of business and government, was in direct opposition to the ascetic, stoic moral values of the Middle Ages. Bacon encouraged others not to retreat from the secular world into asceticism and contemplation but to participate wholeheartedly in the world and thus find personal fulfillment.

On the other hand, this did not lead him to abandon religious faith and philosophical reflection. In fact, Bacon asserted that a deep study of philosophy would lead people closer to religion because a contemplation of final causes demands an intelligent designer. The irony, or hypocrisy if you wish, was that his ongoing dedication to religious faith did not lead Bacon to be overly strict in his own self-discipline. He often spent beyond his means and, as noted before, ended up in serious debt at one point. It appears that Bacon's avid pursuit of worldly success and sensual pleasure caused him a great deal of struggle and strife at various times in his life, which would seem to be at odds with his prescription of pursuing worldliness for personal happiness.

Perhaps Bacon's greatest contribution to epistemology was his dedication to doubting all received dogma and his influence on others after him to do so and find ways to discover the *real* truth. He felt there needed to be a radical revolution in the standard methods of doing research and the intellectual search for truth. His answer to this need was his idea that the greatest mistake of the Ancient Greeks and the Middle Ages was spending too much time thinking about theory and so little time conducting observational studies (Sargent, 1999). He raised serious doubts about the objectivity of pure human thought and pointed out that humans tend to impress their own ideas, emotions, personal experience, and values on the phenomena they seek to describe or interpret, thus causing a distortion of reality. The conclusions reached then become pictures of the ones doing the research, not neutral interpretations of the objects themselves. This is what we now call *projection*. He also made the point that once a conclusion has been reached, people tend to seek out or distort later data to support their conclusions. This is what we now commonly refer to as *confirmation bias*. By carefully reviewing the many ways people distort reality for their purposes, often with the best of intentions, Bacon concluded that people must question all assumptions and propositions and actively seek out raw data to confirm or reject their hypotheses. This method of inductive reasoning must be done in a highly controlled and systematic way to avoid error.

In alignment with the spirit of the times, Bacon wanted this method to be used not just to understand the world better but to give humans the power to control nature and create a utopian society. His interests were quite practical: the betterment of human life in the face of so many natural horrors and limitations that confound people. For instance, Bacon was well aware of the lack of real medical knowledge in his time and its inability to deal effectively with even the most basic of medical problems like illness and infection. People at the time went to doctors out of desperation rather than any real faith the doctor could heal them. While, sadly, Bacon did not make any breakthroughs in medicine and specifically mental illness himself, he did call loudly for science to find the real causes, course of, and treatments for illnesses. He saw progress in this area as being nothing less than the foundation of future human peace and happiness.

Francis Bacon did not just explore the abstractions of epistemology and science, however. He was interested in the mundane, day-to-day realities of human psychology and sociology. He asserted that the best way to avoid civic discord and promote harmony was an equitable distribution of wealth. Rather strangely, he did not like the idea of socialism or even democracy, as he did not trust the masses and dreamed of an aristocratic government, led by a philosopher king. His psychology was almost behaviorist, believing that everything we do is caused by preexisting conditions or factors. He was very curious about the interacting effects of education, culture, habit, social influence, praise and punishment, parenting, and all the extended influences we now refer to as social psychology. He provided self-help–style advice on achieving success in life. He advised others to know themselves and others as well as possible. What are people's strengths and weaknesses? What are they open and secretive about? Who are their friends and other influences? What is their basic temperament or personality? What do they want, and what are they afraid of? He advocated being friendly with others but not too close, seeking to know more than being known. This rather Machiavellian advice stemmed from his basic approach to life, which seemed to be more utilitarian than idealistic.

However, despite his somewhat cynical advice for achieving success, Bacon offered a more romantic vision of a more elevated human happiness. He asserted that philosophy was his deepest love. He felt that only philosophy offered the wisdom and understanding that brought peace to the turmoil of life. He felt that learning and philosophic reflection help to mitigate the fear of death and unavoidable misfortunes of life. They provide a deeper, more fulfilling basis for life than the lust for material things. Fortune and fame can come and go (as he well knew from his own experience), but inner wisdom and peace cannot be taken away and continue to be a succor when all the gold in the world cannot help one. Conversely, despite his strong support of the Protestant faith, Bacon spent little effort exploring more spiritual virtues and their connection to human redemption, if not outright happiness. His explorations were intellectual, philosophical, and worldly, as was his life.

By taking this direction in his life and writings, Francis Bacon was, in many ways, the penultimate man of the Renaissance. He strongly supported the traditional church and aristocracy but demanded a modernization of science and philosophy. He was greatly distrustful of the "common man" but extolled the power of the human intellect to find truth and reject superstition, all for the common welfare. His life reflected the fact that, by the end of the Renaissance, Europe was a cauldron of conflicting ideas, beliefs, religious practices, and principalities. What was to emerge in the coming years was the scientific revolution, religious pluralism, more advanced humanism, and the modern state. Bacon's life and work presaged the emerging scientific revolution which would start the slow ascent of modern psychiatric knowledge and practice. Overall, the Renaissance saw the rise of a religious pluralism that gave people more choice in how (or if) they worshiped. Its humanism gave people individual dignity and rights. Its new, more secular states gave people control over their own destinies in ways never previously imagined. Together, these changes sparked a revolution in the concepts of mental health and mental illness that took place during the Enlightenment.

CHAPTER 6

THE ENLIGHTENMENT

The Enlightenment took place in Europe roughly during the seventeenth and eighteenth centuries. It grew out of the Renaissance and brought the changes of that era to a new level in regard to the knowledge, beliefs, and practices in politics, economics, philosophy, religion, medicine, art, and literature. As usual in this book, we cannot review all the achievements and consequences of the time but will focus instead on their influence on the conception of, and to some extent, practices regarding mental health and mental illness.

At the end of the Renaissance, courageous people had struck blows for a more objective, realistic view of humanity and the universe. Their names are well known: Galileo, Copernicus, Machiavelli, Michelangelo, Paracelsus, Bacon, and many others. They brought the Western world to a turning point, away from superstition and reliance on authority, and toward objectivity and empirical observation. The Western world, in particular, was experiencing profound changes to how people thought about themselves and their place in the world. The achievements of the Enlightenment represented a much more complete break with the ideological realities of the past, especially those of the Middle Ages. As noted in the last chapter, the humanists of the Renaissance had promoted human confidence in their own intellectual abilities, while the Reformation had undermined the authority of the Catholic Church. The Enlightenment continued to move humanity solidly toward the modern world of empirical science, secular society, representative government, and the overall primacy of human-centered psychology, values, and personal interests in all things affecting people.

The first major contribution to this movement in regard to psychology was the development of a more rational, mechanistic view of human thought and action. Thomas Hobbes (1588–1679) asserted that sense perceptions were the only source of psychological activity. He emphasized that these perceptions were associated in the order they were perceived (temporal), thus forming chains of ideas and beliefs, which lead to behavior. He also linked this process to biology, asserting that these perceptions and their organizing processes were driven by the underlying desire to stay alive, pursue pleasure, and avoid pain – in other words, a species-based but individualized self-interest. Philosophers like John Locke (1632–1704) differentiated between external perceptions (sights and sounds) and internal perceptual experiences (impulses and feelings). Others, such as George Berkeley (1685–1754) and David Hume (1711–1776), took this idea further to assert that although it was true that all real knowledge must come from objective data (empiricism), it was also true that everything we know about the world comes through the filter of our subjective experience, and thus, absolute knowledge is impossible. This conclusion would set the foundation for later thinkers to doubt all knowledge, stressing that all truth is individual, subjective, and thus relativistic. But before we get too deep into philosophy, it is important to announce that finally, in the seventeenth century, psychiatry emerged as a medical specialty, a full two centuries before psychology would do the same.

THE BIRTH OF PSYCHIATRY

Prior to the seventeenth century, as we have discussed before, psychiatry was still in thrall to the Classical era and its limited knowledge of the brain and mental illness. Dominated by humoral theory and Christian restrictions on the study of physiology, the field of medical psychiatry made very little progress for more than 1,500 years. The loosening of religious restrictions and the challenging of classical theories (i.e., Platonism and humoral medicine) that started in the Renaissance increased during the Enlightenment. Doctors like William Harvey (1578–1657) and Thomas Sydenham (1624–1689) contributed tremendously to the field (Alexander & Selesnick, 1966). While it wasn't until the advent of the Modern era (nineteenth and twentieth centuries) that we would see the full development of psychiatry as an independent profession, with its separate training, practice, and research, the Enlightenment was the birthplace of that later development. The Enlightenment saw the establishment of empiricism as the epistemological foundation of modern psychiatry. It also saw the rapid growth of a major institution of clinical practice at the time, the asylum. By the end of this period, "mentalists" were practicing throughout Europe, tens of thousands of people were interred in asylums, and psychiatric textbooks were being written by specialists who were attempting to develop a nosology of mental illness (Scull, 2015).

Going back to the beginning of the Enlightenment, William Harvey focused primarily on organic medicine, but he also described the effect of emotional tension on heart activity. This was important for a number of reasons. First of all, it was based on careful observation and questioning of actual patients, not references to humoral theory. Second, it established the importance of an empirically based connection between the psyche and the somatic. Viewing the dynamic of mental health and illness as the nexus point between psychological experiences such as emotion and cognition and the structure and functioning of the human body, primarily the brain, became the foundation of modern psychiatric theory and practice. While the eventual academic field of psychology, drawing from the Enlightenment developments in philosophy, remained trapped in Cartesian dualism (mind–body split), psychiatry developed along a parallel but strikingly different track, reflected by Dr. Harvey's work. Mind and body were seen as integrated, with the psychological experience of the mind being the end result of the actions of the brain. Psychological problems were increasingly conceptualized as brain problems. This was the foundation of what would later become known as the *medical model* of psychopathology.

Thomas Sydenham came from a Puritan family and served in Cromwell's army, studied at Oxford, and practiced medicine in London in the late 1600s. As one would expect of somebody whose family was Protestant, he rejected the idea of reliance on any human institutional authority for truth. He took a critical stance toward historically held medical theories, rejecting the idea that they were valid just because they seemed rational or logical or that sometimes the symptoms or outcomes happened to correspond to a theory. His empirical attitude was severe and uncompromising. He distrusted books, knowing that most were written by authoritative "experts," based on religiously supported philosophy. He trusted facts and the empirical evidence of his own eyes and clinical experience. Most of his contributions were in the field of traditional medicine, but he also advanced psychiatry, describing the symptoms of hysteria. He correctly noted that men, not just women, suffered from this disease, thus refuting the ancient belief that it was caused by a displaced and wandering uterus. He also recognized that hysteria could simulate virtually any form of organic disorder, and thus at least part of the etiology of hysteria was based in the mind.

Of course, no discussion of the history of mental illness is complete without mention of Richard Burton's *Anatomy of Melancholy* (1621). An Oxford dean of divinity, Burton was not a medical doctor, and his famous book is mostly filled with a complex mix of historical misconceptions, superstition, mythology, and pretty much everything he could throw together from his study of depression. What makes the book a significant historical contribution to the field was that so much of it consisted of his own self-reflection. Burton was a self-diagnosed melancholic. He blamed his condition on not receiving enough love from his parents, which left him bitter and chronically dissatisfied with the world. His own emotional pain left him acutely aware of the limitations, inaccuracies, and impracticality of the existing state of knowledge on the subject. His introspection constituted the second great exploration of the psyche in the Western tradition, after St. Augustine's *Confessions*. He described his internal struggle with feelings of hostility, jealousy, frustration, ambivalence, and their knitting together in a tangled ball of resentment, guilt, self-hatred, passive-aggressiveness, and all the rest of the cognitive-emotional dynamics of neurotic depression. It should come as no surprise that in an age which did not yet have psychotherapists or even professional psychologists, the greatest insights into mental illness would come from the self-exploration of sufferers who had the social status, education, and courage to write honestly and effectively about their experiences while refusing to describe themselves in terms passed down to them from a now-discredited and dusty library of scholastic tomes.

THE RISE OF THE ASYLUM

The emergence of modern psychiatry and thus the foundation of our current conceptions of mental illness can be traced to the expansion of mental asylums throughout Europe in the seventeenth and eighteenth centuries. This expansion has been chronicled and discussed in many books and articles through the years (Alexander & Selesnick, 1966; Foucault, 1965; Millon, 2004; Porter, 2013; Scull, 1993, 2017; Shorter, 1997). The academic work on the subject has gone in many directions, including those who emphasize the rise of the asylum as part of a historical *reform movement* designed to address the horrific state of affairs when it came to identifying and treating the mentally ill (most of the psychiatric historians tend to take this tack), while others focus on the increase in the asylum population as a sign of increased stigmatization and cultural control of those who were deemed *different* or *disturbing* (Foucault famously took this approach). In other words, some look at the asylum movement as deeply flawed but well meaning, while others see it as deeply pernicious, with the progressive attitudes expressed about it at the time being mainly a smokescreen for its true intentions.

Of course, like so many complex and far-reaching historical movements, it seems likely that both points of view have some validity but can easily be taken too far and become crude caricatures of themselves. On the one hand, prior to the eighteenth century, the vast majority of people who were severely mentally ill were treated at home or not at all (Foucault, 1965; Scull, 1993; Shorter, 1997). They could be found wandering the streets, begging for food, being driven from villages and cities into the countryside, being beaten and otherwise abused, and being thrown into prisons as part of the unwanted "refuse" of society. The asylum was a place where, by definition, the mentally ill could (hopefully) find succor and treatment. Eventually separated from criminals because of their unique needs and treated as suffering from an illness and not moral or spiritual disturbance, they deserved pity and help, not condemnation and punishment. From this perspective, the increase in asylum placements constituted a humane reform of then-existing practice, seeking to better understand and treat the mentally ill.

On the other hand, a number of forces were at work that actually increased the public and professional condemnation of people who were mentally ill and sought to lock them up in secure institutions, far away from "decent society." One of those forces, which has likely been around for a very long time, as it is foundational to human psychology is what Edward Shorter described as the "horror of those who were different" (1997, p. 2). This horror drove the mistreatment of many who were mentally ill and would lead to the public perception of a need for reform. Because treatment usually took place at home, and for many family members, their response to severe mental illness was horror, revulsion, moral condemnation, and/or rage, the result was often gross maltreatment or outright rejection. Shorter provides a number of examples – a man chained to a wall by his own wife for five years, a youth locked in a pigpen, eating slop from a bowl with his mouth like an animal. These were the kind of conditions that were discovered when local officials looked into the matter. As late as the 1870s, investigators in Germany were finding rural areas, where most people saw mental illness in the family as shameful and thus would not even seek out care in the asylums that was available, but either kept the sufferer at home, often chained or caged in an isolated room, or cast him or her out to become a homeless wanderer. This was the situation that led many to seek reform and create a local or even a national network of mental hospitals or asylums that could offer proper housing and care.

Another force driving the increase in asylums was the general increase in population. By the time of the Enlightenment, Europe was recovering from the population loss during the plagues and wars of the Middle Ages and Renaissance. Between 1500 and 1750, the overall population of Europe doubled in size, from about 65 million to about 130 million (Levine, 2019). This meant that there were more people who were mentally ill and were being treated at home or were wandering the roads and waterways, never finding a place of refuge or care. Combined with the overall population increase was the rising number of people living in cities. While the urbanization level (percentage of overall population living in cities and towns) would not increase much before the nineteenth century and stayed around 10% during the Enlightenment, the increasing overall size of the cities pushed both the demand for services to deal with the public health problem of mental illness (homelessness, criminality, etc.) as well as the tax base to support such services.

Mental illness presents unique problems in a large city. The high level of population density in a city leads to a higher number of people exhibiting signs of severe mental illness in a relatively small geographic area. This is amplified by the tendency of such people to congregate in and around public spaces, because severe mental illness is so debilitating that it typically leads to chronic homelessness. When this occurs, other residents begin to complain about the "problem" of mental illness, as they are concerned about or irritated by the presence of people who may be "disturbing" in a number of different ways. The mentally ill will often present as emotionally agitated, talking to themselves, dressed in unusual ways, moving around in unusual ways, being socially intrusive or inappropriate, and presenting as a perceived or actual risk of robbery or assault. In short, their presence leads to public calls that *something be done*. One of the results of these complaints in Europe was the expansion of asylums.

As noted in previous chapters, asylums had already been around for nearly 2,000 years but were still quite rare, provided minimal treatment, and were expected to care for only the most disturbed or disruptive individuals (Scull, 2017). They were often associated with religious charity and provided as a public service. While there were a few in Europe, there were many more in the Islamic world, including in Spain when it was under Islamic control (Alexander & Selesnick, 1966). In religiously supported institutions, there was little demand to provide any type of professional assessment or treatment. It was enough that they provided charitably motivated refuge for the suffering. Given the limited and misleading knowledge regarding mental illness at the time, the lack of serious treatment was not seen as a particular problem. By the age of Enlightenment, not much had changed in regard to available professional information. There was still no clearly established nosology for assessment and diagnosis of mental illness or empirically established norms of treatment. What had changed was the public demand for an increase in institutional, custodial care, partly because of the factors previously discussed.

Another factor in the increase in asylums, and one more directly connected to our central topic, involved the changing beliefs about mental illness. As noted in the last chapter, the rise of empiricism started to shift secular, cultural, and political forces away from conceptualizing mental illness as a moral and spiritual problem and toward being seen as a medical issue. This meant that more families would seek outside help, more medical professionals would see providing help as part of their chosen field, and more politicians, administrators, and taxpayers would see providing help as an appropriate and even necessary use of public funds.

This demand led to the expansion of many existing monastic hospitals or prisons and turning them into publicly funded and administered institutions for custodial care of the mentally ill. It also led to the building of many new institutions for that purpose. This established, for good or ill, the idea that identifying and treating mental illness was a public or societal responsibility. This took the subject matter out of the relative privacy of the family and the church and placed it in the better funded, more transparent, and accountable public sector. Things that are paid for with public money demand a "full accounting," and they are open to serious questions. What is the need? How do you measure it? How much of it is there? What is an effective and financially efficient way of dealing with it? These questions naturally arise and must be answered. Those answers may be biased by specific religious beliefs or local folk wisdom, but they should be objectively sought and easily accepted by everyone and thus based on empirical knowledge and the authority of professionalism. This drive toward objectivity, empiricism, and professionalism naturally increases as societies become more heterogeneous, secular, educated, industrialized, and generally modern.

The increasing sense of public responsibility for providing institutional care for severe mental illness ironically contributed to the public perception of the dangerousness of mental illness, both in relation to those afflicted with mental illness and to the asylums that were built to treat them. This was because as the number of institutions increased, and they housed involuntary patients behind locked doors and shackled to the wall if necessary, the public image of mental illness as extreme and dangerous naturally increased. The very image of the "madman" chained to a wall in a dank fortress of a "hospital" was amplified in the public mind as the truth of mental illness. Perhaps the most infamous of these publicly funded and thus publicly accessible institutions was Bethlehem, outside London. Often mispronounced "Bedlam," its very name became synonymous with insanity, as well as the dangers and horrors associated with it. People began to visit such places as a perverse source of entertainment, to see the raving lunatics and experience firsthand the horrors of the insane asylum. They could then return home and spread tales of the spectacle they had witnessed.

As noted previously, an important contributor to this discussion of how people conceptualized mental illness is Michel Foucault. He wrote about many topics but is best known in the field of psychology for his study of the history of insanity, which has become infamous for its historical interpretation of the rise of the asylum in this era (1965). I say "infamous" because his ideas have inspired both strong support and equally strong criticism. As an intellectual, Foucault was particularly concerned about the relationship between power and knowledge, a topic he addressed in his writings and lectures on a number of subjects. In regard to the subject of psychiatry, he looked at this in two ways. The first had to do with the changing conception of mental illness in the premodern era (the Renaissance and the Enlightenment). The second had to do with the practical application of this change of conception, which was the increase in population of involuntary patients in asylums. Foucault referred to this increase as the *great confinement*.

So what was Foucault's thesis regarding the changing concept of mental illness? The key to exploring this question is to consider the fundamental debate regarding whether mental illness exists as a real, ontological entity or rather a cultural, historically contextualized creation. Is insanity a natural phenomenon that cultures *respond* to, or does a culture's *response* to what it finds unusual or disturbing in human nature constitute something it decides to call insanity? Foucault clearly falls in the latter camp, as did Thomas Szasz, who was writing around the same time, in the 1960s and 1970s. Most historians of psychiatry take the first position and think of mental illness as a real entity, although it is obviously *affected* by cultural phenomena, and thus may appear and be treated differently from culture to culture, but that does not change the fact that something we call mental illness actually exists separate from what we think about it. For instance, Shorter (1997) noted that changes in the nuclear family, with membership becoming more about emotional/social intimacy rather than property and lineage, led to less acceptance of behavioral disruption. This decrease in the family-level acceptance of deviance led to more referrals to asylum care. This dynamic would quickly become synergistic, as the increase in demand pushed the construction of more asylums and thus greater accessibility. However, in Shorter's analysis, this was *not* because the changes in family dynamics *created* a form of mental illness but rather that it *changed the reaction* to mental illness experienced by individual family members.

This argument from mainstream, modern psychiatry focuses on the historical reaction to the deviancy of mental illness. Foucault took a very different tack and looked at *deviancy itself* as the primary factor in society's response. In his analysis (1965), personality attributes that were acceptable in the premodern era became increasingly unacceptable in the early Modern era, especially in relation to the emerging capitalistic mindset, which valued a disciplined work ethic, self-control, rationalism, and materialism. People who were more impulsive, emotional, overly spiritual, and socially inappropriate would no longer be tolerated and deserved punishment or rehabilitation. To Foucault, asylum populations increased not as an empathetic response to true mental illness but as a cultural punishment for people who did not fit the needs of an increasingly modern, capitalist society. He described the shift from the "ship of fools" to the hospital as the development of cultural control over the definitions and meaning of madness. No longer roaming free at the fulcrum point of God, humanity, and dreams of reason, the emerging modern culture of Europe needed to redefine madness in a medical, secular way, conforming with the needs of an increasingly urban, family-based, capitalist, and materialistic society. A state of mind that is irrational and undisciplined is highly problematical in such a place and needs external censure and control. In such a place, madness emerges as the *prince of fools*, calling out the nakedness of the king, "an ironic sign that misplaces the guideposts between the real and the chimerica" (Foucault, 1965, p. 37). As Western society, driven by the empirical revolution of the Enlightenment, raised rationality and productivity as the supreme values of human nature, the agitated disturbance of the disturbed became increasingly unacceptable and the need for confinement justified as being for the "common good."

In Foucault's analysis, the *voice* of madness needed to be silenced. He placed the landmark date of this shift at 1656, when a French governmental decree founded the General Hospital in Paris (Foucault, 1965). On the surface a mere administrative reorganization, it actually increased the power of the state to incarcerate the poor and troublesome. Its directors were given the power of "correction and punishment" over all citizens of Paris who caused trouble. This meant it wasn't just a hospital in the modern sense but also a prison, and the two roles were not clearly differentiated. The insane were detained, housed, and treated the same way as common criminals were. The hospital housed murderers, pickpockets, madmen, pregnant teens, juvenile delinquents, the physically disabled, epileptics, the mentally retarded, etc. The disowned, unwanted, and difficult to manage of Paris were all placed together in a filthy, overcrowded facility with no clear dictate to choose between treatment or punishment. Twenty years later, the king of France extended this practice to the entire country in an edict proscribing the establishment of a general hospital in every city of the kingdom. By the eve of the French Revolution, these hospitals could be found in 32 cities throughout France. Similar movements were occurring in other parts of Europe, especially Germany and England. As in France, most of the institutions opened at this time had multiple functions. They served as hospitals for the insane, confinement for criminals, emergency housing for the poor, and hospice care for the variously disabled. In the modern world, we are so used to these functions being provided in different ways, in different institutions, that it seems very strange to us that people with severe mental illness would be confined alongside and treated similarly to violent criminals.

It soon became clear that different types of people had different needs, different problems, and different relative strengths and weaknesses. People with medical problems needed medical care and may not have needed forced confinement. The behavior of criminals may have called for some kind of punishment, but not that of the mentally ill, who by any reasonable definition could not control their misbehavior. Many of the groups, including the criminals, resented being housed with the mentally ill, finding it unfair to be housed alongside people so disturbed and thus disturbing. By the eighteenth century, there was already solid movement toward a clearer differentiation of these groups and the treatment they should receive from the public sector of society. Thus, it was the rise of the public sector's social welfare activity (as the religious sector waned, secular society strengthened, capitalism spread, and the modern state was established) that helped drive a new understanding of mental illness – more medical and less religious or moral in nature. Foucault points out the "strange contradiction" that on the one hand, the confinement served to hide the shame of insanity from the public, while on the other hand, it *exposed* mental illness by placing it in a highly visible, institutional form. This exposure itself affected public perception and conception as people reacted to the horrors of institutional confinement (from drawings, paintings, novels, plays, newspaper exposés, and government reports) as well as the disgusting spectacle of their fellow citizens flocking to madhouses for the entertainment of watching the insane "perform" for them in their debasement, suffering, and dramatic, abnormal behavior.

During the Enlightenment, these institutions established their reputation for being grossly unhealthy dumping grounds for the unfit and unwanted. Some modern historians (Porter, Scull, and Shorter, for instance) have made the point that it is unfair to blame this on a semipurposeful sociopolitical "great confinement" to punish and rehabilitate those who failed to fulfill the emerging capitalist values of rationality and hard work. On the other hand, Foucault and Szasz, among other, more sociologically oriented historians, make the competing point that the rise of institutionalization of the mentally ill was driven not just by a more enlightened interest in helping the mentally ill and saving them from abuse and neglect at home. They say that this historical change was also motivated by more malign impulses involving fear, revulsion, ignorance, and yes, the emerging modern Western values regarding individual responsibility, self-discipline, rationality, and economic productivity. Thus, the shortcomings of the asylum movement in the seventeenth and eighteenth centuries created the impetus for the reforms that would follow in the nineteenth and twentieth.

THE MEDICALIZATION OF MADNESS

As noted before, the Enlightenment can be seen as a time of transition, from the medieval to the modern, in the conception of and consequent treatment of mental illness. This was just discussed in connection to the rise of the asylum as the focus point of treatment. However, along with the increase in asylum care, there was a more *general move* toward a medical model of understanding mental illness. To this day, most historians, especially those from a psychiatric background, view this as a positive, progressive change – moving away from the superstitious, witch-hunting days of the Dark Ages and into the humane, empirical light of modern rationality. On the other hand, the doubters are deeply skeptical of the supposedly objective validity of modern empiricism in its ability to understand madness. The intellectual children of the Romantics of the nineteenth century, they explore and value the dimensions of mental illness that are lost or dismissed in the antiseptic and glaring light of medical empiricism.

Foucault was, of course, one such critic. Part of his view of insanity was that it reflects the underlying, irrational, animalistic core of human nature. He referred to madness as the "limit in the realm of animality" (1965, p. 81). As such, it was sanctified in the Judeo-Christian worldview. The point of the Fall was that there was nothing in the experience of humanity that could not be redeemed. Not only was nothing outside the bounds of *grace and forgiveness*, but sin was inevitable. Depravity was the natural condition from which humanity needed to be saved by God. If madness was, in some way, the lowest point of human experience, then its presence signaled the opportunity for and required starting point for *redemption*. The dark night of the soul, the wandering through the wilderness, the days of temptation, the resurrection after passing through Hell, and *Pilgrim's Progress* all point toward a necessary journey through darkness and suffering to eventually reunite with God in paradise. Foucault makes the historical point that the Enlightenment despiritualized madness, moving it squarely into the realm of the secular (medicine, politics, economics). Stripped of its spiritual import, madness became a public health problem – the irritating homeless rather than the *spiritually lost and suffering*.

By pointing out this change in the way mental illness was conceptualized, Foucault was establishing a new dialectic regarding madness. Rather than seeing knowledge about insanity as developing over time, as objective information is accumulated, moving from ignorance to enlightenment, he saw such knowledge as always being a reflection of the values, beliefs, needs, challenges, and power structures of a particular point in time. He was as impressed by what was *lost* in the increasingly modernized vision of mental illness as by what was *gained*. He saw madness in our *relationship* with our passions and our fixed ideas; that meeting point between the soul and the body. Anger, sadness, lust, and hunger, along with delusional beliefs and irrational thought processes, are experienced and communicated in the body and mind/soul together in what he called "the symbolic values of common qualities" (1965, p. 87). By this, he meant that the empirical structure of causality was lost because there is no real separateness of body and soul. He asks if our joys and sorrows are the cause or the result of the physical activity of the nerves. In fact they are both, and thus it is pointless to ask if irrational impulsivity is the cause or the result of madness. The modern doctor looks for a linear etiology to the experience of madness, but this is a projective inflation – a single referent from what is really a matrix of meanings, perspectives, and mutual influences. He reminds us that imagination is not madness, but when the mind binds itself to the imagined and takes it for reality, forsaking affirmation or negation, then madness can be said to be present. The problem is that the demystification of the modern world narrows the range of socially acceptable imagination and psychological experience. Then madness becomes an epithet we throw at those whose imagination differs from our own.

It is the issues of personal psychological experience, including feelings, ideas, affirmations, and negations, that led Foucault to conclude that language itself is the "first and last" structure of madness. It is language that provides descriptions and meanings, thus framing the perceived sources, purposes, and outcomes of all psychological phenomena, and thus no less the experience and conceptualization of madness and sanity. Foucault accepted that there is objective truth, at least physical truth, versus moral truth. So madness was *real* for him, reflecting a person's self-deception and error in analysis and judgment. The problem, from Foucault's perspective, was that the madman does not wake from his dreams – he is blind to rational analysis, and thus insanity becomes the impossibility of reason. Reason reflects symbols of order, unity, and the familiar structures of meaning and thought itself. The symbolism of madness focuses on shadows, darkness, and the nighttime world of monsters. What exists from the daytime work of judgment becomes enthralled to the night's hallucinations and delusions. In other words, Foucault's referring to the central importance of language does not mean that he thought that madness was nothing but an empty word or *only* a social judgment. Instead, he asserted that language is the nexus point of reality and human experience. As such, it is the alpha and omega of all attempts to understand this phenomenon of human existence.

Prior to the Enlightenment, as discussed previously, insanity was viewed through two lenses. The first was the rational but flawed medical theories of the Classical Age. The second was the Christian faith of the Medieval Age. The two lenses formed an awkward and ultimately unsustainable vision of madness. It didn't work on a practical level as the empirical failings of Classical medicine became increasingly clear – its descriptions and prescriptions simply did not work – they did not fit the emerging medical reality that the scientific worldview was revealing. It also did not work on the conceptual level. The singular, authoritatively based Christian faith of the Medieval world was disintegrating – set off by the hammer strokes of Martin Luther's 95 theses on the door of All Saint's Church in Wittenberg in 1517. As the next two centuries progressed, the Christian view of mental illness had become splintered. The Inquisition was over, belief in witchcraft was waning, and an increasing number of people throughout the Western World were ready to view insanity as a medical problem, not a moral or spiritual one.

This change in attitude was fully aligned with the public perception of what would become the medical specialty of psychiatry. This happened in two ways. The first was the fact that the asylum was, more or less, a medical institution and seen as such by the public. Its very existence in the community spoke loudly of a medical response to mental illness. However, the failures of the asylums to cure and their notorious abuses of their wards became public knowledge and would damage the reputation of the nascent field of psychiatry. This did not change the fact that whatever the quality of care being offered, the reality that it was being offered in a medical context became the accepted norm and solidified the public conception of mental illness as a medical problem.

While modern critics like Foucault and Thomas Szasz emphasize the issues of culture and power in the identification of mental illness, others like Edward Shorter (1997) see the increase in asylum care during the Enlightenment as reflecting real changes in the perceived and actual frequency of mental illness at the time. The change in perception reflected the shift from home-based to institutional care. In other words, more people were being "counted" as mentally ill and publicly known to be mentally ill because they were being placed in asylums rather than remaining "hidden" at home with family. There was also probably an increase in the actual number of the mentally ill. This would have been caused by an increase in neurosyphilis, alcoholic psychosis, and of course the raw increase in population.

In pursuing the story of this history, the first two factors in the actual increase in cases of mental illness, neurosyphilis and alcoholic psychosis are particularly important, as they raise but do not provide a clear answer regarding the important question of etiology, or causation of mental illness. The common assumption is that madness is connected to either social problems (isolation, alienation, abuse, cultural judgment) or with abnormalities in brain functioning that are genetic in nature. Mental problems caused by direct physical damage (head injury) or chemical influence (methamphetamine abuse) are typically thought of as nonpsychiatric medical problems rather than mental illness. It pushes the boundaries of what most people think about as mental illness to include the neurological side effects of other illnesses, physical trauma, or substance ingestion.

In regard to syphilis, it was typically contracted through contact with prostitutes and would result in initial signs of infection that would typically go away. A year or more later, however, the spirochetes (the microorganisms that originally caused the disease) could invade the meningeal lining of the brain and spinal cord. A decade later, either the host has successfully fought off the infection and stays symptom free for life, or the immune system become overwhelmed and the host begins to experience various symptoms, including problems with speech, mania, delusions, inflated euphoria, and eventually full-blown dementia. Because the symptoms would emerge long after the initial infection, they could easily be misdiagnosed as traditional mental illness. This was exacerbated by the fact that many sufferers did not want to admit that they had contracted syphilis from a prostitute and preferred to be thought of as mentally ill. Of course, people who developed psychosis as a result of alcohol abuse did not have the luxury of denying the cause of their mental problems.

The general increase in the number of mentally ill and the increase in the number of patients with biologically based insanity fed the growing public conception of mental illness as a medical issue. However, it is important to remember that the Enlightenment was still a point of transition. When exploring the history of mental illness and the difficult questions regarding social versus biological causes (and thus conceptualization) of psychological problems, it is important to remember that during the Enlightenment, there was not yet the clear demarcation of the social and the biological that would emerge as a hallmark of modern Western thinking and debate. During the Enlightenment, mental illness was still commonly seen as a weakness of the spirit or the soul, not just of the brain and body. As such, it was not clearly demarked from other social problems such as criminality and poverty. That is why treatments, ranging from moral cures (attempting to talk someone into rationality and prosocial attitudes) to physical ones (purges, bloodlettings, elixirs) had no meaningful distinction, and people with any of the three basic problems (insanity, criminality, poverty) could be detained together in the same institution and likely receive much the same treatment.

Not only was this a time without a clear distinction between the social/moral and the physical/biological, it was also a time when so little was known about biological functioning that the treatments offered tended to be equally effective or ineffective, no matter who received them, for whatever problems they might have. Purgings had no greater or lesser chance of success whether one was insane or criminally oriented. Thus, the relative lack of distinction between the moral and the physical, along with the general lack of effectiveness (especially differential effectiveness) of any of the treatments available, put the emerging field of what we now call psychiatry in immediate disrepute and fed a public fear of mental illness. The mentally ill could be detained (whether it was crude and rough or thoughtful and concerned), but they could not be cured. Since the old beliefs about etiology were losing power and new ones were embryonic and typically equally as misguided as the old ones, public fears could run wild.

One such fear was the idea that mental illness could spread through the air. This idea was based on the emerging concept of airborne illness, which likely started because of the obvious, observational evidence regarding the spreading of diseases like influenza and the common cold. Added to this was the fact that asylums for the mentally ill quickly became known for the foul stench associated with them. Describing such places in France, it was said, "Even the air of the place, which can be smelled four hundred yards away – everything suggests that one is approaching a place of violence, an asylum of degradation and infortune" (Foucault, 1965, p. 202, Mercier, 1783). These were places of fear and contempt, as they became the literally stinking repositories of the human refuse of society. The smell, combined with the idea of vapors, led to a fear that the madness of the asylum could spread like a contagion of evil and putrid rottenness. It is easy to imagine such fears, especially in cities, where the lack of sanitation and density of population regularly led to outbreaks of deadly disease. It is no coincidence that the image of the countryside, with its clean, pure air, would become a meme of healthy living (both physical and moral), while the urban world would become associated with physical and moral decay, degeneration, and dystopia. The public conceptualization of mental illness became imbued with the confabulation of stench, illness, public hygiene, moral degeneracy, and the relative problems of urban versus rural life.

Obviously, there are many other historical and social factors involved with this conceptual distinction between the urban and the rural. For the purposes of our topic here, however, it should be noted that this theme has always been a powerful force in psychiatry, with medical advice often promoting the benefits of clean air and water, a slower pace of life, and regular exercise – the hallmarks of country living. This goes back to the Ancient Greeks and Romans and reemerged with the rise of the asylums, which initially were built in or near major cities, often because they were general hospitals, not designated for housing just the mentally ill. Later, in the nineteenth century, they would be built more exclusively for the mentally ill and placed far outside cities, partially because it was less expensive but also to take advantage of the perceived health benefits of the country life. For these and the other reasons discussed earlier, madness has typically been associated in the public mind with urban life. Two more modern examples of this dynamic are the movies *The Joker* and *Seven*, both of which portray insanity as arising from the conditions of urban decay. This paradigm, or meme if you prefer, has been a regular refrain in cultural criticisms of urbanization that may have their roots in earlier periods but got a strong boost during the Enlightenment (Mumford, 1961).

Foucault (1965) makes another point about changes in the conceptualization of mental illness during the Enlightenment when he discusses the professionalization of the issue. Stemming partly from the rise of asylum placement, mental illness was increasingly understood and assessed through observation by professionals, particularly medical doctors. Historically, although the disturbing *behavior* of madness was an important consideration, the internal psychology and subjective experience of the mad was primary. Foucault noted the growing importance of patients being observed and held responsible for their behavior in institutional settings; thus he focused on the role of the asylum in a change of emphasis from the internal experience to the observable behavior of the insane. Another factor in this change of emphasis was the rise of empiricism in determining what was real and true. That which cannot be seen and cannot be measured is automatically suspected as being unreal, untrue, or at least unworthy of serious consideration. In the twentieth century, this epistemological position would spur the rise of behaviorism at the expense of psychoanalysis. In the seventeenth and eighteenth centuries it spurred the rise of observational psychiatry over conjecture regarding the internal psychological state of the sufferer. To the extent that the places of observation (asylums and doctors' offices) and the medical doctors saw themselves as serving the processes of science and professionalism, they would focus increasingly on the observable signs of mental illness rather than its reportable but unobservable symptoms.

This professional objectification of mental illness, and by extension the mentally ill themselves, was aided by the asylum's creation of psychiatry as a separate science and medical practice (Scull, 1993). It provided a setting for various professionals to specialize in mental illness. This movement was accelerated by the institutional separation of the mentally ill from the poor and eventually the criminal. Setting aside insanity from other "problems" that required professional intervention was an important historical process. Previously, doctors and administrators alike approached the mentally ill as generalists. Administrators were more focused on the challenges of running a secure institution than on the specific needs or difficulties of the mentally ill. Doctors were also generalists. The mentally ill were widely dispersed in the community and typically not wealthy, making them a very small part of almost any doctor's caseload. Asylums brought the mentally ill together in one place, so a group of doctors could now specialize in their diagnosis and care. While many would see this as a great benefit to the evolving understanding of mental illness, Foucault was concerned with the problems that emerged from this process. He pointed out that it served to give these doctors almost magical powers of supposed understanding, as well as very real control of the patients, whose dignity and autonomy were reduced to the extent that they acquiesced to the power of the medical establishment.

This power could be expressed in two major ways, one hard and one soft. Hard power existed through the process of confinement itself – involuntary, behind stone walls, in often horrific conditions, with shackles, straitjackets, ice baths, and beatings for misbehavior. This was all done *for the patient's good*. It was *prescribed* based on existing medical knowledge and wisdom. What was one to think about oneself when the best authority available regarding the psyche said one deserved to be physically removed from society, put behind bars, and treated with cruelty and harsh coercion when one did not think, feel, or behave the way they thought one should? Even more insidious was the exertion of soft power, the influence of social position and public discourse. Hard power is transparent – it can be seen, recognized, separated from one's sense of self, and rebelled against as an assault from without. Soft power is different. It is hard to see and recognize as coming from outside oneself. It is easy to internalize, to accept as "just the way things are," and thus to submit with shame and guilt if one does not live up to its quiet demands. The combination of hard and soft cultural power is incredibly difficult to oppose. To disagree is to be called an idiot, a fool, immoral, and antisocial. It leads to being shunned, ignored, condemned, confined, abused, tortured, or even killed. Nathaniel Lee, an English dramatist of the seventeenth century, was detained at Bedlam for five years and famously said, "They called me mad, and I called them mad, and damn them, they outvoted me!" (2020). The social construction of mental illness (and, by contrast, mental health), increasingly driven by a professional field of mental health doctors and administrators, forced people's lives and very self-conception into boxes of identity as sane or insane, with very real consequences.

THE EARLY EVOLUTION OF PSYCHIATRIC THEORY

As the Western world transitioned from the medieval to the modern, there was a period of time when the emerging world of psychiatry had to give up the humoral theory and the moralistic conceptualizations of the Classical era but had not yet developed the knowledge and theories of modern medicine. With little empirical data to go on but an overwhelming need to explain biological processes, both how they work and how they can go wrong, a slew of ideas was proposed to filled the gap. This was in sharp contrast to other sciences, where real advances were being made in astronomy, physics, chemistry, physiology, optics, and all the areas of mechanical engineering. In psychiatry, medical professionals recognized that the brain was the center of psychology, and they referred to nerve functioning, but they had virtually no idea how the central nervous system worked or how it was functionally organized. As a result, Alexander and Selesnick called it the "era of quacks" (1966, p. 123). For instance, Friedrich Hoffman (1660–1742) believed that mental illness was caused by excesses or deficits in an unspecified material substance in the body. This idea was supported by many professionals of the time, as it was related to a longstanding belief in such an essence or substance, sometimes referred to as "animal spirits." Embracing more a metaphor than a scientific doctrine, Enlightenment thinkers like Descartes referred to a mysterious fluid that circulated throughout the body and controlled virtually all aspects of life, including psychological functioning. While not particularly helpful in understanding real physiological and psychological processes, it did constitute an early attempt to place mental illness in an internal, biological process, dissociated from external cultural, religious, and moral issues.

A thorough review of the strange and grossly incorrect understandings of mental illness at the time would take too many pages and has already been well covered by others, so let's take a quick look at just two of the more famous and influential but misguided theorists of the time, Franz Joseph Gall (1758–1828) and Franz Mesmer (1734–1815). Ironically, both men not only share a first name but graduated from the same school, the University of Vienna School of Medicine. They also both have the distinction that their theories were not *just* wrong but helped inspire research that led to better understandings of both normal psychological functioning and mental illness. Franz Gall was a serious medical scholar who dedicated his professional life to the study of the brain. He made a number of contributions to neurological science, including a much better understanding of brain development, but is best known for his phrenological theory. He identified 37 different character traits, localized them to 37 parts of the brain, then proposed that one could assess psychological functioning by feeling the bumps and dips on the outside of a person's skull. Although he was right in a general sense that different psychological functions are localized in various parts of the brain, he was extraordinarily wrong about how the brain differentiates those functions, how they are distributed throughout the brain, and whether the relative strength or weakness of the brain's functional areas is reflected in the pattern of bumps on the exterior of the skull. Despite his fundamental errors, Gall's work and professional success did inspire further research in cerebral localization, as well as trait theories of personality.

Like Gall, Franz Mesmer thought of himself as a serious academic and sought the acceptance of the medical authorities of the time. That acceptance eluded him, but he succeeded in creating public interest in his methods and inspiring research into his ideas that led to actual progress in the field. Mesmer alluded to ideas about both animal spirits and magnetism in his concept of animal magnetism. In many centuries, people had conceptually linked electricity to the biological life force, leading to various treatments for physical and psychological problems that involved magnets and other means to manipulate electrical energy. Mesmer built on these common-sense (but basically incorrect) linkages in the development of his concepts, which involved identifying mental health with the free flow of energy in the body and illness with its restriction. Because of the generic nature of this theory, a wide variety of psychological problems could be linked to a problem with energy flow. The problems were not just the severe mental disorders generally recognized at the time but less severe issues with depression, anxiety, sexual dysfunction, social problems, and what later professionals would call hysteria. These problems were not the focus of the "mad doctors" of the asylums, because people suffering with them were functional enough to stay out of such horrific places. Instead, people who struggled with these issues flocked to costly but highly charismatic healers like Mesmer. By doing so, they contributed to the emerging science of classifying mental illness and differentiating it from mental health. The clinical attention paid to the "worried well" was reinforced by Mesmer's widespread and (at least partly) successful practice, as was the felt need in the medical profession to develop a better understanding of what kinds of mental illness existed and how to distinguish severe mental illness from less severe neuroses and from psychological wellness. This meant there needed to be better understanding of both clinical nosology and etiology. This was highly motivating for the psychiatric professionals of the time, if for no other good reason but to discredit charlatans like Gall and Mesmer.

THE BIRTH OF NOSOLOGY

As noted previously, there was an explosion of human knowledge during the Enlightenment. That explosion created an increased need for new and expanded classification systems for that knowledge. The fields of chemistry (Antoine Lavoisier), botany (Carolus Linnaeus), and many others experienced this revolution. The new information made old systems of organization discredited and obsolete. The sheer mass of information demanded new ways of organizing it in terms of types and relationships. One of the challenges of doing this was finding ways of organizing the information based on empirical findings. Planets are fundamentally different than stars. Sheep are fundamentally different than starfish. But how are they different? What aspects of their structure or function can be identified and recognized as important elements of typological differentiation? For a nosology to make sense and be functionally useful, it needs to reflect objective, measurable aspects of the underlying phenomena. It also helps, and follows logically, that it reflects (or ultimately suggests) a conceptual understanding of the ontological and relational *meaning* of the phenomena. The differential phenomena need to be *important*. Two heavenly bodies may be different colors, but is relative color a meaningful or important differentiation? If not, then what is?

This is where the development of a nosology becomes quite complicated and becomes a proverbial "double-edged sword." On the one side, following the data to a conceptual conclusion about an overall field of study is useful. It brings order to chaos, increases real understanding of the world, and provides the foundation for both future research and practical applications. On the other side, producing a conceptual "overview" of any field of knowledge risks many problems, including (1) the conceptual errors of the past may be continued, with new information being manipulated to fit preexisting conceptual categories and understandings; (2) new concepts may be produced that are spurious and just plain wrong and thus divert a field into gross misunderstanding; (3) new concepts can be over-relied on and create "self-fulfilling prophecies" in which we only search for knowledge that fits the new concepts and ignore or reject information that does not fit; and (4) there is always the problem of what systems of power and authority support a particular concept, with their own interests and values that are not empirical. As the professional field of psychiatry began to grow as a "specialty" in the West, it developed idioms of belief and practice that, as all idioms do, would become entrenched, self-interested, and self-fulfilling. In some ways, this development was helpful to the extent that it relied on empirical science and professionalism (in the good sense of the word), leading to more accurate understandings and ethical practice, but it would also create a number of problems, as its scientific focus was limited in scope (observable behavior, individual pathology, and neurology) and blinded by its own conceptual and professional interests.

Around the time in question, however, in the eighteenth century, a practitioner appeared who came to epitomize this double-edged sword of progress. He was not the only one to emerge as a leader in this new profession, but his contributions to the field and historical prominence make it appropriate to discuss his unique life and career. His name was Philippe Pinel (1745–1826), and he was born into a poor family in the south of France. His father was a doctor, and after studying mathematics for a while, Philippe followed his father into medicine. He became involved in the French Revolution and was particularly enthralled by the humanitarian movement and Enlightenment philosophy of his day. He was put in charge of the Bicetre Hospital in Paris and was horrified by the conditions he saw. The patients were chained, abused, and denied any reasonable level of freedom or respect. They were treated like prisoners, or worse. They were considered society's refuse rather than people suffering from illness. Virtually no thought was given to treatment, and in fact, the common belief of the day was that the insane could not recover. Pinel took a very different view of mental illness. He saw the mentally ill first and foremost as human beings deserving of basic care and respect. He also saw profound differences between individuals and noted that some experienced periods of remission between bouts of more severe symptoms. This meant there was hope, and he became committed to the provision of actual treatment to help "developing and strengthening their faculties of reason" (1801, p. 253). Although much of Pinel's work and fame centered on his approach to treatment, and thus is outside the scope of this book, his reforms were based on his underlying assumptions about mental illness that both reflected the spirit of his times and helped establish a more humanitarian conceptualization of mental illness as European society moved toward the modern age.

As alluded to previously, Pinel was influenced by the French Revolution, which in turn had been a reaction to the traditional hierarchal ordering of French society in which the aristocracy saw itself as fundamentally superior to commoners and thus enforced a political, social, and economic system of extreme "haves" and "have nots." This basic philosophy (some groups of people are naturally superior to others) was the norm in the vast majority of cultures throughout the world, particularly in "advanced" societies in which the complexity of social and economic relations led to extreme human disparities that were then taken as a natural "given" of reality. In short, when everyone in society has to perform relatively equal work (hunting, farming, childrearing, etc.), the power structure tends to be relatively egalitarian. In large, complex societies, the division of labor and other cultural responsibilities grossly exacerbates the natural social hierarchies seen in the animal kingdom (for instance, when a dominant male chimpanzee gains sexual access to females that is denied lower-ranking males). The eighteenth-century revolutionaries rejected the arguments that rigidly structured human hierarchies were natural. Instead, they insisted on the basic equality of all human beings, which then calls for a certain basic level of valuation, concern for, and equal treatment of everyone . . . . even the mentally ill. Pinel embraced this idea and sought to reform the institutions he worked in to reflect that humanitarian spirit. He thought of the people under his care as *human beings with a mental illness* rather than simply as *the insane*.

Pinel also contributed to the growing emphasis on the need for an empirically based classification system for mental illness. While he was not really a pioneer in this area and simply expanded existing systems (those of de Sauvages, Whytt, and Cullen, for instance), his work was helpful, and his prominence made him uniquely influential as the field moved forward. He contributed to the understanding of the clinical features of what we now call the antisocial personality, noting that some individuals engaged in impulsive and self-damaging yet (ironically) selfish behavior but with unimpaired rationality. This constitutes insanity without delirium – a mental illness not centered on mood (depression or mania) or disturbed cognitive functioning (psychosis or developmental problems) but rather on self-image, social functioning, affect, and impulse control. Sometimes called "moral insanity," these sorts of conditions were not previously considered by many to constitute mental illness but were simply considered personal moral failing or sinfulness. It was only in the context of a medical model of mental illness that such psychological syndromes could be considered a disease. To this day, there is controversy regarding the inclusion of syndromes that are primarily behavioral or problems with the internalization of moral or social values as mental illnesses. Pinel was important in moving the needle on including personality characteristics like these in a nosology of mental disorders.

Like the systematizers before him, Pinel sought to organize mental illness according to collections of symptoms, gathered by careful observation. The collective knowledge of the field grew as clinical observation and description became the norm, and various practitioners read each other's work and contributed their own. William Cullen was the first to use the term "neurosis," de Sauvages had obsessively categorized every aspect of nervous disorders, and Whytt divided neuroses into hysteria, hypochondriasis, and nervous exhaustion. Pinel's descriptions of mental illness were detailed, objective, and systematic. In addition to his contribution regarding the antisocial temperament, he separated psychotic illnesses into melancholias, manias with delirium, manias without delirium, and dementia. He also distinguished between problems of memory, judgment, affect, attention, reality testing/delusion, hallucinations, energy level, and impulsivity (Alexander & Selesnick, 1966; Millon, 2004).

Like virtually all nosologists of the time, Pinel was also interested in etiology. He wanted to know what *caused* mental illness. He was well aware of the various theories that had been forwarded. Collectively, they had tried to move beyond the discredited humoral theory and sought to understand mental illness as based on real physiological/neurological processes, but as noted before, they were based on such limited empirical knowledge that they amounted to little more than biased guesswork. Pinel considered them meaningless physiological fictions. Instead, he proposed a much more academically modest and humble approach. On the physiological side, he maintained the importance of brain lesions and other neurological and hereditary malfunctions. He was limited in his conjecture, however, insisting that empirical research was required to better understand the biological substrates of mental illness. Therefore, he was equally insistent on an appreciation of sociological etiology. He believed that a sufferer's upbringing and life experiences were vitally important in the development of his or her psychological problems. This attitude may have been driven by his close clinical work with real patients, combined with his humanistic leanings. Pinel believed that physicians who worked with the mentally ill should have an extensive understanding of what we would now call psychology: human motivation, personality development, and the impact of both negative and positive life experiences on emotional and cognitive functioning. He recognized that the horrific conditions of most asylums at the time could actually contribute to a patient's dysfunction. This multifactoral and dynamic perspective on mental illness created the foundation for what we now call the biopsychosocial model.

Pinel was more evolutionary than revolutionary in his approach to mental illness, but his overall impact on the field was stronger than his specific contributions. He came to embody the spirit of a rational, empirical, multifactoral, empathetic, and fundamentally humanistic understanding of mental illness. His influence was felt by other reformers of the era, including Benjamin Rush, Vincenzo Chiarugi, Johann Reil, and the best known, Jean-Etienne-Dominique Esquirol. Esquirol (1772–1840) was Pinel's student and successor at Salpetriere. He established a number of new hospitals, based on Pinel's teachings, lectured extensively on psychiatry throughout Europe, and published a hugely successful textbook on mental illness, *Des Maladies Mentales* (1838). In this book, Esquirol established his loyalty to Pinel's principles, particularly the importance of systematic observation and description of patients to understand their mental illness, along with a rejection of unsupported theories regarding physiological etiology and a humanistic approach to both understanding and subsequent treatment. Esquirol supported this approach so strongly that he is often considered the founder of this tradition, especially the centrality of *descriptive* psychiatry in providing a framework for any valid classification system.

He also extended Pinel's belief in the interaction of developmental, psychological issues with whatever physiological vulnerabilities were contributing to the patient's mental problems. It is the word "contributory" that is key here. Esquirol detailed numerous environmental difficulties that he felt were causal factors in many clinical conditions. This psychological approach led him to be interested in and explore his patients' inner lives. What were they thinking and feeling? How had that pattern been established through the experiences of their lives? How did it lead to the particular delusions, hallucinations, obsessions, and impulses now being experienced as symptoms of mental illness? His approach prefigured Sigmund Freud's much more complex and detailed theories about human development and its impact on mental health and mental illness. Although not as complex as Freud's psychological theories, the work of Pinel and Esquirol was successful in setting off a profound debate in the field of mental illness over the next two centuries – the battle between the psychological and physiological explanations of mental illness. Overall, the field, dominated by medical doctors, tended to focus on physiological causes of mental illness, but with the leadership of Pinel and Esquirol, the human-istic reformers of the seventeenth and eighteenth centuries threw down a gauntlet that was profoundly threatening to the medical status quo of the time.

The story is not that simple, however. While the reform movement sought to change how patients were conceptualized and treated, it was fully supportive of the basic *need* for asylums. Severe mental illness was still thought of as so disabling that it required (mostly) involuntary detention under the control of (increasingly) well-meaning overseers. The reforms instituted were therefore focused on changing the *attitude* of those overseers toward their charges, seeing them as unfortunate suf-ferers of illness rather than lumping them together with criminals and other social deviants. However, what had not changed yet was the core assumption that one was sane or insane. This simplistic, binary approach to understanding was (ironically) reinforced by the increase in asylum care. As more beds became available, both in America and in Europe (although much less so in other parts of the world), the question of insanity increasingly became connected to putting someone in a virtual prison (however humanistic the treatment approach), usually against their will, and potentially keeping them there for years, with little hope of ever being able to lead their own independent, successful lives in the wider community. While progress was being made regarding the identification of different *types* of madness, the picture regarding different *levels* of insanity was becoming increasingly complicated and problematical.

As noted before, on the one hand, there was the increasing availability of asylum placement, within a now well-established professional field of assessment and treatment. The proof of this newly found professionalism was reflected in the Napoleonic Code of 1838, which required that potential patients in asylums be certified by a medical officer, not local authorities or family members. This grow-ing field of clinical psychiatry was increasingly centered in the asylums – doctors seeking this specialty would train in these institutions, working extensively with this clientele, make it their academic and research focus, and often live on the grounds of the institutions in which they worked. Working with severe, debilitating mental illness was their vocation and the foundation of their being able to continue think-ing of themselves as medical doctors.

On the other hand, there were lots of people who experienced mild to mod-erate psychological distress whose resulting functionality was not so impaired that they were candidates for the asylum. Mental health professionals now euphemis-tically refer to these folks as the "worried well," and today, there is an immense system (in the Western world) for their care, including self-help books, seminars/

workshops, wellness centers, yoga/meditation classes, psychotherapy/counseling, and various over-the-counter and prescriptive medications. But what was available for these people (with common sense telling is there were far more of them than there were people experiencing severe mental illness) in the eighteenth century?

ENLIGHTENMENT PHILOSOPHY AND MENTAL HEALTH

In many ways, the attitude toward mental health, or psychological well-being, to use a less clinical term, began to change during the Enlightenment. It became more secular and professionalized. Ideas about being happy in the face of the many problems of life took a philosophical turn, reflecting the humanistic and empirical idealism of the time. More people sought out professional help, not so much from established mental health professionals but from practitioners who promoted a wide variety of physiological theories, based on nothing but the fact that the era called for a more scientific, nonhumoral explanation for mental problems. We have already introduced Franz Mesmer as an exemplar of this approach, using his personal charisma and scientific sounding theories to build a client base, make a lot of money, and become famously successful. Of course, this grassroots system of wellness professionals was nothing new, as people had sought out cures for life's everyday problems (depression, social problems, stress, sexual problems, etc.) for thousands of years. The change that occurred during the Enlightenment was that this cottage industry began to reflect the intellectual and philosophical movements that would soon evolve into what we like to call the Modern world.

One Enlightenment figure who contributed greatly to the emerging field of mental health was Benedict Spinoza (1632–1677). Born in Amsterdam into a Jewish family that had escaped the Spanish Inquisition, he was a studious young man with grandiose dreams. Spinoza aspired to develop a unified system of all human knowledge about the world (Hampshire, 1956). In pursuing this dream, it was natural that he would disagree with Descartes's separation of mind and body; instead, he saw all the phenomena of the world as interconnected. On the human level, that meant that the psychological and the physiological were two aspects of the same basic unity – a human being. He also delved into areas that would become the province of psychoanalysis – deep, underlying psychological conflicts and the interconnected importance of these conflicts and related psychological experiences to ethics, morality, and the basic motivations in people's lives. He felt that what people call morality stems from the basic experience of pleasure as good and pain as bad. People's greatest desire was to increase pleasure and decrease pain, thus pursuing what later psychologists would call the pleasure principle (Sigmund Freud) or self-actualization (Abraham Maslow). This pursuit is complicated, of course, by all manner of conflicts, contradictions, and limitations, not the least of which is the inevitability of physical and emotional suffering and death itself. In Spinoza's view, the only way past these roadblocks to happiness is a pursuit of rationality, insight, and true understanding. Ultimately, knowledge of self would lead to knowledge of God, for God is the source of all and thus is ultimately one with nature itself. In other words, Spinoza believed that logic and reason lead to knowledge, which produces a feeling of contentment because acceptance of true knowledge *is* union with God.

Of course, not everyone agreed with the inevitability of a union between reason and faith. In fact, during the Enlightenment, it became increasingly common to separate the two. The various positions taken included (1) maintaining the traditional lack of separation of faith and reason, (2) making faith and reason completely separate but coexisting issues, and (3) making faith and reason competing epistemological positions, meaning that one or the other was valid but not both. The three basic positions can be called *conjoined, coexistent,* and *competing.* As one can quickly surmise, Spinoza took the *conjoined* perspective. And while it obviously reflected a premodern, pre-Enlightenment epistemology, Spinoza updated the concept by prioritizing emotion over faith in a way that actually makes his thought relevant to even fully modern neurologists (Damasio, 2003).

Renee Descartes, by asserting the separateness of body and mind – soma and soul – helped establish the *coexistent* position (Descartes, 1998/1637). It created the epistemological possibility of considering mental health and illness from either a physiological or a metaphysical position. The positions could be considered separately. The problem, of course, was that by separating them, Descartes set the emerging modern world on a trajectory of self-alienation that continues to haunt us today. Recent attempts to solve the dilemma started with the Romantic movement of the nineteenth century then continued with existentialism, postmodernism, structuralism and poststructuralist theory, and phenomenology. All these philosophical approaches to relativism try to reconcile the gulf between subjective experience and objective materialism. All struggle with the fundamental dissatisfaction of concluding that reality is what anyone *thinks it is* rather than existing independently of human experience. While Descartes was by no measure an existentialist, he unwittingly set us on that path. His audacious demand to question everything was necessary for the cognitive and moral development of humanity – to awaken from its thrall to the ancient gods and demons of its ancestors – but it created the problem of epistemological relativism. How am I to figure out what is right or wrong, meaningful or absurd, with no ontological basis for making these judgments? Can the objective and subjective really coexist in a stable and unified way?

From the perspective of the *competing* position, the answer is no. Partially founded by the most famous thinkers of the Enlightenment, John Locke and Thomas Hobbes, the conflicted position asserts that there is a fundamental, objective reality to be discovered. It is difficult to do so, because people approach the truth through so many veils, including the limits of their biological senses and preexisting beliefs. That does not mean that the truth does not exist. People need to dedicate themselves to dropping their preconceptions (with a nod to Descartes), including the unproven faith in the existence of God (definitely not in tune with Descartes) and seeking to cognize and understand that which truly exists. The measurable facts must be used as a guide, utilizing the clarity of logic, to reach objective conclusions about reality. If one's subjective, felt experience tells one something different than the facts would suggest, then one is in conflict and can choose to either stay in error or adjust one's thinking to fit what is true. That is the spirit of empiricism and what would become known as modernism. The hero of the emerging age was the clear-eyed scientist who could rise above the sound and fury of the culturally driven human fray of beliefs and see the mountaintops of a world laid out *as it is*, not how he or she wants or fear it to be.

These three basic positions and the ongoing debate between their adherents became the foundation of various movements over the ensuing centuries to find truth, meaning, human peace, happiness, fulfillment, and ultimately redemption in this world and, in some cases, the next. John Locke was the first major theorist to oppose Descartes, by emphasizing the primacy of constructing hypotheses about what is true, based on analogies, and then seeking supportive evidence rather than believing that one can find the truth by cognitive analysis. In other words, he rejected the concept of innate truths. Instead, he asserted that people develop their ideas about the world through direct experience, with more complex ideas deriving from combinations of more simple ones.

One of the consequences of this antidogmatic approach to epistemology was that it led him to reject patriarchal and monarchal government. Instead, he supported representational government and the right of the misgoverned to rebel. If a preexisting right to govern others (divine right of kings) is a baseless fantasy, then a more objective foundation must be established for government. What is it for, and how should it be designed? These questions reflected the growing beliefs that (1) societal structures should serve the common people not preordained elites, and (2) it is the *right* of people to change those structures to better support their well-being. This led to the conclusion that the only rational and moral type of government was democracy, because it was the most effective way to build a structure responsive to the desires and well-being of the most people. As is well known, Locke's writings helped form the philosophical foundation of both the American and French revolutions. This point is important because in the professional field of mental health, we often explore changes in clinical thought and practice but rarely the larger philosophical movements that are dramatically impactful on the psychological well-being of large groups of people.

One example of this, well known to Western readers, is the move toward separation of church and state in the new government following the American Revolution. In fact, the entire revolution could be examined as it relates to the emergence of the modern psychological principle of *self-efficacy*. The assertion by Thomas Jefferson that humanity is endowed with "inalienable rights of life, liberty, and pursuit of happiness" was truly revolutionary in this regard. That discussion could easily take an entire book itself to explore. So instead, let's focus on just separation of church and state as it relates to this issue. Jefferson wrote the Virginia Statute for Religious Freedom in 1777, and it was enacted by the Virginia Assembly as law in 1786. At the end of his life, when asked what he wanted on his tombstone, Jefferson included it as one of the three great accomplishments of his life, along with writing the Declaration of Independence and founding the University of Virginia. In the statute, Jefferson makes a number of vital and interconnected points, which helped sum up his thinking and its empirical and humanistic foundation (Smith, 2018). He asserted that (1) God gave us free will, so exercising free thought is in line with His intentions; (2) besides, trying to force others to believe and act the way you do leads to bitterness and hypocrisy; (3) human beings are, by nature, imperfect, so we cannot trust others to be right, and thus should not give people the power to force their opinions on others; (4) we don't need religion to tell us what are rights and responsibilities are, they are common sense; (5) allowing the government to enforce one set of religious beliefs over another denies human freedom and is arbitrary, as leaders will naturally want to support their own; (6) thus, the government should only enforce particular beliefs and practices when it is necessary to protect others and civic order; (7) and finally, these precepts are not just a good idea in this particular situation but reflect the *natural rights* of all people at all times. What this constitutes is a detailed expansion of his assertion of the "inalienable" rights of humanity in the Declaration of Independence. It provides a rationale for individual self-efficacy and a humanistic manifesto for the modern world. It declares the people should be free to choose their own beliefs and practices to further their well-being and should not be coerced into following other people's beliefs and practices unless they are directly hurting others.

This intellectual foundation for human happiness and well-being, inspired as it was by the philosophy of the Enlightenment, helped lay the foundation for the modern principles of religious liberty, personal freedom, free speech/thought, and democracy as the best form of government. Modern debates regarding how far those freedoms should extend (for instance, does one person's religious beliefs/ freedom give them the right to restrict another's access to goods and services by refusing to serve them in a privately owned business?) have often been framed around the conflicts and ambiguities inherent in such a foundation. For instance, one person's freedom will naturally conflict with another's on a regular basis, and it becomes very difficult and tricky to work through *competing rights*, such as the right to life itself of an unborn fetus versus the right of biological self-determination of the mother. Prior to the Enlightenment, these debates occurred at the highest levels of cultural hierarchy (or at least they only mattered if carried on at the highest levels) and were based on interpretations of "received authority." After the Enlightenment, these debates have occurred at every level of society and often take the form of (1) ongoing conflicts *between* humanistic principles and received authority and (2) attempts to work out compromises and establish a hierarchy of values *within* a humanistic or authoritative tradition.

As just noted, conflict and ambiguity are inherent in a humanistic foundation for human wellness. This is because (1) all people are considered equal, so no one person's beliefs or rights are considered automatically superior to another; (2) there is no established authority on beliefs or practices to help avoid conflict; and (3) various rights, beliefs, and practices often do conflict. These fundamental difficulties will be explored in much more detail in later chapters. For now, it is enough to recognize that the combination of empiricism and humanism led to a new approach to human happiness. As autonomous reason increasingly established itself as the path to truth, independent self-interest, individual experience, and personal, ethical reasoning came to be seen as the foundation for human happiness. While innate beliefs and the preordained powers were losing their legitimacy, the belief in self-will, the honoring of the individual, and the inherent equality of all people gained validity. The power of the church was threatened and the monarchies were shaken, while people formed more private and public organizations to assert collective power based on mutual self-interest. Trade associations, democracy movements, social societies, scientific organizations, and various religious sects all blossomed within the spirit of Enlightenment humanism. Not yet hobbled by the failure to establish an objective standard of truth, the empirical humanism of the Enlightenment was vibrant and (literally) revolutionary. People began to make their own choices (religious, social, governmental, economic) and, by extension, to take control of their own path to happiness. That is the key. Rather than obey and align, people began to rebel and individuate. What is good and meaningful became, in the new definition, what is right for *me*.

NON-WESTERN APPROACHES TO MENTAL ILLNESS

Of course, this discussion has so far been focused on the Western world. It has explored changes in epistemology, theory, and practice in Europe and, increasingly, in North America. This is important because those changes have led to the now-dominant views and practices of mental health care in most of the world. But that is not all that was going on during the time we call the Enlightenment in the Western world. For most of the world, things went along pretty much as before, with theory and practice following the norms of local culture that had been established long before. But there were two other dynamics in play. First, significant changes took place in certain cultures that need to be addressed. Second, there was the powerful force of colonization that began to overthrow (and to some extent integrate) local cultures and force a Western view upon subjugated populations.

In regard to the first dynamic, it is beyond the scope of this book to provide an encyclopedic discourse on the wide range of world cultures that existed at the time, but we can take a look at one or two of them. It makes sense to choose ones that have continued to influence a large number of people on the planet and are currently impacting the dominant Western view of mental health and mental illness. Probably the most powerful of these is the religio-culture of Buddhism. It was first introduced in Chapter 4, and we will take a closer look at its spiritual and philosophical approach to human wellness. As noted earlier, Siddhartha Gautama lived sometime between the fourth and sixth centuries in the northeastern part of what is now India (Skilton, 1994). He sought to escape the sufferings of his human life. He initially engaged in hedonism, indulging all his worldly desires, but this led only to more psychological suffering. Then he became an ascetic, engaging in extreme self-denial. This did not work either, as he found that as much as he rejected his material self, he was still a living being, and only physical death could free him from the sufferings of his earthly life. So he sat under what is now called the Bodhi Tree and went into deep meditation, seeking the wisdom that would rescue him from the bonds of his dilemma. After a series of spiritual experiences, he became enlightened, having attained awareness of the four noble truths and how to attain liberation from suffering and the cycle of birth, death, and rebirth. The set of beliefs and practices connected to these *truths* and *liberation* are at the heart of the Buddhist approach to mental illness and mental health (Fellows, 1979).

The first noble truth is called *Dukkha* and is the core Buddhist insight that in the material world, all things are impermanent, and thus all attempts to fulfill wishes and desires will ultimately be unsatisfying. Every meal leads to more hunger, all sex leads to more lust, and in the end, disease, decay, and death are inevitable. Mortal life is bound to pain. The second noble truth (*Samudaya*) is that our suffering is the result of craving something different and clinging to our wishes and desires. This constitutes psychological suffering. The sources of pain cannot be changed because they are embedded in the temporal and material nature of the world. Time passes and things change. All life forms come into being, engage in the vicissitudes of material life, and pass away. What *can* change is our attitude toward that reality. Suffering constitutes a psychological relationship with reality based on conflict and resistance; "this is something that should not be." Change the relationship and one is left with pain, but not suffering. That is the core of the third noble truth (*Nirodha*) that peace of mind (*Nirvana*) can be attained if we release ourselves from clinging to our desires. This suggests that pain is inevitable, but suffering is optional. It is a psychological state and thus can be adjusted. Of course, it is not easy. Even the Buddha could not simply snap his fingers and be free from suffering. It required, for him, a long process of (1) hiding from the pain (the early part of this life), (2) becoming overwhelmed by the pain (his crisis of awareness), (3) attempting solutions that failed to work (his ascetic period), (4) seeking a better way (sitting under the Bodhi Tree), and then (5) dedicating himself to a solution to attain liberation and then maintain it. It is this fifth step that is embodied in the fourth noble truth (*Magga*). This truth says there is a path to enlightenment and liberation, and it is embodied in the eightfold path.

The eightfold path is a guideline for life practice that leads to nirvana. It starts with right belief (wisdom of the four noble truths), leading to right intention (a personal dedication to living out these truths) – together, these steps on the path constitute foundational wisdom. The resulting wisdom needs to be followed up with right speech, right action, and right livelihood. This means that having a good idea means little if it is not carried out in all areas of a person's life. The last three steps are right effort, right mindfulness, and right concentration. These may be considered the maintenance steps, guiding ongoing meditation practice to reinforce the mental approach necessary to attain and sustain enlightenment. Only the most naive of practitioners would think that one can simply sit down, contemplate Buddhist wisdom, and snap forever into a state of nirvana. Buddhist practice is a lifelong process in which the final and most difficult challenge is the paradoxical need to let go of the desire for nirvana itself!

The challenges of this approach to spirituality, and by extension mental health, are evident in the historical development of Buddhist monasteries. Like

Christianity before it, Buddhism quickly found that belief and practice were two different things, and not only was it difficult to maintain an agreed-upon set of beliefs, it was very difficult to put them into practice in the profane world of everyday life, where one is beset with temptations, responsibilities, threats, and demands. Monasteries create a buffer between the secular world and the communicant. They seek to create an environment that supports people's ability to manifest their faith in how they live their day-to-day lives. Separation from many of the distracting or conflictual demands of "normal life" makes it easier for people to maintain right attitude and action in their lives. The structure and rules of the monastery help keep people "on the path." Controlling how the residents eat, sleep, treat other people, make a living, worship, pray, and meditate reduces the stress and distractions of normal daily life, along with the potential conflicts with uncooperative friends and relatives and a higher possibility of failure.

The reference to Buddhist monastic life was made to amplify the implicit difficulty of the Buddhist approach to mental health, especially in the context of trying to attain nirvana, or some semblance of psychological peace and well-being, while living a "normal" life, with a job, a family, bills to pay, and social demands to meet. The reality, of course, is that the vast majority of Buddhist adherents try to do just that. Not only that, but in most cultures it encountered, Buddhism did not supplant but rather was integrated with an existing religious system. This actually aided the dissemination of Buddhism throughout most of Asia. So by the time of the European Enlightenment, Buddhism was dominant in only a few places but highly influential in many more. This provided a model to aid the integration of Buddhist philosophy with Western culture without undue fear that it would completely replace the existing dominant religion or way of life.

A typical example of this kind of quiet revolution was in Japan, where Buddhism was first introduced around 500 AD and was initially most popular with the aristocracy (Skilton, 1994). It was seen as a civilizing influence and was encouraged by Japan's leaders. However, it made little impact on the general population. By the eighth century, government patronage of Buddhism had resulted in a growing problem with corruption and loss of integrity, which became worse as it became more integrated with the native Shinto religion. This began to change in the Kamakura period (1185–1333), when a break from Chinese influence allowed for the growth of a more characteristically Japanese form of Buddhism, thus increasing its popularity with the public. One result of this change was that Japanese Buddhism became more simple than other forms. This was a reaction both to the imposition of overcomplicated and confusing forms from a foreign culture (China) and the felt need to have a clear, simple response to the chaos and corruption of the times. One outcome of this development was the popularity of Zen Buddhism. While this form did not originate in Japan, it found a hospitable climate there and, by the time of the European Enlightenment, had become the form most closely associated with Japanese culture. It deemphasizes the importance of complex knowledge or doctrine and focuses instead on rigorous self-control and meditation practice. This paralleled the developing Japanese style in visual and ceramic arts, literature, architecture, and even cuisine, which tended to value high quality imbedded within simple forms. Ironically, Zen Buddhism's relative lack of emphasis on complex teachings and literature has made it particularly popular in the West, where, as in Japan seven centuries ago, its perceived simplicity helps make it easier to integrate with existing cultural beliefs and practices.

The good news about Zen Buddhism, for our purposes here, is that its valuing of simplicity invites a concise description that is not misleadingly reductionist. Eschewing the unnecessarily (and counterproductively) complex, Zen advocates an approach to living that is simple, humble, and fully embodied (Suzuki, 1970). Truth is best considered from the perspective of beginner's mind, an openness to direct experience of the object of question, free of preconceptions. This allows people to see things "as they are" and not how they are taught they are. Full attention and engagement are the goals, not obscure logic or expert opinion. For instance, an empty or clear mind easily perceives and accepts the simple ethics and morals that are required for right practice and enlightenment. Do not kill, do not steal, do not lie – it doesn't need to be complicated, and when it is made so, it can easily lead to confusion, disconnection from the thing or principle itself, and profound errors such as self-serving hypocrisy. This attitude also encourages the practitioner to trust him or herself. Truth is found through direct experience not complicated teaching. The deepest Truth is that all people share a Buddha-nature, meaning that all have the potential for enlightenment, and just as the Buddha achieved his enlightenment by looking within, so can everyone else. Looking outside, even for supposedly wise teachers, will only confuse and distract.

It would be easy to consider the Buddhist approach to wellness as individualistic or even selfish, but it is important to remember that Buddhism developed in a more collectivist culture than the West. From a collectivist perspective, morality and ethics are not just individual concerns. Being *good* is directly connected to the general welfare of the community (Triandis, 1995). Behaving in a way that profits the individual at the expense of the community is inherently immoral and unethical. It promotes conflict, disruption, and societal dis-ease. Therefore, in seeking individual peace, happiness, and well-being, one must be aligned with the general good and the welfare of others. This is not sought, as in the Judeo-Christian view, as an external rule imposed by God, to be rewarded for its adherence in the afterlife. Instead, in the collectivist view, it is inherent in the human psyche to find peace and happiness in the collective well-being of one's society.

This follows from the collectivist perspective that the individual, the social collective, and the wider world/universe are all connected at multiple levels of meaning and interaction or mutual influence. In that view, the connections are not just symbolic but actual. What one does affects the collective as well as the universal (although at that level of extension, the effect will be rather weak), and the universal affects both the collective and the individual (in this direction, the effect is quite strong). This is one of the reasons why *seemingly* individualistic philosophies like Buddhism can be integrated so easily with other non-Western religious systems. The individual is not seen as separate from the collective or the universal – such a perceived separation is understood as illusory and superficial, while the underlying connections are more fundamental and thus real. The individual is simply one level of a multilevel reality. From that perspective, one can embrace Zen Buddhism and still practice ancestor worship, astrology, Taoism, Christianity, Islam, etc. In fact, the roots of Zen Buddhism lie, in part, in Chinese Taoism (Watts, 1957). As noted previously in this text, Taoism reflects an ancient Chinese approach to the world that is part philosophy, part religion, and part cultural belief system.

Again, this kind of integrated approach to mental health is more typical of non-Western societies. In the West, especially as empirical professionalism within the Enlightenment progressed, the corresponding subject areas involving mental health became increasingly differentiated, as exemplified by the separation of psychiatry from general medicine. That differentiation did not occur outside the Western context, at least not until the Modern era, with an increase in cross-cultural contact that began during the Renaissance but increased dramatically during the period of more recent colonialism (seventeenth to nineteenth centuries). By the mid nineteenth century, many non-Western societies had been strongly impacted (passively or by force) by Western ideas regarding the separation of religion and philosophy, mental health and mental illness, the psychological and the physiological, and psychiatry and general medicine. This process was only beginning during the European Enlightenment, and most of the Eastern cultural areas we are considering, under the influence of Buddhism (China, India, Japan, Vietnam, etc.), were still relatively free of Western influence. Given that state of affairs, it is fair to conclude that at that time, the non-Western cultures still experienced the questions of mental health, mental illness, religious faith, philosophy of life, medicine, and even astronomy and physics as fundamentally interconnected.

Since that was likely the case, let's consider an example of psychiatry from a non-Western culture that existed at the time we are exploring. Building on the previous exploration of Buddhism's approach to mental health, let's look at a Buddhist model of mental illness. Terry Clifford did just that in a detailed and insightful analysis of Tibetan Buddhist psychiatry (1984). She described Tibetan medicine as a unique system of healing that blends spiritual, psychological, and rational/empirical beliefs and practices. Its foundation can be found in Indian Ayurvedic medicinal tradition that stretches back more than 2,000 years to the Vedic period. It was imported to Tibet in the seventh century AD as part of the spread of Buddhism throughout most of Asia. According to Clifford, Tibetan medicine became renowned throughout central Asia and is based on a close integration of Buddhism with medical beliefs and practices in Tibet. This integration is profound and includes not just general medicine but also what the West now refers to as psychiatry.

The Tibetan understanding of mental illness is based on the fact that Buddhism is primarily a religion of psychology and philosophy. Illness and suffering are conceptualized as resulting from craving and attachment. It is important to note that Buddhist thought includes a very different conception of self-identity than is typical in the West. In the West, people (including psychologists and psychiatrists) tend to view the self as a very real and central entity. It (or me) is the most important thing. I seek happiness. I want to be well. I want to reach my goals in life. As noted before, in Buddhism, this conscious self-identity is viewed as a delusion, a problem to be overcome, obscuring the real truth of things. Attachment to ego and self-identity is based on an ignorance or misunderstanding of its transitory and illusory foundation. A meditational approach to this "problem" can be to sit and remind oneself, as thoughts, feelings, and impulses pass through consciousness, "I am not that." That is not meant to imply that one's thoughts, feelings, and impulses are not part of the individual but that they are not *all* that one is. One should not confuse the core of his or her being with the passing psychological phenomena that seem so central to reality on a moment-to-moment basis but are in actuality only a part of the overall picture and not really the most important or foundational part of the individual.

This existential position extends to Tibetan psychiatry. Psychological suffering, in all its forms, is seen as following from a dysfunctional attachment to the self, leading to negative emotions, dysfunctional relationships, mental distortions, and a resulting sense of turmoil, agitation, or misery. Therefore, despite psychological suffering being caused by ignorance, it is holistically integrated within the person's being and overall functioning. It is connected to the patient's biology, spirituality, and psychology, as well as his or her social functioning and overall life situation. In regard to the biological, the Tibetan system relies on the ancient humoral theory. The basic three humors (air, bile, and phlegm) are understood as corresponding to the three basic psychological failings – air with craving, bile with hatred, and phlegm with ignorance. As with the Ancient Greek system, it is humoral imbalance that causes illness. These imbalances relate to a variety of factors, including diet, astrology, spiritual forces, life problems, karma, and the influence of past lives. These last two are particularly interesting and quite different from Western conceptions of mental illness. The karmic force (basically the law of cause and effect working on the universal or metaphysical plane) exerts an influence on the patient, stemming particularly from past life experiences. Some mental diseases are seen as purely karmic in nature and will not respond to medical intervention but instead call for a spiritual or religious treatment. Severe mental illness is a bit more complicated. Tibetan psychiatry takes a holistic approach, conceptualizing psychosis and other serious mental disorders as being caused by one or more of six factors, including (1) karma, (2) poison, (3) negative emotions and emotional conflict, (4) humoral imbalance caused by life difficulties (stress, poor diet, relationship problems, love-sickness, overwork, loss, isolation, etc.), and (5) destructive spiritual factors or demons. Only two of these are seriously considered in the modern, Western perspective, which leaves the Tibetan approach quite alien to Western psychiatry and too easily dismissed as "naive" or "backward."

In regard to types of diseases, the Tibetan system typically identifies four kinds: karmic diseases, evil-spirit diseases, current or immediate diseases, and life diseases. Although all mental diseases are karmic, in that they are all impacted by karma and past lives, some are exclusively spiritual in nature. They are sometimes identified by the fact that regular medicines don't work, and thus, rigorous religious interventions are called for. Evil-spirit diseases are also treated with religious interventions, combined with various oils and herbal medicines. Evil spirits are often identified as the cause of insanity and the more severe psychiatric problems. Immediate diseases come and go quickly, and little is necessary to treat them, as they tend to resolve themselves. Life diseases are more serious and typically call for somatic and lifestyle changes, as they reflect humoral imbalances caused by poor diet and sleep, psychological factors, behavioral problems, and environmental issues. These can include such things as having too much jealousy or pride or leading an immoral or unvirtuous life. By the way, it should be noted that traditional Tibetan psychiatric diagnosis does not include children or the elderly – these groups are assessed separately, with their own concepts and categories. Children, for instance, are considered especially vulnerable to invasion by evil spirits and should be protected from avoidable startling, as the moment of shock constitutes a suspension of consciousness through which an invading spirit can enter.

Although Tibetan psychiatry does not have a clearly delineated nosology like the DSM in the West (the holistic quality of its approach means, first of all, that all cases are unique, and second that almost all diseases have both somatic and psychiatric symptoms), air is the humor most closely associated with psychiatric distress. Wind is connected to the concept of both mind and insanity. Most psychiatric problems are considered to be, at least partly, caused by "disturbed air," and severe neurotic behavior and intense anxiety problems are understood as a life-wind disorder and called "sok-lung." The psyche becomes disturbed or even insane when the internal winds do not circulate where or how they should. For instance, if they inflate the "life-vein" at the heart (this is conceived as a "subtle channel" made of light not a physical vein), this can weaken the person's mind force and result in hallucinations, delusions, and a variety of cognitive distortions. Of course, given the holistic nature of the Tibetan system, this problem is also associated with high blood pressure and other cardiovascular diseases. Life-wind disorder is often caused by stress, worry, overwork, sorrow, or anger. For instance, the loss of a loved one may be followed by these psychological symptoms, as well as dizziness, insomnia, loss of appetite, or lack of coordination. The subtle channels and inner winds or energy movement are directly associated with chakra theory in tantric practice, with the heart chakra most closely associated with emotional disturbance.

Of course, far more could be said about Tibetan psychiatry, and for those who are interested, I strongly suggest Terry Clifford's excellent book, but this short review will have to do as an example of a non-Western approach that developed during the Western Enlightenment era. It is still utilized to this day but is under severe stress given the combination of the aggressive takeover of Tibet by China and the more general cultural invasion by Western psychiatry. The period of the European Enlightenment may have been the last time that many non-Western approaches, not just Tibetan psychiatry, were able to sustain their development and practice with relatively limited impact from the West. Of course, by that time, there had already been incursions into native cultures by European explorers, and various native cultures had, from ancient times, intermingled cooperatively or by force, so it is not accurate to describe the period as "pristine" by any measure. It can only be said that many cultural systems, with their psychiatric theories and practices, remained strongly intact but were about to be impacted in dramatic ways by the emerging tidal wave of colonialism and Western psychiatry in the Modern era. The changes that would occur may have begun in Europe, but they would transform the world landscape of mental health and mental illness almost as dramatically as they would that of the Western world itself.

CHAPTER 7

THE MODERN AGE

The Modern age generally refers to the period of time from the beginning of the nineteenth century to the early twentieth century. It covers an enormous number of dramatic changes in the human landscape. These include the industrial revolution, high levels of colonization and then postcolonization, the emergence of universal education, mass urbanization, the Romantic movement, modern medical science, an explosion in various technologies that directly impacted how people live, two world wars, a revolution of human rights, and the list goes on. These particular changes were listed not only because they represent some of the more important impacts on the shaping of the period itself, but they all had a powerful influence on how mental health and mental illness were experienced and understood in a changing world. In the interest of brevity and space, only passing references to these events will be possible in this chapter, but hopefully enough will be included to impart the importance of these cultural dynamics to the changes in both psychiatry and the soon-to-be-brand-new field of academic psychology.

Our tale enters the 1800s, and the world is changing fast. Within a few years there will be steam engines, machine guns, popular nationalism replacing monarchy and tribalism in most places, and in 1844, Francis Rynd, an Irish physician invents the hypodermic syringe and symbolically launches modern medical science. The world of mental health and mental illness was also changing fast. Psychiatry developed into a full-blown medical specialty, with its own practitioners who would spend their careers working exclusively with mentally ill patients, often in psychiatric hospitals. At the same time, for the first time in history, academic psychology emerged as a separate discipline. Students could obtain advanced degrees in the field, and although it started by studying "normal" human psychology, a clinical specialization emerged and by the beginning of the twentieth century, students in a number of universities could study psychopathology with an eye toward working with mentally ill patients. A dynamic emerged, which is still active today, of professional competition between psychiatry (medical) and psychology (academic), with the two fields sometimes having overlapping responsibilities for diagnosing, assessing, treatment planning, and even treating clients. This competitive dynamic would become quite charged. The two disciplines, although supposedly studying the same subject, often seemed to be coming from very different points of view. How could that be if they were both objective, empirical sciences, researching and applying the results within the same subject field? It turns out they could, and this chapter is going to tell the story how such a "crazy" thing could happen.

ROMANTICISM VERSUS SCIENTISM

In their history of psychiatry, Alexander and Selesnick (1966) make the point that the philosophers of the Enlightenment tried to build a new world based on a rational, empirical understanding of reality, but by the beginning of the nineteenth century, the enthusiasm for rationalism had turned to disappointment, criticism, and disillusionment. The dream that rationality could describe, understand, and heal the human condition ran aground on the hard reality of the limits of human knowledge and the underlying irrationality of the human psyche.

The result was that the nineteenth century was marked by a profound split between those who rejected the rational approach to life and those who wanted to continue the effort to develop an objective, rational, and empirical approach to understanding ourselves and improving the human condition. At times, these two forces could work together, but often, they were at odds. By the beginning of the twentieth century, these forces had staked their claims in the fields of psychiatry and psychology, but neither had a hegemony in its respective school. On the one side, instinct, emotion, and the unconscious mind became the new focus of much psychological theory. On the other side, medical science was emerging as a serious discipline, and a series of new findings in neurology and the brand-new scientific theory of evolution placed psychiatry in the position of supporting the empirical, biological side of the coin. Of course, nothing is quite this simple. Despite its alignment with biological medicine, the field of psychiatry would embrace the more conceptual notions of Sigmund Freud, and psychology would become enthralled with the empirical rationality of behaviorism and the research laboratory. In other words, both fields were caught up in the conflict, and we need to go back to the beginning of the nineteenth century to see how it got to that point.

At the start of the 1800s, the Western world was being transformed by the industrial revolution, which was driven by science and empirical rationalism. It was radically transforming the individual and collective lives of people, breaking up families when individuals moved away to work in factories, disrupting traditional family values when females began to receive education and get jobs outside the home, and transforming whole communities when people started moving from rural to urban areas. People's psychological horizons widened as trains allowed them to travel far beyond their historical limits and contact cultures different from their own. Technology became more powerful and important than the people wielding it. Wealth was expanding but only for the few who controlled the mechanisms of industry and government. In the crux of the industrial revolution, many people began to feel like cogs in an economic machine, working dangerous, soul-killing jobs, unable to afford the luxuries the new technologies created, and increasingly alienated from traditional sources of meaning, purpose, and fulfillment. The response by many to this problem was to reject the emerging modernism, with its soulless science and technology, and embrace the irrational values of emotion, aesthetic pleasure, ecstatic faith, sexuality, and love of nature. This movement, originally led by philosophers and artists, became known as Romanticism and featured writers like Byron and Poe, composers like Schumann and Wagner, painters like Blake and Goya, and thinkers like Coleridge and Schlegel.

THE BIRTH OF PSYCHOLOGY

In the world of psychology, this meant turning away from purely cognitive, philosophical approaches to understanding the human psyche. Interest turned to the emotional life and deeper levels of what might be called the soul, including those aspects that are not available to conscious reflection. For the first time, we begin to hear about a human condition that we now call alienation: the suffering of an individual (and, by extension, entire groups and cultures), who is disconnected from the world around her and even from herself. This disconnection from the external world can include a lack of emotionally nurturing relationships with friends, family, and romantic partners. It can include a sense of cultural disconnection with the group one has been "born into." It can include a sense that the life one is living is unfulfilling, meaningless, and even absurd. On the internal level, it can include a disconnection from one's emotions or life energy. It can include a disconnection from one's deeper sense of self or life-purpose. It can include either a vague, nagging feeling of unhappiness, anxiety, and dis-ease or a more powerful sense of rage and despair. Behaviorally, it can feed a variety of responses, including drug and alcohol abuse, violence toward others, participation in a wide range of groups that promise to "fix the problem" (religious, political, sociological, cultural), and in extreme cases, violence toward others or the self, and even suicide. The Enlightenment project of human progress began to be seen as both "thin gruel" to address these issues, and actually part of the problem, conceptualizing the human psyche in mechanistic, philosophical ways, and championing an empirical, scientific approach to reality that triggered the industrial revolution and its dehumanizing, technical mechanization of human life and destruction of traditional, more fulfilling ways of life. In other words, modernism freed people from the mental and physical shackles of traditional ways of life but replaced it with the horror show of an inhumane existence of individualism, materialism, and overreliance on technology.

Developing in the context of this cultural situation, the period from the latter part of the eighteenth to the mid-nineteenth century saw the birth of academic psychology. At first, this nascent field was populated by philosophers, physicians, and artists describing the human condition in new ways. By the mid nineteenth century, the movement had evolved and inspired the founding of the academic and, later, the professional field of psychology. At the beginning however, there were physicians like Johann Christian Reil, who strongly promoted hospital reform and something we would recognize today as psychotherapy for the mentally ill. His advocacy of psychotherapy stemmed from his belief that mental illness was caused primarily by psychological issues. He did not reject the idea that physiology was a factor but felt it needed to be integrated with an understanding of psychological phenomena. Therefore, he believed anyone working in the field of mental health needed to be grounded in a deep understanding of human personality not just medicine. Despite his interest in the integration of soma and psyche, Reil did not develop a comprehensive theory of personality, and his ideas remained vague and speculative.

In the meantime, there was a different line of thought advancing in the philosophical world that would become a major element in modern psychology. This was the study of existentialism and phenomenology. These were responding to the same problems in the modern world (the limits to rationalism and the inhumanity and social disruptions of the industrial revolution) that many social and political protesters were. They also rejected an approach to the human psyche that relied exclusively on an objective and empirical epistemology for understanding. Instead, phenomenology asserts the primary importance of the human *experience* of things over the objective qualities of things themselves. Existentialism built upon that basic truth assertion by adding that the primary questions and issues of people's lives are based on the lived experience of life and the naturally resulting issues regarding alienation, purpose and meaning in life, and the fundamental problem of the inevitability of death. Eventually, these two strands of thought would lead to postmodernism, but already, in the mid-nineteenth century, they constituted a radical departure from the rational scientism of the Enlightenment.

The precursors of existential phenomenology can be found in the works of Voltaire (1694–1778) and Jean-Jacques Rousseau (1712–1778) (Millon, 2004). Voltaire was an author of great renown in France but was little known in the English-speaking world except by virtue of his famous name. Through his many writings, he advocated freedom of speech and religion. He dared to attack the Catholic Church and the aristocracy and, by extension, all forms of established power in favor of the right of people to choose their own beliefs and control their own lives. His faith was not in the god of his fathers but in the innate goodness of humanity and his confidence in the drive of people for their own highest purpose and its natural alignment with the well-being of others. These ideas foreshadowed the concept of self-actualization developed by Abraham Maslow, Carl Rogers, and other twentieth-century humanists.

In contrast to Enlightenment thinking, Rousseau famously thought of people as "noble savages" not empirical philosophers. By this, he meant both that we are, at our heart, animals dominated by our emotions and that this reflects what is best in us. In his view, the forces of civilization, religion, and government converge to corrupt the human soul. The empiricists had asserted that the center of human nature was in seeking to know, while Rousseau argued that the core of the human psyche was the capacity for feeling. He agreed that intellect was important to attain goals, compete with others, figure out how the world worked, and develop a "social contract," but if one gives oneself over completely to a cognitive, mechanical state of being, one has lost the heart of his or her humanity. It was culture that tried to weaken people's emotional lives and make them live in unnatural ways. This idea that society itself was a source of emotional alienation and suffering was taken up by Søren Kierkegaard (1813–1855), who was one of many philosophers of this era who started out in life grounded in the Christian faith but at some point felt compelled to find the source of human suffering and its redemption in the individual heart and soul rather than the authority, truths, or prescriptions of society or religion. He asserted that society created the increasing sense of depersonalization found in modern people, and the problem was amplified by the intrinsic subjectivity of human existence. In his view, people are all forced to live their lives, to some extent, psychologically separate from others, alone, in despair, and painfully waiting for death. This perspective described what would later be called existential angst. Together, Rousseau and Kierkegaard can be seen as establishing the dichotomous counterpoints in the existential continuum – ranging between the hopeful, positive pole of human goodness and striving and the negative pole of hopelessness, isolation, and suffering.

The founder of the field of phenomenology was Edmund Husserl (1859–1938). He introduced the term in 1913 and defined it in terms of the structures of consciousness that enable one to refer to or re-cognize external phenomena. In other words, he was focused on how people psychologically *experience* the world or "being" itself (Tarnas, 1991). Of course, the mind can cognize both real and imagined phenomena, so one should not *assume* the objective reality of anything. The only reasonable approach to truth is to try to take an unbiased stand in relation to all phenomena, putting aside one's preconceptions, in an attempt to see the thing *as it is*. This assertion naturally raises the question of whether it is possible, as a separate, subjective being, for any human to take such a stance. While it may be a worthy goal, is it a fool's errand? In the twentieth century, the postmodernists would insist it is, and the best we can do is to explore the nature of inter-subjective reality, recognizing our inherent inability to see the world as it is, as opposed to how we subjectively create it. Already, in the nineteenth century, serious doubts were being raised.

The reason existential phenomenology is so important for our topic in this book is that while traditional psychiatry and even much of conventional psychology has focused on observable, measurable symptoms of mental illness or the basic, everyday problems of life like social difficulties, the existentialists provided the foundation for psychology to explore and work with the deeper issues of life. Digging deeper in the psyche than the level of psychodiagnoses and daily functionality, this approach reveals layers of the personality, or soul if you prefer that term, that are the closer to the heart of modern culture, revealed through its art and literature, as well as the people who live in that culture, hungering for a rich and fulfilling life amid the dreams and nightmares of modernity.

EVOLUTION

Going back to the early nineteenth century, however, these postmodern musings were only just emerging and were not fully developed. What did explode into Western consciousness at that time was the new science and philosophy of evolutionary theory (Bowler, 2009; Millon, 2004; Tarnas, 1991). The idea itself goes back to the Classical era, when pre-Socratic philosophers like Anaximander and Empedocles speculated that an organism could descend from another type. However, this concept was opposed by both Plato and Aristotle, who believed that existing organisms emerged from eternal forms, reflecting divinely designed order. It was this idea of the Platonic ideal that fit easily in the Christian worldview, as well as those of most other world religions. God (or gods) had designed the world, pretty much as it is now, and progressive, natural change to that order was impossible.

Over time, though, this belief was weakening. First of all, as the centuries passed, many religiously based beliefs about the natural world were being contradicted by scientific facts, and, one by one, had to be given up by religious leaders. The most famous of these was the idea that the Earth was the center of the universe, a belief contradicted by the observation that the Earth actually revolves around the sun, not the other way around. Also, moons were observed orbiting other planets, not the Earth. In more recent centuries, scientific investigation was accumulating real and practically useful information and was quickly becoming the primary source of information about the natural world, rather than the Bible. The Bible had nothing to say about chemistry, biology, mechanical engineering, or any of the other scientific areas that were transforming human life, often for the better. Next, the Reformation had broken the hegemony the Catholic Church had on all beliefs. The Western world had become a competitive arena for religious and other epistemological truths. Finally, over the centuries, there had been wholesale manipulation of species by human intervention. Farming and ranching had utilized selective breeding to change the characteristics of many plants and animals. Humans had selectively bred wild wolves and cats into a wide variety of house pets, with various qualities they happened to like. While there was still a valid question regarding the immutability of the different species, the truth that significant change within species was possible, and in fact was easily controlled, was becoming increasingly obvious.

By the time Charles Darwin came along, thinkers like Pierre Maupertuis, Jean-Baptiste Lamarck, Georges-Louis Leclerc, and Charles's own father, Erasmus Darwin, were speculating about evolutionary processes. The fact that evolution was "in the air" in scientific circles at the time was evidenced by the fact that Alfred Russel Wallace was famously writing his own paper on the subject at the same time as Darwin, and they presented together at an 1858 meeting of the Linnaean Society of London. The reason this point is important is that many opponents of evolutionary theory, then and now, try to paint a picture of the theory being the singular product of a particular person, Charles Darwin, thus supposedly weakening its validity. Some insist on calling it Darwinian Theory, ignoring the facts that (1) it reflected multiple tracks of research and theory in both the natural and social sciences at the time; (2) it has continued to be developed over the subsequent 160 years and thus is no longer strictly Darwinian; and (3) it has become the foundational theory for a wide variety of the natural and social sciences.

The basic outlines of evolutionary theory are well known and thus do not require a great deal of time to describe. The basic idea is that the biology of living species is flexible, thus allowing them to adjust to challenges and opportunities in the natural environment over the course of generations. Those attributes that aid survival tend to get passed on to the next generation. Those that hinder survival are less likely to. Historically, the fossil record shows a clear progression, with the earliest life forms being the most simple and basic, and later ones showing greater complexity, developing tools such as teeth, eyes, ears, flippers, and increasingly large brains to better fit the competitive demands of their environment. The overall process of evolution led from exclusively water-based creatures (fish) to those that could live both in water and on land (amphibians) to those living only on land (reptiles). Attributes such as sex-based reproduction and extended gestation periods increased the viability of animals by increasing genetic diversity and the time needed to grow bigger brains and learn complex living skills for survival (mammals). This overall process is natural and automatic, not requiring a designer or a goal. It continues to this day and into the future. Human beings are the result of the process, just like the rest of the animals. This does not mean that humans are the "endpoint" of evolution or generally superior to the rest of nature. The one special attribute for human survival is our giant brains. Compared to many other primates, humans are slow, clumsy, and weak. Humans evolved a bigger brain because our key to survival was using superior intelligence to work together in complex ways to perform tasks more effectively than could be done individually. It led to the development of tools, the ability to plan and prepare for the future, and the development of complex societies to augment the capacity for mutual protection, food production, and child-rearing. The amazing result is human beings can live in almost any location on our planet (and even in space) and have expanded its population from barely a billion people around 1820 to approximately 7.7 billion just 200 years later.

This explosion of the human population is testament not just to its biological evolutionary success but more so to what is commonly called "cultural evolution." This process follows the same general principles as biological evolution but focuses instead on beliefs and practices that enhance group success. It involves the development and transmission of knowledge, concepts, skills, customs, language, religion, family dynamics, government, and technology. Like biological evolution, it typically (but not exclusively) involves the progression from simpler to more complex forms, for instance from small hunting bands to settled farming villages, and eventually to civilizations with governments, armies, and universities. In the nineteenth century, the focus of theories of social evolution was unilinear, often called "social Darwinism," and emphasized a particular idea of "progress" or improvement of society, which led to an academic reinforcement of the idea that Western civilization was "superior" to non-Western ones. By the twentieth century, this approach was being criticized as too limited and ethnocentric, which led to the development of a theory of multilinear cultural evolution, or neoevolution, which considered the ways that different cultures respond to similar environments, the ways that many different cultures share similar patterns of development, and the different patterns of long-term, general development versus more localized, short-term adaptive change. In other words, evolution is very complex and can work in different ways, in different situations, and does not always appear as "progress" in the stereotypical meaning of the word (Nolan & Lenski, 2015).

What this means is that in the field of psychology, we need to consider the collective effect of both biological and cultural evolution in how people think, feel, and behave. While the academic field of evolutionary psychology emerged in the 1930s with the work of biologists studying animal behavior, including Nikolaas Tinbergen, Konrad Lorenz, and Karl von Frisch, the application of evolutionary theory to human psychology began with Charles Darwin in the mid-nineteenth century. He foresaw the future of psychology being based on evolutionary theory, and some of his later works focused heavily on the subject (Darwin, 1871/2004). For the first time in a long time, a truly new concept emerged in the field of psychology: adaptation. This refers to the ways that an organism or group changes its structure or functioning to better fit its environment for survival and reproduction. From this perspective, the question becomes, what *psychological* traits evolved as adaptations to aid survival and procreation, or how has our functioning developed to increase environment fitness?

These questions lead in many directions, including biological/physiological issues such as the increase in brain size, which, of course, relates directly to overall intelligence. As noted previously, intelligence was the primary adaptive advantage for early humanoids. More than any other animals, humans needed highly complex, socially oriented thought and communication, including speech, to survive (Pinker, 1994). As early societies became more complex, divisions of labor and hierarchies of power emerged. A great deal of information needed to be shared, opinions noted, options considered, and decisions made. Grunts and cries were not enough to handle the communication demand, so speech evolved to fill the need. As brain size increased, along with intelligence, females' hips widened to provide passage for bigger-headed babies, and parental investment increased as those babies took much more time to develop the skills necessary to function effectively within the group. This likely decreased the female role in some activities (hunting) and increased it in others (childcare). Changes to reproductive physiology were not just limited to pelvic size. The estrous cycle changed, intensifying menstruation and creating conditions for nearly continual sexual activity (Wilson, 1975). This, combined with the demands of extended child-rearing, led to longer-term mate pairing, romantic love, and the "nuclear" family (Buss, 2008).

According to Darwin (1871/2004), mental traits evolved along the same basic principles as physical ones, with the difference between humans and other animals being one of degree rather than kind. He noted the existence, in other animals, of the basic roots of empathy, love, altruism, fear, anger, jealousy, and so on. Even moral and ethical instincts have evolved (Wright, 1994). Interestingly, morality and empathy lead civilized societies to protect the weak, who, from an overly simplistic evolutionary perspective, should die or at least not procreate. Support for these people is seen as a drain on limited resources and could potentially weaken the larger group. In the nineteenth century, this idea would lead to the eugenics movement, which sought to strengthen the population by sterilizing those identified as weak or otherwise detrimental in body or psychology. Darwin himself did not take this position. He felt that moral sympathy was a powerful attribute provided by evolutionary psychology, with many benefits, and therefore society must bear the unintended negative consequences or else experience a deterioration of its most noble characteristics. Obviously, this view was not shared by all, and many would use evolutionary theory to argue that society should utilize at least some of the principles of selective breeding to increase overall fitness and improve the population. It would not be until the end of World War II that the full horrors of such an approach became publicly evident and led to the wholesale repudiation of that agenda (Bruinius, 2006).

Another area that Darwin discussed was sexual selection. He asserted that males, through the use of tools and weapons, had become superior to women, both physically and intellectually. Like many Westerners at the time, he saw women's natural and appropriate place in society as limited to taking care of the home and children and not in the public space, engaging in economic, cultural, and political activity. Darwin made an evolutionary argument for this. However, it met with almost immediate criticism and has been a point of debate ever since. A particularly salient aspect of the debate has been the role of social evolution in the roles, abilities, and status of the genders. For instance, the apparent physical superiority of males in strength and speed gave them an advantage for many centuries in the areas of physical labor, hunting, and fighting. However, the technological development of tools of work and warfare, along with the radically increased proportion of non–labor-intensive work, have largely removed that advantage and leveled the playing field; hence the larger role of women in almost all advanced societies today.

A third area of controversy in the early days of evolutionary theory was the question of race. At the time, in the nineteenth century, many academics thought that there were a specific number of clearly differentiated races that constituted nearly separate species (Bowler, 2009). It was thought that these races had widely different qualities, and many in the West (not coincidentally) believed that the Caucasian race was superior to the others, especially in the psychological areas of intellect and morality. Darwin directly challenged this belief, asserting that all races had a common evolutionary source and were of the same species, as supported by the facts that the different races could successfully mate, becoming mixed, that the races had highly variable characteristics, and that there were many similar characteristics across the races. Together, these factors suggested that humans were monogenetic and the different races emerged through sexual selection. As in the case of gender differences, his arguments sparked a debate about biological versus social evolution in the area of race and racial differences.

At the time of Darwin's publications, the idea of evolution was (as it still is) highly controversial. Many of the leading figures in science and society rejected the notion both as contradictory to religious faith and as a moral affront to human dignity. Humans were seen as holding a special and superior place to the rest of nature. Created in God's image, they could not be "just another animal," evolved from apes, similar in many ways to their simian cousins, and continuing to change in response to their environment. While public polling was not yet in vogue, it is safe to say that the large majority of the public opposed the idea. It may also be said that the introduction of the concept of evolution to the natural and social sciences (including psychology) in the nineteenth century helped build a wall between academia and the general public – a wall of mistrust of the "findings" of science and academia, especially for those more religiously inclined. The difference between those who were highly educated and those who were not was not just about how much one knew but what one thought was true about human nature and the world in general.

Why is this important for our particular topic, the concepts of mental health or wellness? Because, while starting with Darwin, psychologists, psychiatrists, and social scientists of all stripes have discussed the impact of evolution on human psychological functioning, both positive and negative, many in the general public (and a solid minority in the scientific establishment) have not. To a large extent, *people are who they think they are.* People think, feel, and act in the context of how they view themselves. If a person sees him- or herself as a uniquely created "child of

God," then their entire psyche unfolds from that perspective. If one sees oneself as an evolved simian, then their core conceptions and personality will reflect that subjective reality. If people have sexual feelings for members of their own gender, will they experience that as sinful, shameful, and something to be changed? Or instead, will they experience those feelings as a natural point on the spectrum of sexuality? If someone points out that other primates sometimes engage in homosexual behavior, will that be taken as confirmation of normality or rejected as having nothing to do with humans because we are not just another animal? The introduction of the theory of evolution in the nineteenth century created a special challenge, not just within a professional field, but around the world, for humanity to see itself in a radically new way. Such challenges are inevitably met with a mix of excitement and resistance.

The excitement of that challenge helped establish the field of academic psychology. In the mid- to late nineteenth century, the new field of psychology was dominated by structuralists (Wilhelm Wundt and Edward Titchener, among others), who were attempting to delineate and define the basic components of the mind and understand how they fit together to create more complex mental experiences. This approach did not need the theory of evolution to support its foundation or agenda. By the end of the century, however, this approach was facing increasing criticism in regard to the validity of its methods (introspection), its potential for practical application, and a number of its core assumptions, including the idea that mental experience can be broken down into separate elements. It was being replaced with a new approach we now call functionalism. A direct outgrowth of evolutionary theory, functionalism sought to understand the utility (adaptivity) and purpose (teleology) of human thought, emotions, and behavior (Schultz & Schultz, 2012).

The first to bring an evolutionary perspective to academic psychology was Francis Galton (1822–1911). Blessed with extraordinary intelligence, Galton was fascinated with the question of how mental attributes are *distributed* among people and the individual differences that result. His approach to this question assumed that such attributes evolve over time and are biologically based. His first major book, *Hereditary Genius* (1869), made the claim that high intelligence occurred far too regularly in certain families to be purely environmental in nature; it must be inherited. He recognized that in order to properly investigate human attributes, there had to be a way to quantify and statistically analyze them. Statistical analysis had already been developed but had not been applied to psychological characteristics. Galton was at the forefront of developing psychological tests, both of direct mentation (such as sensory capacities he thought were related to intelligence) and indirectly, through questionnaires and word-association tests. He was also a believer in the unconscious mind, wrote about its impact on the overall personality, and was likely a strong influence on the work of Sigmund Freud. While it is not necessary to believe in evolution to appreciate Galton's approach to measuring psychological attributes, it is vital to understand that his interest was driven by his belief that such attributes developed and are distributed in any given population by genetic dynamics, driven by evolution.

FUNCTIONALISM, PRAGMATISM, AND THE EMERGENCE OF ACADEMIC PSYCHOLOGY

If you take that particular point of view and accept that humans evolved from other animal species, than it makes sense to study human psychology from the perspective of its utility and purpose of behavior in order to maximize adaptability. In contrast to existentialism, which focused on uniquely human issues, functionalism highlights that part of human nature that is shared with other species. These include primal emotions like affection, fear, and anger. It includes core drives like lust and hunger. It includes the basic processes of learning and reinforcement. Rather than referring to the ancient well-being of fitting in with society or the religious concepts of sin and atonement, functionalism reminds us that people are flesh-and-blood creatures, driven and attracted by the many of the same emotions and drives as other animals. Some may find that dehumanizing, but it is hard to summarily reject the idea that whatever the truth may be about our spiritual nature, we are certainly also biological beings, and perhaps primarily so.

However, even the functionalists did not necessarily believe that the academic study of human beings had to stop at attributes we share with other animals. For instance, William James (1842–1910) argued that psychology should be a division of biology, and its main focus should be the study of adaptation, he was also interested in the whole, living person and embraced the new philosophy that included the irrational, the subconscious, and even the spiritual side of the human personality. He saw consciousness not as a collection of discrete mental sensations but rather as an integrated stream. Despite this wide-ranging interest in human nature, James focused primarily on his belief that consciousness has a biological utility, namely the ability to exert willfulness and purpose on the environment. Consciousness allows the human organism to conceive of, plan for, and cooperate with others to reach goals based on self-interest and seeking psychological well-being.

This common-sense and fundamentally evolution-based concept regarding consciousness correlated with James's strong support for pragmatism. First postulated by his good friend Charles Sanders Pierce, the basic tenet of this approach to epistemology is that the truth or validity of an idea or concept lies in its practical consequences. A uniquely American kind of philosophy, it supports the idea that "if it works, it must be right." One of the consequent positions of this approach is that there can be multiple sound or valid ways to conceptualize reality. This is because truth is a function of the relationship between postulates, none of which holds a special position of being unassailable or universal. So, in a sense, there is no ultimate truth, only practical or useful-to-believe truths. This means that in the world of science, what matters is how well it (science) predicts phenomena, not how well it describes the world. This fits well with the American spirit, which was heavy on practicality, common sense, and a "can-do" attitude and not as concerned about ultimate truths and fine, philosophical distinctions between phenomena.

This is particularly relevant in the world of psychology, which is replete with reifications – that is, taking a concept and treating it as if it is something concrete. Sometimes it may be true, but it may not be, and more likely it will not mean the same thing to someone else as it is to the writer. If I write about love or the self or intelligence or a thousand other psychological concepts, do they really exist, and if so, in what form? If I write the word "love," are you and I thinking about exactly the same thing? That is doubtful. Pragmatism is a philosophy that is aware of this problem. It calls for humility in the face of the unknown and, to a large extent, unknowable. It recognizes that all too often, the best we can do is predict the outcomes of our concepts, see if reality aligns with that prediction, and if so, then conclude that either we were right or at least the original concept has practical utility.

This core understanding of truth led William James to criticize much of the early work in psychology, seeing its research as discovering a great deal about very little, with doubtful validity, and thus he felt free to move beyond the official bounds of the field. He was so disgusted with the direction that academic psychology was taking that he left the field and spent the rest of his career exploring religious faith, parapsychology, and education. He recognized that his ideas were exploratory, and he was not establishing significant truths, but as far as James was concerned, the only things that could be empirically established in his chosen field were very narrow concerns not the big questions that actually matter in human psychology.

The nineteenth century had begun with no formal, academic field of psychology and ended with a very dynamic one, but it was in deep conflict. Should it study abnormal psychology or leave that to medical psychiatry and explore only the psychology of the normal? Was this a field of empirical research or speculative philosophy? Should it sell its services in the public marketplace or stay in the ivory tower and seek pure knowledge? By the beginning of the twentieth century, academic psychology was gaining ground in the universities but hadn't had much of an impact on widespread conceptions of either mental health or mental illness. Its emerging ideas were still speculative, impractical, and largely hidden in the notebooks of the few students who found their way to its lecture halls. Early leaders like James were tempted to turn away in disgust, wondering if they were wasting their time. Little did they know how the field would explode in creativity, popularity, and public influence in the coming century.

THE PSYCHIATRISTS

In the meantime, as noted at the beginning of the chapter, the world of psychiatry began the nineteenth century by embracing the Romantic movement. Writers like J. Moreau de Tours and Johann Christian Heinroth developed a view of psychopathology that foreshadowed the psychoanalytic theories of Sigmund Freud, but in a sense, they were too early (Alexander & Selesnick, 1966). Both theorists predated Freud by decades by postulating that psychological disturbance arises from conflicts between the (largely) unconscious, biologically based drives and internalized morals, and their ideas will be discussed in more detail later in this chapter. The psychiatric world was not ready for such ideas, though. Instead, from the middle to the end of the nineteenth century, the world of psychiatry moved in a biological direction and established itself as both a science and a clinical practice. Building on the work of Pinel and Esquirol, these pioneers developed neurology as the foundational science of psychiatry and made significant progress in developing a detailed nosology based on clinical practice and observation. Although it was not yet able to directly link the new findings in neurology with specific disorders, psychiatry did finally break free of the bonds of belief and practice that had enslaved it to ancient medicine for many centuries. Many physicians at the beginning of the nineteenth century were still working on the basis of humoral theory, but by the end of the century, all had embraced the modern sciences.

The work of a number of researchers between 1750 and 1850 had advanced neurological science, establishing the electrochemical nature of nerve impulses, the identification of neurons, the localization of mental functions in different parts of the brain, the cellular theory of tissue, chloroform anesthesia, and the measurement of nerve impulse speeds (Scull, 2015). Researchers like A.L.J. Bayle and J.L. Calmiel discovered that many patients who had psychotic symptoms and muscle weakness (paresis) turned out to have brain lesions. As a result, the first true textbook on neurology was published by Moritz Romberg in 1840. Psychiatry would forever after be linked with neurology, and medical psychiatrists increasingly saw their patients' mental disorders as neurological problems, not psychosocial ones.

Advances in other medical fields were establishing connections between medical problems (syphilis, lack of iodine, etc.) and symptoms associated with mental illness (depression, anxiety, psychosis, etc.). As a result, it became important to differentiate psychiatry from the rest of medical science. Doctors like Wilhelm Griesinger (1817–1868) drew the distinction by asserting that the proper realm of psychiatry was diseases of the brain, which could properly be called mental illness. From that perspective, disorders centered in other parts of the body may include psychological symptoms or impact the brain but are not mental illness.

This approach changed the fundamental perspective of psychiatrists and increasingly set them in contrast to the new field of academic psychology, which was concerned with normal functioning, the role of evolution in psychological processes, and psychosocial explanations for mental disorders. Psychiatry's more biological approach led it to focus on neurological research and, in the clinical world, to identifying symptoms and diagnosing categorically recognized mental disorders.

It is to the second world, that of clinical work, that we now turn. As always, in this text, we are not as concerned with treatment. Instead, we will keep our focus on the concepts of mental health and mental illness. The first point to make here is that because of the increasingly medicalized approach of nineteenth-century psychiatry, questions of mental health virtually disappear. More and more, the field became fixated on the presence of and types of mental illness, based on what we now call the medical model. The concept of mental health faded into the background and simply became the *absence* of symptoms of mental illness.

It has already been noted that the first practitioners to develop a modern nosology were Pinel and Esquirol. Building on their work, neurologists were grouping psychological symptoms into syndromes and diseases. The next step in this was taken by Karl Kahlbaum (1828–1899). He thought that all psychiatric symptoms could be organized into groups and therefore into syndromes or diseases. He introduced a number of important new terms, including cyclothymia (alternating mood states between depression and mania), catatonia (a state of rigidity, mutism, and social withdrawal), and the symptom complex (regularly occurring groups of symptoms with no immediately obvious common etiology). A student of Kahlbaum's, Ewald Hecker (1843–1909), added the concept of regressive behavior, which he called hebephrenia and thus helped identify and differentiate different phenomena associated with psychosis. This regression or degeneration was a common feature observed in psychotic patients and helped convince researchers that psychosis had a biological basis and reflected an inherited vulnerability to some form of brain deterioration. Benedict Morel (1809–1873) noticed that many of his patients who were psychotic had first experienced their symptoms in late adolescence or early adulthood. This commonality led him to believe it was an inherited form of early-onset dementia, and thus he called the condition "demence precoce," a term that was later changed to "dementia praecox" and eventually labeled schizophrenia by Eugen Bleuler.

Since degeneracy (lack of concern for others and internalized morals) was an important psychological problem that concerned both doctors and the general public, it made sense to look at this as a possible psychiatric problem, not just a moral one. Thus, psychiatry began to explore antisocial attitudes and criminal behavior as a mental problem. James Prichard (1786–1909) came to view these problems as a form of insanity and identified the syndrome as a distinct mental illness. Cesare Lombroso (1836–1909) took this one step further and theorized that criminality represented a form of biological degeneration. While taking a purely biological approach to criminality clearly had its limits and has since been discredited, the effort to identify such life patterns as specific forms of insanity led to the concept of a *personality disorder*, which remains in the psychiatric lexicon as an awkwardly separate category of mental illness.

As the nineteenth century progressed, the growing mass of information from neurology, as well as other medical sciences, demanded a nosology based less on superficial observation and more on underlying, biological processes. To the present day, this effort has been largely unsuccessful, but its starting point in the mid-nineteenth century was the inspiration for the work of the most famous nosologist of the era, Emil Kraepelin (1856–1926). He was a German, born, ironically, in the same year as Sigmund Freud. He studied both psychiatry and psychology in school (an accomplishment that would be nearly impossible today). He kept incredibly detailed records on all his patients, including their clinical symptoms, personal history, and the outcomes of treatment. He wrote a highly successful textbook on psychiatry, which made him famous and well respected in the field, amplifying the influence of his ideas. Ironically, he did not set out to create a new nosology for the field. He did not develop a unique theoretical model of mental illness or propose a specific classification system for such a model. Instead, it was the way he organized his detailed descriptions of different mental illnesses in his textbook that provided an impressive and influential categorical structure for the field. Also ironic was the fact that in his categorization, he did not emphasize the possible neurological foundations of the disorders, which was becoming so popular among researchers. Instead, he continued to emphasize the overt, observable manifestations of the various disorders. This likely reflected the fact that far too little was known at the time about neurobiology to create a biologically based classification system, so while he was responding to the exploding amount of medical knowledge in his field, Kraepelin felt compelled to organize his classifications based on observable phenomena. Despite that, he still conceived the basis of mental disorders as being endogenous and biological. This may seem contradictory or irrational, and to some extent it was, but it reflected the basic problem that existed (and largely still does) that while psychiatrists would assume that symptoms of mental illness were largely caused by biologically based dysfunction, they did not know what those dysfunctions were, could not "see" or measure them, and definitely could not link them to specific disorders.

Kraepelin made an exception to the idea of biological etiology when considering the milder disorders. He saw neurosis, hysteria, and anxiety as more psychologically driven (Kraepelin, 2018). He did not make it clear just how some disorders are biological and others psychological or why depression issues could be physiologically based and anxiety issues not, but Kraepelin apparently considered the more severe disorders as chronic, reflecting an inborn temperament, and thus biological in origin. Other psychological problems reflected a reaction to life circumstances. More specifically, he differentiated various types of *cyclothymia*, including the *hypomanic, depressive, irascible*, and *emotionally unstable*. He described an *autistic temperament*, typified by a quiet, shy disposition, with little interest in friendship and high levels of self-absorption. He described a number of different types of criminally oriented personalities, including those who were without conscience (what we would now call sociopathic), those who were impulsive, and those who were basically immature and irresponsible. He also anticipated the concept of the borderline personality to describe those who exhibited severe fluctuations of emotion and were highly reactive, often self-destructive, and behaved in erratic, often contradictory ways, especially in relationships with others. By establishing these differences in personality (including elements of emotional intensity, relationship style, overall energy, morality, etc.) as representing forms of mental illness, Kraepelin extended the realm of psychiatry beyond the more severe forms of madness traditionally associated with residents chained to a wall in dungeon-like asylums. It could now include the "worried well" as mentally ill, and although he did not consider them victims of biological dysfunction, classification systems typically do not make such distinctions. The biologically mad and sociologically mad sit side by side in the textbook nosologies, as they would in the waiting rooms of their doctors.

Of course, Kraepelin was not alone in his development of a modern classification system for mental illness. Others, like Eugen Bleuler, Philippe Chaslin, and Adolph Meyer made significant contributions to the enterprise. Meyer was particularly influential in the early 1900s, supporting Kraepelin's basic categorical definitions but ascribing a greater role for environmental factors to the development of many psychiatric disorders. Initially reacting to the extreme nature of some psychiatrists' insistence on universal biological etiology, he asserted that traumatic and stressful life events were a powerful influence on the emergence and course of many mental disorders, even schizophrenia. This psychological approach to mental illness drew him into sympathy with the views of a young psychiatrist at the turn of the twentieth century, Sigmund Freud. Although he eventually turned away from

Freud based on his discomfort with some of the latter's more esoteric theories and practices, Meyer's basic agreement with Freud helped win mainstream professional acceptance of the maverick doctor's main ideas.

THE BIRTH OF THE UNCONSCIOUS

If the mid- to late part of the nineteenth century saw the birth of psychiatry, dominated by neurology and efforts to categorize mental illness, the end of it witnessed the explosion of an entirely new conceptualization of insanity. The idea here was that the human psyche is largely unconscious, and the unconscious side is actually the main force behind the development of mental illness and the human struggle to be psychologically well. While many students think this began with Sigmund Freud, they are mistaken. Freud ran with the idea, but he did not create it.

An early contribution to the conception of the unconscious mind was offered by J. Moreau de Tours (1804–1884), who was mentioned earlier in this chapter. He explored the more irrational and unconscious aspects of the psyche and proposed that, in order to understand mental illness, it was necessary to perceive the whole personality and the underlying, unconscious forces creating the madness. Moreau was the first to introduce the idea that people's dreams were a rich source of information about these foundational, underlying aspects of the human personality. While he did not use the term "unconscious," he established the idea of a "double life" of the psyche, on one level consisting of our conscious, external orientation to the world and at another, deep inside the psyche and below the level of conscious awareness. Decades before Freud, Moreau saw dreams as the "meeting" point between these two levels of the psyche, providing powerful hints about the underlying, irrational forces that shaped the personality, for good or ill.

This introductory idea of the "total personality" was expanded through the work of Johann Christian Heinroth (1773–1843), who took a more religiously oriented approach, and conceptualized the psyche as naturally conflicted between selfish desires and Christian morality, resulting in chronic guilt and inner conflict. This conceptualization presaged the work of Freud and proposed a similar three-part structure of the personality, with the deepest level being instinctual and pleasure seeking, the middle level being the psyche's self-awareness and development of ways to operate in the outer world and get one's needs met and desires fulfilled, and the third level the higher conscience, or set of morals, ideals, and values internalized from the environment. Nearly identical with Freud's id, ego, and superego, Heinroth also saw them in developmental terms, with the infant being born almost entirely instinctual, with the intellect slowing emerging to negotiate between the internal and external worlds, and the moral conscience emerging last, embodying an inherent conflict between the self and the highest moral truths (of religious origin, in Heinroth's thinking) that are attained through reason, thus appearing later in development and remaining relatively weak in most people compared to their selfish, instinctual urges. Heinroth saw mental illness being the result of ongoing conflicts between these three functional areas of the psyche and mental health stemming from proper integration of the three areas, with the conscience taking the lead. Of course, since this kind of moral development is relatively rare and demands a disavowal of selfish desires, he had little hope for the mass of humanity attaining freedom from internal conflict.

The work of thinkers like Moreau and Heinroth helped established what would later be called the psychodynamic approach to mental health and mental illness. That approach would become a dramatically powerful force in the world of psychology, but at the time, the lack of specificity (they did not propose a well-developed system or structure of description, pathology, or treatment) left it as visionary but not practical. They proposed an integration of psyche and soma but provided no methodological system or tools to implement that integration in the real world. As a result, their contributions did not gain much traction in the fast-growing psychiatric world, would mainly influence the artists and philosophers of the era, and had to wait until the end of the nineteenth century to be rediscovered and reintroduced by Freud. To what *extent* Freud knew of this original work or gave proper credit for it has been an area of debate for the last 100 years.

What we do know is that Freud was strongly influenced by the work of one of the great figures of modern psychiatry, Jean-Martin Charcot (1835–1893). He was born in Paris, to a renowned carriage-builder, and was a brilliant student. As a young medical intern, he was assigned to the famous Salpetriere hospital, where he came into contact with numerous patients with mysterious neurological diseases of unknown origin (Ellenberger, 1970). They experienced a multitude of symptoms that would typically be associated with neurological impairment (paralysis, sudden blindness, convulsions, pain that shifted between different parts of the body, etc.), but there were no other signs of neurological damage or dysfunction. This suggested that their symptoms were of psychological rather than neurological origin. This condition came to be called hysteria and posed a significant problem for the young neurologist. How could a patient experience neurological symptoms strictly from psychological causes? What could those causes be? And most intriguing, how could it be that, as they regularly found, the patients had no *conscious awareness* of the psychological factors or traumatic events that likely led to their symptoms? Fascinated by these questions and the challenges they posed, Charcot was able to distinguish the subtle differences between the true neurological cases and the hysterics. He then needed a technique that could bypass the conscious mind to reach a deeper level of the psyche.

As historical fate would have it, it turns out that just such a technique had recently been developed. In the previous chapter, we presented the strange career of Franz Mesmer. He utilized a method of trance induction then called mesmerism that would later be renamed hypnosis (evidently, this term was first used by James Braid in 1843). We do not have the space to explore the long, amazing history of trance, hypnosis, and related phenomena in human history (Gauld, 1992), but it is enough to say that this method was highly controversial in the professional circles of the mid-nineteenth century. Most medical professionals rejected hypnotism as quackery – the province of wandering snake-oil salesmen, manipulating the gullible with tricks and sleight of hand. Few of them believed that it was a real phenomenon that, in some unknown way, bypassed normal waking consciousness. Charcot studied the technique, found it valid and effective, and utilized it with his hysteric patients. He found that he could produce new symptoms and remove existing ones, thus confirming the psychological basis of their disorders. By 1892, he was able to identify dynamic amnesia, in which a person had "lost" a traumatic memory but could bring it back to consciousness under hypnosis. Later in his career, Charcot even reported that he was aware of valid cases of "faith healing," where patients had gone to Lourdes and returned healed of their medical afflictions. Despite these findings, Charcot remained a neurologist at heart and concluded that the hysterics' suggestibility and hypnotizability were the result of an underlying weakness of the nervous system not their traumatic experiences.

Pierre Janet (1859–1947) studied under Charcot and basically agreed with his mentor, supporting the theory of neurological weakness, but he added a unique element to the clinical picture. He concluded that the biological weakness was related to a lack of psychological integration or cohesiveness. He called this *psychasthenia* and theorized that this syndrome could follow traumatic experiences, such as extreme fatigue or shock. He believed that the lack of psychological integration would result in parts of consciousness becoming "split off," leading to hysterical symptoms and vulnerability to various dissociative processes. He hypnotized many of his patients and often found that in that state, they remembered long-forgotten traumatic experiences related to their symptoms and further that they sometimes recovered from those symptoms through the cathartic experience of remembering and sharing those memories with the doctor. Josef Breuer (1842–1925) had discovered the same thing, but Janet published earlier and got the credit for this important finding.

The career and findings of Charcot and Janet might have remained an interesting but largely unknown side-street in the history of psychiatry except for that fact that Charcot's fame and professional demonstrations of his methods drew the attention of a young neurologist from Vienna named Sigmund Freud. He was born in 1856 in the Moravian town of Freiberg. He became a medical doctor, graduating from the University of Vienna in 1881. He was appointed a docent in neuropathology and then became a professor in 1902. He lived and worked in Vienna until he moved to England to escape the Nazis in 1938. Freud's early work was in cerebral anatomy, and he conducted important work in neuropathology, including aphasias. A crucial point in Freud's career was when he learned that because of his Jewish heritage, his options would be limited in the academic and research worlds. He was encouraged to start a private practice instead. This change of direction led Freud to take his interest in neurology to the professional arena of outpatient treatment. Prior to Freud, most clinical work in neurology had taken place in hospitals, with severely disordered patients. Freud's patients were functional enough to live in the community and come to his office for assessment and treatment. They did not require direct medical intervention. It is important to remember that at that time, the field of academic psychology was focused on "normal" psychological functions and processes. Clinical psychology did not yet exist. People with emotional troubles went to a medical doctor, and if they had neurologically related symptoms, they would be sent to a medical specialist, like Freud.

The result of this professional situation was that Dr. Freud found himself with a series of patients who had what was called hysteria. We have already explored what that was and how it was being addressed at the time, especially through the research of Charcot. In 1885, Freud went to Paris for a three-month fellowship to study with Dr. Charcot. He was deeply impressed regarding the validity and power of both the unconscious mind and hypnosis. He returned to Vienna to apply the theory and techniques with his own patients. What Freud discovered reinforced his belief that the unconscious mind was real and was the primary driver of our conscious attitudes and behavior. However, he lost faith in the effectiveness of hypnosis. Both of these conclusions had major impacts on the twentieth-century understanding of mental illness and mental health. Freud's theories regarding the unconscious mind strongly influenced the subsequent ideas about the origins and development of both healthy and unhealthy personalities. His abandonment of hypnosis drove him to find an alternative method to access the unconscious mind, which led him to the practice (versus the theory) of psychoanalysis. This influenced not only the evolution of psychotherapy as a form of treatment for mental illness but also a tool to increase psychological wellness for those without mental illness but still struggling with a "normal" level of life's distress and impairment. The combination of psychoanalytic theory and practice became a powerful force, convincing the Western world that we are all a little neurotic, that we are so because of early-childhood problems in development, and that self-insight (with or without psychotherapy) can help us lead happier, better-adjusted lives. In fact, it could be said that Freud helped exacerbate a felt sense of unhappiness in the modern world by convincing us that we have a birthright of happiness that was stolen from us by bad parenting, which can be reclaimed through therapeutic means. In the next chapter, we will explore the rise of therapy for "normal" people, the self-help movement, the human potential movement, and the rise of pharmacotherapy for the "worried well," but here we will briefly discuss the basics of Freud's theories of psychopathology and psychological wellness so we can see just how they influenced later developments.

Freud conceptualized the structure of conscious as having three basic levels and three basic functional areas. The three levels are the unconscious, the preconscious, and the conscious. The three areas are the id, the ego, and the superego. Very simply put, the unconscious is truly unconscious and can only be accessed indirectly through such techniques as hypnosis, free association, and dream interpretation. It is the repository of repressed memories, attitudes, and impulses that are unacceptable to the conscious mind. The preconscious includes that mental material that is not in immediate awareness but can be easily accessed when needed. The conscious mind is what people are aware of in any given moment. In regard to the functional areas of mind, the id includes the core biological drives and morally unacceptable impulses. The superego serves as the internalization of culturally acquired morals and ethics. The ego serves as the rational mediator between the two, seeking to find ways to function well in the world, get as much of what one wants as one can, and avoid punishment (outside forces) or guilt and shame (inside forces). In terms of development, babies are born almost entirely id based and hedonistic but immediately begin to internalize the rules and morals of their family and society through the people around them. This creates conflicts between what the individual actually wants and what they *should* want. Children then begin to experience guilt and shame and develop the psychological skills to mediate between the two opposing forces, based on the reality principle, that constitutes the emerging and strengthening ego. Difficulties and challenges in doing this lead to the development of a variety of ego "defense mechanisms," including denial, projection, repression, reaction formation, regression, rationalization, sublimation, and others. Freud also postulated a number of distinct psychosexual stages of development based on a theorized center of pleasure, starting with the oral (0–2 years), then the anal (3–4 years), then the phallic (4–5 years), then giving way to a latency period before puberty and the subsequent adult, genital focus of pleasure.

This confluence of theoretical submodels constituted Freud's approach to the structure and development of personality. It provided a level of depth, complexity, and detail far beyond anything previously proposed. The previous paragraph's description was obviously a gross oversimplification of Freud's theories. However, in a book of this type, whose purpose is to provide an overview of a wide variety of perspectives on a topic, it is impossible to give a proper exploration of any one of them. I will have to beg the readers' forgiveness, invite you to read more thorough reviews of Freudian theory such as those relied on for this brief introduction (Ellenberger, 1970; Mitchell & Black, 1995; Rickman, 1957), and try to make some pertinent points regarding our present thesis.

The questions are, in that regard, what was Freud's basic conception of mental illness and its differentiation from mental health, and what was the impact of those ideas on the world, both professional and cultural? That is still a lot to cover in a short time. One of the best courses I ever took as an undergrad was called The Freudian Revolution, co-taught by two professors, one from the psychology department and one from the history department of my university. The course was pertinent because few people in history have had such a transformative impact not only in their own field but on the wider culture as well. In the Western world, how people see themselves in terms of both mental health and mental illness changed dramatically as a result of the ideas of Sigmund Freud.

I say impact because, as previously noted, there were precursors to Freud's ideas. He did not come up with the concepts of the unconscious, the primacy of emotions in psychological life, neurosis, the importance of sexuality in human psychology, or even the importance of experiential trauma on the etiology of mental illness. However, nobody had integrated these concepts in a highly detailed, holistic model of human psychology, psychopathology, and cultural dynamics. Freud did. This does not mean that he was always right, and one of the main criticisms of Freud has been that many of his ideas are difficult if not impossible to prove one way or the other. In his own time, Freud was accused of being unscientific, which was a bitter pill for him given his background as a highly trained and successful neurological researcher. Alexander and Selesnick (1966) make the point that part of Freud's audacious bravery was his willingness to develop and propose ideas, based on his clinical experience, that he knew would trigger severe resistance from his peers and society in general and could not be fully proven in the then-current state of psychological research. Despite the resistance – and it was severe – Freud's ideas found a receptive audience and spread beyond the tight circle of psychiatry into the wider culture. He was decried by some as a crackpot and a pervert, and many found his ideas profound and valid, especially in the light of evolutionary theory.

The linkage to evolutionary theory is important for two reasons. First, as previously discussed, the theory of evolution was (and still is) highly controversial and quickly became a *public* issue in the nineteenth century. It challenged the prevailing view of human nature as being the creation of God, in His image and immutable. Instead, it proposed an image of human nature as having naturally developed over time, with biological, animalistic roots and as being multileveled, with biological, psychological, and sociological dimensions. Many in the public rejected this notion, finding it both morally objectionable and theologically unacceptable. Many others accepted the idea of evolution and began to use it to better understand themselves and others around them. It was quickly taken up by academics in many fields, not just biology but the emerging social sciences as well, including psychology and what would become known as sociology.

The second reason is that Freud himself supported the theory of evolution and used it as a basis for his thinking about human development and psychological processes involved in personality (Scharbert, 2009). For instance, he conceptualized the id as the functional area consisting of biological drives, such as sexual desire, connected to the organism's need to survive, pursue self-interests, and procreate. These would have developed early in human evolution and been part of our biological inheritance in the same way that drives and instincts are for other primates. Moral and ethical values necessary for group cohesion in a complex social environment would have developed later; thus Freud postulated the superego as emerging later in childhood due to interaction with others in a person's society. The evolutionary value of morality is obvious, but as a "late addition," it can be provided through social evolution rather than a biological inheritance. The natural conflict between the two (I want to take that orange because I am hungry – but stealing is wrong and I might get caught and punished) requires a third psychological process to mediate, thus the ego. The key here is the interaction between the evolutionary need for individual survival (my needs), procreation (species needs), and group survival (our needs). Group success often calls for individual sacrifice, but I want my needs met, so I may refuse and face collective punishment for my "selfishness," or I may choose to be altruistic and enjoy the benefits of being a "hero." Of course, I may feel so strongly about not wanting to be altruistic but not wanting to feel guilty or ashamed for refusing to be a hero that I engage in an ego defense to protect my psyche. I could *rationalize* the problem: "I really wasn't the best person for the assignment anyway." I could *deny* the problem: "It wasn't really a sacrifice they wanted, they just wanted a scapegoat, so it wasn't really altruistic." There are many ways people can deal with unpleasant realities to protect themselves and further their self-interest.

The complicated interplay of development (both general and specific to the individual) and the structure of the personality is central to Freud's conception of mental health and mental illness. Ironically, given his background as a neurologist, Freud's ideas were primarily psychological in nature. He always believed that psychological processes were based on a neurological foundation but recognized that the state of neurological science at the time did not allow him to directly connect the two. Thus, he focused on the psychological and left it to future researchers to make the connection. This framed his career as a counterpoint to mainstream psychiatry at the time, which continued to focus on the physiological and often saw Freud's ideas as elaborate fantasies with no basis in biological science. Sadly, as we have already explored, that dedication to biological science did not (and still has not) lead to a clear understanding of the biological basis of mental illness but only to the creation of a nosological system, which was *assumed* to reflect underlying biology but had little empirical data to support the assumption. This actually left an opening for Freud's ideas to infiltrate psychiatry and become the dominant theory for much of the twentieth century, but that is a story for the next chapter.

Returning to the early days of psychoanalysis, Freud saw human nature as fundamentally conflicted. What the individual wants is naturally at odds with what the environment is willing or able to provide. The baby demands love and nurturance that the mother has only so many resources to supply. The wider environment does not provide everything the child wants when the child wants it and increasingly says "no" and "you must," against the child's desires. "No – you can't have another cookie, no – you cannot hit your sister, and you must do your homework rather than watch television, and you must clean your room." This combination of frustrations and demands naturally creates anxiety, resentment, guilt, and shame. Narcissistic wounding is inevitable. Thus, human suffering is inevitable. In the healthy scenario, the ego develops a strong capacity to mediate the internal and external conflicts, resulting in a sense of integration, confidence, and competence. People can develop an adequate ability to relate well with others, have fun, get a decent amount of what we want in life, and engage in work that is productive, fulfilling, and beneficial to society. In the unhealthy scenario, the individual fails to develop a strong ego and thus is dominated by either the super-ego (becoming moralistic, rule bound, emotionally constricted, and guilt ridden) or the id (remaining impulsive, selfish, emotionally unregulated, undisciplined, immature, and irresponsible). In either case of inadequate ego development, the person often experiences themselves as "split"; in painful conflict with both themselves and the outside world. There is a profound sense of a lack of integration. This sense is not always consciously experienced. It may be so repressed that it only emerges through dreams, free association, and various "Freudian slips" or unwanted behavior, when the competing aspects of the psyche break through the defenses. The superego-dominated individual may find him or herself acting in passive-aggressive ways that are rationalized and cannot be experienced as authentically their own, "I want to do my work well and on time, but I keep finding myself procrastinating, turning in things late and sloppily done, and getting in trouble, which feels unfair." One's own thoughts, feelings, and behavior are experienced as alien or egodystonic (to use more technical phrasing).

One aspect of Freud's conceptional system which is particularly important for our topic in this book is that it is dimensional rather than categorical. In the psychoanalytic model, people are not simply placed in binary categories – psychotic or not psychotic, depressed or not depressed. People are more or less psychotic, more or less depressed. Psychological health is understood along a continuum, ranging from psychotic to borderline to neurotic to healthy. This is quite different than the then emerging medical model in psychiatry, which recognized an increasing number of distinct mental disorders, which people had or did not have. In mainstream psychiatry, then as now, one has schizophrenia or not, and there was little consideration for the idea of being a *little bit* psychotic or the idea of psychosis being a dimension of or functional level of the overall human personality.

When you combine these elements of Freudian theory – the power of the unconscious mind, a complex personality structure, the inevitability of psychological conflict, and the dimensional nature of mental health and illness – you get a model that would powerfully influence society at large. Psychiatry was not just about the small number of severely mentally ill people in the world. It was about everyone and society in general. Entire cultures could be assessed based on how healthy or ill they seemed. Nobody was safe from psychoanalysis. This was amplified by the fact that psychoanalysis offered not just a vision of what was wrong but a cure. It is interesting and not a little ironic that the term "psychoanalysis" refers not only to the assessment of the psyche, but also the psychotherapeutic cure. As always, in this text, the focus is on the underlying concepts of mental health and illness, not treatments. However, it is important in this case to briefly visit the practice of psychoanalysis because it is so bound up with the underlying concepts and the impact of those theories on the wider world.

As noted previously, Freud was not the founder of what we call psychotherapy – the use of verbal discourse to change the course of mental illness. Moral therapy had already been attempted centuries before, but Freud fundamentally changed how it was conceptualized and practiced. Moral persuasion had been utilized to actively change how patients thought, felt, and behaved. Their irrational, delusional thoughts were directly challenged, and there was an active attempt to persuade the mentally ill to lead more moral, self-controlled lives. Doctors even tried to help them develop better problem-solving skills. What they found, however, was that these attempts were not particularly effective, and few in the psychiatric field saw this as a really helpful part of treatment. They focused more on what we now call milieu therapy – providing a safe (from themselves and others), insulated (from the stresses of everyday living), and therapeutic environment (clean, orderly, natural settings, with gardens and friendly, supportive staff), along with a widely varying collection of physical interventions (hydrotherapy, massage, sensory restriction, etc.) of dubious effectiveness. By necessity, these interventions were provided in a residential setting and thus were provided only to the most disturbed and dysfunctional in the population. What we would now call outpatient psychotherapy was nearly nonexistent outside of commonsense advice and informal referrals to visit a spa or go on a relaxing vacation.

Freud changed this picture. He worked in private practice not a hospital or asylum. His patients were well enough to function in the "outside" world. He had to find a way to alleviate their suffering in the context of a normal, noninstitutional life. Impressed by the work of Charcot, he initially used hypnosis to try and alleviate his patients' symptoms. As previously noted, he quickly became frustrated by this approach. He found that not everyone is easily hypnotizable and that the effects were widely varying and inevitably temporary. What he did recognize was that his patients' problems were driven by unconscious forces – what he needed was a better way to access the unconscious and effect changes in the overall psyche of his patients. In regard to access, he discovered that he could identify subconscious elements of the psyche through an interpretation of three things: (1) dreams, (2) unintended behavior and verbalizations, and (3) free association, in which patients were invited to say anything that came to their minds with as little direction or self-censure as possible. In regard to actual change, he found that the amount of emotional intensity connected to this access of material was related to therapeutic *movement*. That is, the fuller the emotional experience of the contact with their repressed content, the more patients actually changed – just talking about it was not enough; there needed to be *abreaction* – psychotherapy had to be a fully lived experience not an intellectual or moral discussion. Thus was the foundation of most modern psychotherapy set – *begin* by exploring a client's life in as full and open a way as possible and provide an intense, emotional experience connected to the client's exploration of their psychological issues. This is best achieved through a therapeutic relationship that is professional, trusting, supportive, and nonjudg-mental. It turns out that Freud's attitude as a caring, responsible, and curious physician who did not judge his patients' symptoms but was intensely interested in understanding and ultimately relieving them was well-suited to achieve such a therapeutic relationship and unleashing the repressed psychological dynamics of his patients.

Because this treatment could be provided on an outpatient basis, it became available to virtually anyone who wanted it and had the resources to pay for it. This effectively shifted most mental health treatment from those with severe mental illness, often in a hospital setting, to the "worried well," functioning adequately, in the community. When that happened, not only did a far higher number of people begin receiving mental health services, but it changed the perception of mental illness. One does not typically receive services for something that is not needed, so the bar for what was considered mental illness lowered considerably. Far more people were not only receiving mental health treatment but actually saw themselves as mentally ill or at least neurotic. This was particularly true for such issues as depression, anxiety, and relationship problems. In the West, people began flooding the offices of psychiatrists for psychoanalysis to deal with a wide variety of psycho-logical problems. While this may have started with patients with what we now call conversion disorders (converting psychological problems into neurological ones), it soon included those with a wide range of psychological and functional problems, more general social difficulties, and generic issues related to unhappiness in life. Psychological treatment began to lose its stigma as being only for severe mental illness and became more acceptable, even normal, for "regular" people. Eventu-ally, disturbed children, acting-out adolescents, and unhappy couples and families would be going to therapy. As the stigma weakened, people would begin talking openly about their treatment and would be called "clients" rather than "patients," and the entire enterprise would become normalized and reconceptualized as build-ing on existing strengths rather than fixing major problems. The point here is that Freudian analysis set in motion a dramatic change in the collective mindset that *normalized* psychological problems as well as the utilization of professional services to deal with them.

By the beginning of the twentieth century, Freud had established a conceptual basis for mental illness as being psychologically based, with profound disturbances of personality development, resulting in a poorly functioning ego and overreliance on primitive ego defenses. But how could this happen? How could things go wrong in one's psychological development? His original belief was that it was the result of profound early childhood trauma, often sexual in nature. The large majority of Freud's patients were women, and under hypnosis (and later free association and dream interpretation), they discovered "repressed" memories of childhood sexual abuse. Freud called it the "seduction theory" and theorized that his patients had been inappropriately seduced and sexually abused by their fathers, leading to intense psychological conflicts, with the original memory of the abuse repressed into the unconscious because of its disturbing nature. This theory was later expanded by various authors to include (1) other types of abuse and neglect, (2) more chronic, lower-level abuse, and (3) the lack of ongoing memory of the abuse being attributed to processes other than repression. This has become a standard part of psychological thinking and is generally referred to as "trauma theory," with the primary factors being stress and adjustment (Noshpitz & Coddington, 1990). Freud himself abandoned the seduction theory, triggering intense criticism (Masson, 1984), and began to think of neurosis as being largely caused by a combination of suboptimal parenting and the individual's distortions of reality. Because virtually everyone receives suboptimal parenting and engages in some level of reality distortion, people are all prone to some level of neurosis. This expanded the net of abusive parenting and subsequent mental illness to include almost everyone.

The treatment was, of course, psychoanalysis. The foundation had been set. Clients (no longer stigmatized by the term "patient") would see a therapist (no longer stigmatized by the term "doctor") in private practice or counseling centers. The therapist would be calm, professional, nonjudgmental, and generally supportive of the client's well-being. The therapist would help the client (1) explore their psychological inner worlds to discover what was not consciously known or understood, (2) identify developmental problems from childhood, (3) unleash powerful emotions associated with these problems to achieve (4) insight and (5) an adjustment of self-concept, better reality testing, better social functioning, and a sense of wholeness and well-being. Western society began to think of human life (both individual and collective) as based on forces below the level of conscious awareness and imbued with conflict. They could have been happy and whole, but childhood problems robbed them of that birthright. They can return to a state of happiness and wholeness if they "work through" the developmental problems they all have. This understanding was augmented with the idea that society itself was deeply problematical and failing to provide optimal conditions for human development and well-being. The treatment here was twofold. First, the individual could overcome societal ills through personal growth aided by psychoanalysis, and second, people could work to identify those ills and change them through social action. Thus, psychoanalysis left the doctor's office and entered the public sphere of political and social activism. This second approach to treatment, through the public sphere, was strongly aided by the loose collection of changes, individuals, forces, and organizations generally referred to as the progressive movement.

THE PROGRESSIVE MOVEMENT

The nineteenth century was a time of amazing change in the Western world. As noted at the beginning of the chapter, a dizzying array of developments converged to transform the West from an agrarian, religion-centered, collectivist, intensely hierarchal society based on traditional patterns of relationships to one that was more urban, secular, individualistic, and egalitarian. It also became more reliant on technology and centralized governmental power. These changes were highly disruptive, even revolutionary at times, unmooring people from traditional sources of self-identity, meaning, and empowerment. They created a "crisis of modernity," forcing people to wonder who they were in this new world, what their values were, and how to discover what Jefferson had referred to as their human rights to "life, liberty, and pursuit of happiness."

There is an almost endless list of topic areas that could be explored to understand this process and its impact on the changing concept of and approach to mental health. In the interest of space, we can only touch on a few of them. We will focus on two in particular: the mental hygiene movement and the social reform movement. These two have been chosen because they have a direct connection to our central topic.

The first topic, the mental hygiene movement, began in the mid nineteenth century. The term was first coined by William Sweetser and then developed by Isaac Ray, who was one of the founders of the American Psychiatric Association. Ray defined the term as referring to the practice of protecting the mind against negative influences designed to damage its qualities and diminish its energy. Its areas of interest included the personal management of exercise, diet, rest, climate, breeding, emotions, and cognition (Ray, 1863). This combination of focus areas indicates the importance Ray and others placed on the integration of the physical and the mental spheres for overall healthy living. They were responding to a concern that urbanization and industrialization were creating living conditions for many Americans that were fundamentally unhealthy for body and mind. The basic idea was that the human organism has evolved a number of functional mental capacities that could be maximized if cared for and managed properly but that many people did not do so. This was seen not just as an individual problem but as a collective one as well, because many of the impediments to healthy functioning were outside of individual control, including such things as access to clean water, food, and air, natural environments, and recreational facilities. People also needed adequate leisure time and freedom from toxic social conditions such as violent crime, racism, sexism, and economic exploitation. These issues are outside the realm of biological evolution. Instead, they are addressed through the process of social progress. As William White put it, "ever higher attributes of social evolution are possible and since it is so, it is incumbent upon human society to discover and attain them" (1917, p. xi). This alludes to the fact that social conditions are a collective responsibility, and thus changing them requires collective action.

This concern was given a particularly strong voice when Dorothea Dix (1802–1887) began trying to help people with mental disorders, was shocked by their living conditions, and exposed these problems to the public, demanding change. It was this latter issue, the demand for change, that made all the difference. The connection between mental health and healthy living habits has been a topic of discussion since the time of the Ancient Greeks (see "The Classical Era"), but there had been no serious claim of a public or government responsibility to *provide* healthy living conditions to impact mental health since the Classical era, when it was seen as a government responsibility to provide public baths, as well as entertainment and exercise facilities.

Dorothea Dix was born in Hampden, Maine, and initially grew up with abusive and alcoholic parents. At the age of 12, she moved in with a wealthy grandmother to escape her traumatic upbringing. Before she was 20, she had already opened her own school and soon began teaching poor and neglected children out of her grandmother's barn. She suffered from depression and poor health her entire life but still had one of the most amazing careers in nursing ever observed. She was a passionate advocate for public health programing, especially as it applied to the mentally ill. She was a central figure in the nineteenth-century reform movement, seeking public funding for asylums, believing that only the government could provide the money and the oversight necessary for the proper treatment of severe mental illness. During the American Civil War, Dix was appointed Superintendent of Army Nurses by the Union Army, and after the war, she continued her crusade to establish and improve the care of disabled veterans, state prisoners, and the mentally ill in America and around the world. Overall, she was a strong advocate for the effective and humane treatment of those who suffered physically and mentally. This advocacy often focused on the responsibility of the government to fund and oversee such treatment. The result of the efforts of Dix and many others in the reform movement was to greatly increase the number and quality of hospitals and asylums throughout America and Europe in the nineteenth century. At a deeper level, they helped establish a perception that it was a public and therefore governmental responsibility to identify and address problems of psychological well-being.

By the early twentieth century, it was clear that mental hygiene books and sporadic efforts at asylum reform were not enough. The mental hygiene movement was officially born when Adolph Meyer co-founded the National Committee on Mental Hygiene in 1909, along with a former asylum patient, Clifford Beers (who famously wrote *A Mind That Found Itself*), and they engaged in multiple projects to prevent the emergence of mental illness (Harrington, 2019). They produced and distributed pamphlets and posters. They arranged traveling exhibitions. By the 1920s, mental hygiene had become a part of many school curriculums and led to full courses in many colleges. In doing this work, the mental hygienists created a new category of people with psychological and behavioral problems that were not yet severe enough for institutionalization – they were the *maladjusted*. This concept subsumed a wide variety of issues, including substance abuse, criminality, poor work habits, social dysfunction, and what we would now call stress. The focus was on proper adjustment or adaptation to the demands of living. This required the ability to engage in appropriate social behavior, do well at school or work, follow the rules of society, and develop an inner sense of peace, calm emotions, rationality, morality, and self-discipline. If the tools of prevention did not work, then early intervention was offered. Outpatient clinics were staffed by psychologists, social workers, and psychiatrists and sprouted up in many cities across America. The focus on prevention meant that there was an effort to identify something called mental health and promote it in any way possible.

The mental hygiene movement had lasting effects on the public, especially in regard to the growing sense of a public responsibility for psychological well-being. The other progressive movement we will discuss had a similar effect. The term "social reform" refers to a loose collection of efforts to create a more egalitarian society. These efforts were connected with the overall progressive movement and included the labor movement, abolition, women's suffrage, environmentalism, immigration reform, anticorruption, and the clean food and drug movement. Nearly every element of modern life was affected, attempting to improve the conditions of life for groups of people who were systematically oppressed or otherwise suffering in the then-current state of affairs, through a combination of social reforms and public (government) policy. We only have space to discuss a few of these. Abolition was arguably the first major social reform movement of the progressive era. It was centered in the Western world, starting in France as early as 1315, when Louis X banned slavery in his country and eventually its colonies. During the Enlightenment, many authors wrote against the evil of slavery as an affront to human dignity and basic equality. England had officially banned slavery by 1700, when Lord Chief Justice John Holt upheld that a slave became free when he or she arrived in England. Already, in the mid-1700s, sectarian radicals fighting the English civil wars had attacked slavery as contrary to the ideal of personal freedom. Despite this, slavery persisted in much of the colonized world and even expanded during the eighteenth and into the nineteenth century. Many Western countries, while banning the practice at home, found it economically advantageous to allow it in their colonies. No doubt this hypocrisy was aided by a racist attitude that saw nonwhites as naturally inferior and thus less deserving of a fundamental right of freedom.

In America, as is well known, the Founding Fathers had reached a compromise on slavery, allowing individual states to decide whether to permit slavery or not. This political expediency reached a crisis point in the first half of the nineteenth century as western expansion led to the creation of new states and an intense fight over whether they would allow slavery. A movement emerged in the North to restrict it, with the ultimate goal of banning slavery across the country. The battle escalated into the most brutal and lethal war of the nineteenth century and ended with abolition, established through the 13th Amendment in 1865. The battle for full social, economic, and political equality of the races continued after the war and reflected the difficulties in changing public attitudes and thus society in general. Despite this problem, the fundamental right of freedom had been legally established, and this strengthened the role of government to regulate such social relations and promote such Enlightenment values as freedom and basic human equality.

The labor movement reacted to industrialism through its concern for safety in the workplace, the use of child labor, and the desire of workers to gain power in relation to business owners who had been free to pay low wages, demand extraordinary hours of work, provide dangerous work conditions, and give no job security. By the end of the era, organized labor had used its increasing power to come closer to leveling the playing field, forcing businesses to institute a 40-hour work week, increase wages and benefits, invest in workplace safety and comfort, end child labor, and respect the right of workers to continue to negotiate for their interests. While organized labor continues to be controversial, it fought hard to promote the interests and dignity of the working class, helping establish the middle class in the Western world and improving the living conditions of millions of people.

The temperance movement was fundamentally a moral crusade, seeking to ban alcohol from public life. The prohibition movement was largely led by religiously oriented women, tired of the widespread moral and societal damage cause by alcohol abuse, including child abuse, public fighting, spousal abuse, financial instability of families, and the general lack of civility stemming from drunkenness. They eventually succeeded in getting the 18th Amendment passed in 1920. Although it was repealed in 1933, the movement succeeded in establishing the idea that the government had a legitimate role in controlling access to mind-altering substances as an extension of promoting the general welfare of society.

The women who led the temperance movement were not only promoting moral behavior in society, they were also establishing themselves as a political force (Hymowitz & Weissman, 1978). This leadership of women in the movement helped to elevate the public image of women as strong, intelligent, thoughtful, politically engaged, and effective. Through their activity, it became harder and harder to argue that women did not deserve equal status as citizens, eventually voters, and then officeholders. This leadership of women extended to other areas of concern as well, including the clean food and drug movement and, of course, women's suffrage. In regard to clean food and drugs, the nineteenth century saw the emergence of industrial-level production of both sets of commodities. As fewer people lived on farms, producing their own food, more and more were living in cities and relying on a fast-growing food production, distribution, and sales industry. This had the benefit of making a great deal of food available to more people at lower cost than was previously possible. Trains made it possible for large amounts of meats and vegetables to be raised in one part of the country and transported to another for sale in large urban areas. Food began to be processed, prepackaged, shipped, and sold on a very large scale. The downside was that the quality of that food was highly variable, and there were no laws controlling that quality. There were no requirements for labeling, shelf life, or even listing of ingredients.

This was also true in regard to drugs. In the nineteenth century, there were no federal laws in America regulating medicines, many of which could be purchased by mail order and often included a variety of potentially addictive (cocaine, heroin) or inert substances that did little or nothing to meet their medical promises and could be downright dangerous or even deadly. This aroused a great deal of concern regarding the health value and safety of these products.

The last of the social reform issues we will introduce is women's suffrage. The term "suffrage" typically refers specifically to the right to vote, but more generally, it has to do with full participation of women in the political life of society. Prior to the nineteenth century, such participation was the exclusive province of men throughout most of the world. In America, women were not allowed to vote and were generally considered the moral and intellectual inferiors of men (Hymowitz &

Weissman, 1978). It must be strongly noted that exclusion from voting, and by extension from all direct power in public life, was not just directed at women. The targets of exclusion included many groups based on race, age, property owner- ship, religion, education or knowledge level, social status, incarceration, residency, disability, and wealth. The focus here on women's suffrage should be considered a single example of a widespread change in the attitudes and practices concerning the question of who has a right to participate actively in the public life of a society.

As recently as 1802, only about 3% of Americans participated in the vote (Keyssar, 2000). The original Constitution of the United States did not specify any nationwide right to vote (with the exception that if a person could vote at the state level, he or she could vote in federal elections), and, like many issues, left it up to the states to decide who could and could not vote. This led to the wholesale restriction of voting rights to a very small percentage of Americans. The first big rise in voting participation occurred in the 1820s and was the result of the removal of land ownership as a condition of enfranchisement in almost all the states. Many restrictions on voting rights remained in place and despite the passage of the 15th Amendment in 1870, which precluded denial of voting rights based on race, color, and previous conditions of servitude. Thus, voter participa- tion was held to less than 20% of the population until 1920. In that year, the 19th Amendment was passed, providing enfranchisement to women.

The story of women's suffrage goes back centuries, and only a few highlights can be covered here. Marie Guyart was a French nun who worked with the Iroquois in Canada in the seventeenth century. She noted that they had female chieftains with the deciding vote in their counsels. The Iroquois, like many other native tribes, had a matrilineal kinship system, with property and social status passing through the female line. Despite her assertions regarding this historical reality, the mod- ern democracies in France, America, and others were typically designed with only males being allowed to vote or hold high-level office. This began to change when a series of principalities including Sweden, the Corsican Republic, the Pitcairn Islands, and the Isle of Man granted women's suffrage. This movement actually started with Sweden in the eighteenth century but gained momentum in the nine- teenth. The American movement officially began with the Seneca Falls Convention in 1848. The first major convention in America for women's rights, it was orga- nized primary by local Quakers, along with Elizabeth Cady Stanton and Lucretia Mott. The convention addressed a number of issues connected to women's rights, including the right to vote. Ironically, Lucretia Mott opposed inclusion of the issue in the convention's Declaration of Resolutions, but the only African-American male present, Frederick Douglass, supported it. The issue continued as a major topic in subsequent National Women's Rights Conventions, which began in 1850. In 1851, Stanton met Susan B. Anthony, and the two formed a strong partnership, advocating for women's right to vote.

While the movement was making limited progress in America, New Zealand first allowed women to vote in 1895, with Australia extending the right in 1902, Finland in 1906, Norway in 1913, Denmark in 1915, and by the end of World War I, England, Canada, Russia, Germany, and Poland. In America, a number of states had passed legislation to allow women the vote in various types of elections, but the country did not pass the 19th Amendment until 1920. African-American women in a number of southern states could not effectively vote until the passage of the Civil Rights Act in 1964. As of the day of this writing, African-American women still face impediments to voting in a number of states, and the United States has not elected a female president or vice president.

Together, these various progressive issues and the social and political movements they produced represent a significant change in modern Western society. The way people see themselves and the empowerment they experience in their lives has been transformed. There are still many who resist this change and believe that life was better in the "good old days." To some extent, this reflects the attitudes of those who feel that they are part of a previously advantaged group that is losing power and primacy in a world that is changing quickly, in unpredictable ways (Jardina, 2019). Rather than being signs of social progress, they see these changes as a disintegration or regression of society. They are particularly sensitive to the relative empowerment of oppressed, nonwhite groups and the role of the government to enforce this change. Ironically, they experience these changes as an assault on their Jeffersonian rights to "life, liberty, and happiness," while those being aided by the progressive movement experience it as a support of long-awaited guarantee of those very same rights.

A question remains, however, about just what the progressive era has to do with our central issue, the conception of mental health and mental illness. To some, this may seem obvious, but for others, it remains unclear. The answer is quite complicated, but I believe it includes a number of components. The first is that mental health is related to a positive sense of self. Sometimes termed self-esteem, this concept refers to a variety of thoughts and feelings about oneself, including the sense of one's value in the world, how *others* think and feel about oneself, and the level of self-efficacy one experiences within his or her society. For many of the groups addressed in the progressive era (women, racial minorities, children, the working class, those with mental illness, immigrants, etc.), it is safe to say that the mistreatment and negative evaluation they received in Western society in general and America in particular had a powerful impact on their sense of self and, by extension, sense of well-being and happiness. Of course, there are many sources of self-esteem, and many people have a high level of resilience, but it can be assumed that the overall population of oppressed groups had to experience some negative psychological impact. For instance, in recent studies, experiences of racism have been found to have adverse effects on both the physical and mental well-being of oppressed groups in society (Hackett, Steptoe, & Jackson, 2019; Jackson et al., 1996).

A second component of the answer is that physical/environmental elements of life impact both mental health and mental illness. These elements include the amount of available leisure time, access to nature, quality of food, air, and water, and availability of quality medical health care. Together, these elements equate to overall quality of life. Through the nineteenth century in the Western world, there was improvement in these elements (improved health care, more food production, increased leisure time) but also a degradation (pollution, increased urbanization leading to less access to nature) and an increasing sense that the wealthy and powerful had access to a better quality of life than that available to the poor and disenfranchised. Quality-of-life issues have become important considerations in the experience and course of mental illness, although significant challenges remain in how to identify them and assess their impact on individual's functioning (Katsch-nig, 2006). Despite these challenges, their impact on mental health was recognized during the progressive era, and the remedy for this unequal distribution of the benefits of modernity was seen by many as using the power of the government to level the playing field.

This last point, using government intervention to level the playing field, itself represents a major component of the answer to the question of the impact of the progressive era on mental health and illness. Prior to the nineteenth century, few saw it as a legitimate role of government to directly intervene in quality-of-life issues. While the Enlightenment championed the concept of democratic, repre-sentative government, it did not promote the idea that government should redis-tribute wealth and other resources to create a level playing field for its citizens. In the nineteenth century, the emergence of Marxian political and economic the-ory helped promote a widely held belief that such redistribution by government was appropriate and necessary for basic fairness and an optimum functioning of society. The experience of capitalism so far had convinced many that this eco-nomic system was good at creating wealth, but it was quite poor at distributing that wealth fairly. The basic idea was that under capitalism, wealth and, subsequently, power tends to concentrate into the hands of a few (bourgeoisie), leaving the large majority (proletariat) exploited and oppressed. The answer for some was to create a socialist system in which economic production and distribution was controlled by a central government enforcing fairness and equality. Ironically, Marx and his followers saw the advanced capitalist nations of Europe and America as ripe for such a revolution, but it turned out to be the less economically advanced countries such as Russia, China, and Cuba that were most open to such a radical change. However, despite the ultimate failure of Marxism to inspire outright revolution in the Western world, it strongly influenced the liberal, democratic revolutions that swept through Europe in 1848, as well as the American progressive movement of the late nineteenth century.

One of the results of this was the creation of the modern political binary of liberalism and conservatism. Liberals, while not typically outright socialists, tend to believe that pure capitalism cannot be trusted to fairly distribute wealth (and there-fore the quality of life it can purchase), and thus government force is required to do so. Conservatives are generally more trusting of capitalism (and averse to the coer-cive power of government) and thus more concerned about the resulting restric-tions on individual freedom. Not surprisingly, leaders of the progressive movement in the nineteenth century tended to be liberals, and they found themselves in con-flict with the more conservative elements of society. The stage was set for a funda-mental public disagreement about the sources of well-being, happiness, and thus mental health. The liberal view became that happiness stems from equality, which must at times be forced from without, while the conservative view was that hap-piness stems from individual freedom, and the proper role of government is not to force equality but to defend individual freedom. It is important to remember, in the context of this text, that these political philosophies developed as idealized visions of the best ordering of society to promote human happiness and well-being. In other words, they are competing models of societal structure, both designed (in part) to maximize mental health.

THE WHITE MAN'S BURDEN, COLONIALISM, AND EUGENICS

So far, this chapter has focused on professional and cultural developments in the Western world of Europe and America. This begs the question of what was occurring in the rest of the world. The answer is twofold. On the one hand, traditional concepts of mental health and mental illness survived in much of Asia, Africa, and South America. Premodern and tribal cultural values, beliefs, and practices continued to dominate for most people outside the West. These factors have been explored previously in this text. On the other hand, the story of mental health and mental illness as it pertains to many of these cultures began to change in the Modern Age, largely as a result of Western colonization. Some of these cultures were radically transformed, with their traditional models virtually destroyed. In other cases, they developed a two-level system, with a traditional model remaining intact (although often "underground") and a Western model increasingly dominating the cultural scene. This was true for most Native American cultures. There were some cultures in which the West had an influence and became integrated in their concepts and practices involving mental health and mental illness. Our previous chapter described such a result in Tibet, where traditional Buddhist concepts were integrated with Western ones. But whatever the level of conceptual and practical incursion, few traditional cultures remained unaffected by Western influence.

One of the primary impacts of this historical dynamic was the effect not just of the change in beliefs about mental health but of the underlying *assumptions* driving the change. In 1899, Rudyard Kipling wrote *The White Man's Burden*, a poem that was written specifically about the Philippine-American war but generally described the "moral duty" of white people to assume control of "less developed" nonwhite people around the world. The central thesis of the poem reflected the view of many if not most white Western people that theirs was a superior culture in virtually every way, and thus it represented a moral good to bring this culture to the rest of the world, voluntarily or not, and thus "help" those people to "rise up." This argument had been utilized in support of slavery, when it was proposed that Africans benefited from whites' management of their lives and introduction of Christianity for their souls. This was thought of in the same way that parents generally think of it as their moral duty to control and educate their children, despite any resistance or thought of a right of autonomy, for their children's greater good. Nonwhites were often characterized as lazy, sinful, impulsive, emotionally immature, intellectually inferior, and generally childlike (Sanders, 1978).

This attitude helped justify an extensive increase in colonialism in the Modern Age, with a shocking disregard for the values, beliefs, practices, and basic human worth of the subjugated peoples. Even Western progressives such as Theodore

Roosevelt maintained an attitude of cultural superiority, enthusiastically supporting American control of the Philippines and appointing William Howard Taft as the first governor of the islands in 1901. He believed that exporting American culture abroad would have an ennobling effect on the world, and he believed that immigrants should set aside their traditional values and beliefs in order to become American. Other progressives, often motivated by religious beliefs, saw it as central to their mission to inculcate their Western, Christian beliefs and values upon the political and social system of America, as well as the rest of the world.

The result of this attitude and associated colonial practice was nothing less than devastating for the people who found themselves placed under the thumb of colonial forces. It also impacted those who were more subtly coerced by well-meaning missionaries, who attempted to "enlighten" native peoples around the world. In 1961, Frantz Fanon wrote *The Wretched of the Earth*, in which he analyzed the psychology of colonized people. He explored the rage, despair, and frustration that follows violent colonization. He showed how such forces disenfranchise the large majority of people, derogates their traditional values and beliefs, exacerbates subgroup conflicts, and empowers a native elite that aligns with the colonizing forces. Every geographical and cultural area of overt and covert colonization has its unique story to tell, but the general impacts of disruption of traditional sources of self-concept, self-esteem, and cultural self-empowerment are universal. To a lesser or greater extent, the attitude of Western superiority disturbs the naturally felt sense of personal and cultural value, instigating reactive rage, passive self-hatred, and often an internalization of the colonial attitude for those natives who then become accomplices in colonization. As noted in the previous section about the impact of sexist attitudes in the West, this leads to an increase in mental illness, along with the obvious impacts on mental health for those who are oppressed.

A corollary movement in the West was the rise of ideas regarding cultural evolution and the eugenics movement. The original development of evolutionary theory focused on changes to physical attributes that would lead to greater adaptability and thus survival. As noted previously, this quickly led to the extension of the theory to behavior and cultural forms of evolution. The idea that culture changes over time, in response to environmental demands, was not new and can be traced back to Aristotle. In the seventeenth century, Thomas Hobbes argued that indigenous cultures were inferior to European culture, which he assumed was the result of Europe's slow progression away from its lowly roots. In the nineteenth century, Herbert Spenser was able to utilize the new biological theory of evolution to develop the idea that humans had originally lived in "undifferentiated hordes" and then progressed into more complex societies, with hierarchies, greater levels of knowledge, specializations, and eventually the sciences and arts (1972). He, like many others at the time, saw increasing complexity as a sign of progress and as naturally superior to simplicity. Thus, evolution was conceptualized as species and cultures becoming more complex and better (a moral value) over time not just better adapted. This was not what Darwin really meant and, as noted previously, has been replaced by the concept of neoevolution. Increasing complexity is only one way that adaptability can be optimized. In fact, germs are very simple organisms, yet they exhibit extraordinary adaptability. Few would argue that the adaptive success of germs makes them morally superior to other organisms – survivability is not a moral value. Spencer's misunderstanding of evolution helped promote the parallel ideas that (1) Western civilization is, from an evolutionary perspective, superior to others and (2) that we should promote those cultural qualities through selective breeding. Selective breeding took two forms. The first was the idea (in various places enforced by law) that superior races should not "mix" with inferior ones. The second was that people who exhibited inferior traits (including mental illness and retardation) should not be allowed to breed at all.

The result of this concept was what we call the eugenics movement, briefly mentioned earlier in this chapter. Described by its proponents as "self-directed evolution," this idea was embraced by people on both ends of the political spectrum and was considered to be at the leading edge of psychology, psychiatry, and the natural sciences at the time (Bruinius, 2006). It began in England but soon took hold throughout most of Europe and America. Frances Galton, a prominent psychologist mentioned earlier, coined the term "eugenics" and believed in a genetic foundation for many psychological qualities and their corresponding behavior, including insanity, criminality, sexual perversion, and laziness, downplaying the possible experiential or developmental factors in such social problems. The result was that tens of thousands of people who displayed such inferior qualities were forcibly sterilized. This occurred in various countries but was most popular in America, where approximately 64,000 men and women were sterilized or forced to have abortions during the movement.

This brutal and racist approach to social improvement was professionally sanctified, especially in the field of psychiatry. Physicians in the nineteenth century were particularly concerned about "nervous degeneration," which was related to the nervous system, thus genetic in nature in their minds, and had been connected to various specific problems, such as alcoholism, feeblemindedness, epilepsy, criminality, and neurasthenia (Scull, 2015). Europe seemed to be awash in neurological decay, which was related to a general intellectual and moral degeneration in society. While some psychiatrists attributed this primarily to the conditions of modern life, many others, like Emil Kraepelin, focused on the influx of Jews and nonwhite races into the European genetic pool as the problem. They were also concerned that acquired social traits could be genetically transmitted to the next generation (Lamarckian evolution) and that the modern welfare state was weakening society by artificially supporting the weak, who would otherwise fail and be "weeded out" by natural selection.

The eugenics movement continued to gain strength into the twentieth century, and although there were those who opposed it, especially those like Freud who proposed a more psychological theory of the development of social problems, it only ended with the horrors of the Nazi movement. While eugenics had been practiced in a slow, quiet way in America, in the seclusion of asylums and other state facilities, the Nazis engaged in a grotesquely aggressive form. They sterilized or killed thousands of homosexuals, the feebleminded, and the mentally ill. They also, as is better known, killed millions of those they identified as racially inferior, including Jews, Gypsies, Blacks, and Eastern Europeans. The world could not turn away from this horror and, at the end of World War II, rejected eugenics as an abusive and wrong-headed approach to social improvement. This rejection was so extreme that for the next 40 years, it became anathema in academic or intellectual circles to consider a biological basis for human psychology or behavior, but that is a story for the next chapter.

PHILOSOPHY AND RELIGIOSITY IN THE MODERN AGE

As noted at the beginning of the chapter, the nineteenth century was a time of intense change, with extremes of technology, capitalism, and practicality on the one hand and spiritualism, Romanticism, and idealism on the other. Many, like William James, were ready to reject the stale authoritarian traditions of Europe. New philosophies, like pragmatism, were ready to help them reject the idea that there were any great, universal truths to discover. At the same time, however, there were forces at play in the Western world that were concerned about the changes occurring in society. They wanted to return to the beliefs and values that they saw as being the foundation of a proper and moral human life.

The Second Great Awakening was not just an American phenomenon but occurred in Germany, England, Canada, and Scotland as well (Hankins, 2004; Orr, 1955). It started in the early nineteenth century as a reaction to the rationalism and religious skepticism of the Enlightenment, as well as the perceived weakening of Christian faith through such modern groups as the deists and the Unitarians. The call was for a return to a more emotional, enthusiastic, and biblically based faith. Church membership soared as many thousands responded to the cry for the restoration of a pure, uncorrupted Christianity, free from intellectual distortions, modern interpretations, and religious political hierarchies. It was about spontaneous, personal experience rather than complicated theology. It was in tune with the Romantic movement in Europe, elevating emotion over intellect. It proclaimed the imminent return of Christ and envisioned the establishment of a truly Christian nation. Thus, when the hoped-for return did not happen (i.e., Millerites and the Seventh-Day Adventists), they turned their attention to transforming American society along the lines of their faith. Ironically, many of these champions of a return to "old-time" religion and values became the core of the progressive movement, and eventually, modern liberalism, which were at odds with many of the values that had originally motivated their activism. At the heart of that activism were the Enlightenment ideals of basic human equality and a rejection of remaining loyal to traditional beliefs because they are supported by authority figures. However, their spiritual foundation was based on a perceived authority of the bible and charismatic religious leaders.

By the end of the nineteenth century, the connection between Christian faith and social activism had combined to form the Third Awakening. Starting in the 1860s and continuing into the early 1900s, this movement was more institutional and socially aware then the Second Awakening. It was supported by the growth of mainstream Protestant churches in the now-established towns of the American West. It also led to the creation of new churches, such as the Christian Scientists and Jehovah's Witnesses. Its ongoing influence was assured through its energy in reaching out to convert others as well as establishing religiously based schools and colleges. It was the Third Awakening rather than the Second that would establish modern evangelical Christianity in America.

Like the progressive movement, the Awakenings of the nineteenth and early twentieth centuries had impacts on the conception of mental health. Religious faith and practice have well-recognized influences on people's self-image and sense of well-being (Koenig, 2012). People of religious faith tend to see themselves as existing in a world that is ordered, understandable, and embedded in a clear set of moral principles. They can see their role and purpose in the world as authoritatively prescribed, with particular rules to follow and practices to perform. Good and evil, right and wrong, correct and incorrect are all categories that are clearly laid out by trusted authorities. Even in a modern society, with religious choices protected by an Enlightenment value of individual freedom, they can choose a faith that aligns with their sense of righteousness. While this makes the choice of faith more complicated than in traditional societies that offer little or no choice, it allows a balance of freedom and authority that is comfortable for many to navigate. The result is a sense of calm assurance that one's values, beliefs, and actions are in accord with God or the gods. One feels aligned with the spiritual truths of the universe. That is a deep comfort indeed.

On the other hand, religious faith can also promote an equally deep sense of guilt and shame when one feels unable to live in accord with one's religious faith or experience other internal conflicts (Geyer & Baumeister, 2005; Miller & Kelley, 2005). Many suffer from self-inflicted punishment, which can manifest as self-loathing, timidity, regular attempts to recommit to one's faith, along with *proper* thinking, feeling, and behavior. This failure to live up to the precepts of faith can also lead to a deep hypocrisy, when one's deeply held beliefs are used to judge others but not integrated in one's own life. From a psychological point of view, such people (and everyone to some extent) protect themselves from self-judgment by focusing on the faults of others. While this protects a certain level of psychological comfort, it creates a profound splitting of the self. The psyche becomes deeply disconnected between an ideal self and a real self. Overall, the relationship between religious faith and mental health is complex and subtle. A source of both comfort and suffering, the one thing that can be said for sure is that the ubiquity of religious faith is testament to the profoundly felt need of people to live in a world that has order, purpose, moral truth, and a creative power.

However, at the same time that these religious movements were occurring, there was a countervailing force at play in the West. Far from the revival tents and Protestant churches of frontier and small towns, there was a different revolution in philosophy happening that would impact how people thought about themselves, the world around them, and the nature of truth itself. The philosophy of the Enlightenment had been largely hopeful and rational – emphasizing human abilities and the paramount possibility and value of rational thought. It invited people to cast off the superstitions and cultural loyalties of the past to create a new world of human-centered institutions, authority, and empirical truth. The philosophy of the nineteenth century came to see such dreams as naive and hopelessly idealistic. Chastened by brutal revolutionary wars during the eighteenth and nineteenth centuries, these philosophers increasingly explored the irrationality of humanity, its deeply conflicted nature, the power of unconscious forces to overwhelm conscious thought and intent, and finally, the ultimate impossibility of knowing much of anything outside the bounds of subjective human experience (Durant, 1926).

The Enlightenment philosophies of the seventeenth and eighteenth centuries, exemplified by Francis Bacon and Spinoza, had exuded confidence in the application of empiricism and logic to understand ourselves and perfect the world. That dream shattered quickly when David Hume pointed out that when Locke proposed that knowledge flows from direct sensation through the mind, he was missing the point that people never directly experience the mind as such, only their awareness of the sensations. Even scientific laws are not immutable but simply the perceived experience of there being a regularity in the universe. That doesn't mean that it is true and that the next experience won't break a rule people think they see. The only thing that is "real" is mathematics, because it follows a strict logic, but even mathematical logic is basically tautological. Still, it is the only "language" of reality that is objective, so if any search for truth is not based on mathematics, it is really only sophistry and delusion, enforced by authority.

This conclusion, which was emerging by the end of the Enlightenment, shocked Immanuel Kant (1724–1804) (Durant, 1926; Millon, 2004; Russell, 1945). Kant was a trim, studious man who rarely traveled outside his native city of Konigsberg, in East Prussia. He was brought up in a strictly religious household but found it increasingly difficult to reconcile his faith with science. Although he wrote about a number of subjects, both philosophical and scientific, it was his work on epistemology and metaphysics that he is best known for. Kant was fascinated by the question of how people develop knowledge and rejected Locke's notion that ideas are built up exclusively through sense perception. Instead, he asserted that the human mind organizes information in preexisting (a priori) categories, an inherited structure of the mind. This suggests two things – first, that to the extent there is external truth to be found, it can only be trusted to the extent it conforms to mathematical or pure logical analysis. Second, to a large extent, what people call truth is really the end result of the mind's capacity to mold sensations to fit innate human categories and modes or laws of thought. Kant called this approach to epistemology transcendental, in that he was asserting that this approach to truth transcended empirical sense experience and focused on the process of correlating incoming data with preexisting forms of conception. In taking this approach, Kant was trying to rectify the rationalists (the world can be validly understood through reason) and the empiricists (knowledge can only be attained through the senses). Kant argued that the mind is the selector, interpreter, and director of the otherwise cacophonous maelstrom of sensation continually assaulting the senses. Beliefs are not shaped by reality as much as they are shaped by the mind itself. In fact, it is the primary *job* of the mind to bring order to chaos – creating perception out of sensation and leading ultimately to conception. Making this job harder is the fact that the mind cannot *know* anything in itself through direct experience but only through the filter of the senses and interpretation. Kant never doubted the reality of the external world, but he raised considerable doubt about the possibility of true objectivity and the ability to trust human conceptions as reflecting reality. This led him to reject the idea of "proving" the existence of God or the validity of any religion. This conclusion, however, did not bring him to atheism or humanism. Kant sought to "save" faith and morality by asserting that there is an a priori sense of moral goodness reflecting a fundamental truth in the world in the same way that the sense of time, cause and effect, and space may be mind-based categories of thought, but these categories *exist* because they reflect real attributes of the world. It would make no sense for the human mind to provide categories of thought that contradict external reality – they are there to assist the mind in making sense of the real world. Thus, Kant saw religion as a practical creation of human societies and felt that it should be judged and directed by a universal moral code, not be trusted to do the judging.

Kant's philosophy, coming at the end of the Enlightenment, set the stage for the next step to come in the Modern Age. His logical assertion of the relativity of truth made it increasingly difficult for others to accept his strained promotion of the absolute and universal in such notoriously subjective and relativistic areas as morality and politics. And so while Kant could have been placed in our chapter on the Enlightenment, he has been placed with the Modernists because the philosophy to come was fundamentally either a building upon or argument with Kant. In general, the nineteenth century response to Kant was a split between those who supported his idealism (Schelling, Hegel, and Schopenhauer) and those who felt his epistemological relativism had not gone far enough – that the logical conclusion of his epistemology was that there were no ultimate truths other than the relativistic reality of subjective thought and experience (Kierkegaard and Nietzsche). The idealists generally supported a religious basis to life, saying that there are universal ideals of goodness, beauty, and social organization. They were the favorites of the Romantic movement, with its idealized vision of human emotions and aesthetics. On the other hand, the relativists sought to expose what they saw as the emptiness of traditional values, which demand people either consciously choose values based on their utility (pragmatism or existentialism) or reject them all together and think of life only in terms of power relations (nihilism). As a leading light of the idealists, Georg Hegel (1770–1831) drew the conclusion that such concepts as God, freedom, ethics, morality, and human progress reflected ontological realities. He built upon these truths to promote idealistic forms of government, religion, and civil society. He felt it was particularly important to consider the role of history in shaping the philosophical views of an era – its zeitgeist. Within philosophy itself, he sought to overcome intrinsic contradictions and tensions, such as subject and object, self and other, and mind and nature, by asserting that they had a dynamic quality that could, over time, lead them to evolve into a unity of thought, or what he called "the absolute idea." This was connected to his concept of God as the Absolute, manifesting the universe through His thought. In other words, the human contemplation of a reconciling of the opposites can lead to a connection with God, which is the ultimate reconciling of all opposites. Romantic idealists of the time found these ideas inspiring, with the underlying belief that God was real and that human civilization was evolving toward an ultimate perfection. Hegel was a favorite of religious authorities, Romantic artists, and political thinkers like Marx who sought to design an ideal political and economic society. He influenced groups as wide-ranging as the American Transcendentalists and the German Nazis. Many critics found Hegel's thought to be fantastical, with flowery and dense rhetoric substituting for serious intellectual analysis of his topics.

Arthur Schopenhauer (1788–1860) can be thought of a transitional figure (Durant, 1926; Russell, 1945; Tarnas, 1991). He certainly shared Kant's position that the world is not directly knowable but is experienced and interpreted by the senses and the mind. He also agreed with Kant's idealism and, in fact, his main point of departure was how far he took that idealism. While Kant had mainly stayed in the arid territory of pure mentation and the ability of the individual to know the world, Schopenhauer was more interested in the "real" world of history and culture. He was interested in the historical foundations of how people tended to interpret the world – their zeitgeist. He was interested in historical movements, art and aesthetics, Eastern philosophy (he was a strong supporter of Buddhism), and the unconscious, irrational drives that he saw as influencing human thought, emotion, and behavior. Like so many of his generation, he was strongly impacted by the violent upheavals and revolutionary fervor in nineteenth-century Europe. They watched European social and political structures disintegrating while many thousands died. Schopenhauer could not sit in an ivory tower, musing about epistemology, without taking into account how these ideas related to real people, with real lives. It probably helped, in that regard, that Schopenhauer was such a difficult character that he struggled to find a safe, comfortable academic position (like Kant enjoyed) and thus was not insulated from the nineteenth-century disruptions of European life and society.

Given this confluence of factors, Schopenhauer directed his work toward what could be called psychology, the dynamics underlying human thought, motivation, emotion, and issues of daily living. As such, he was a major influence on the emerging field of psychology represented by such figures as James and Freud. For instance, he proposed a fundamental human drive to live. He called this drive *will*, and by it he meant a biologically based drive not only to stay alive but to meet all the desires of the individual. It is not surprising that Schopenhauer, a man of intense and often frustrated desires, would place such a drive at the core of his philosophy and human psychology. Rather than the Enlightenment tradition of placing conscious, rational thought at the center of its philosophy, Schopenhauer saw people as driven by the largely unconscious, irrational, and instinctual part of their being. He saw it as being the unifying element of the psyche, providing a powerful center that holds together otherwise disparate thoughts, beliefs, and motivation. It creates what we call personality and character. We are not what we think or wish ourselves to be but what we are invisibly driven to be at the biological core of our being.

If this sounds familiar, it is because this concept would form the basis for Freud's ideas about the unconscious, the id, and libido. Influenced strongly by Buddhism and his own experience, Schopenhauer pointed out that human desires are regularly frustrated and that this results in suffering. As long as the soul is filled with will, a never-ending hunger, then it follows that pain is a constant, and happiness is only the all-too-quick respite from that pain, soon to be followed by a new desire. Thus, life is essentially hopeless because there is no chance of remaining happy by quenching desire, and increasing knowledge only makes it worse because one simply becomes more aware of the ultimate hopelessness of his or her situation.

Only the simple and naive can have some form of happiness, because they still think that they will be happy if they get what they want. And in the end, there is only decay and death. Religion arises from the collective fear of death and the wish for an escape, but the wise can see that this is a schoolboy's dream and cannot join it with any sense of integrity and courage. Since worldly satisfaction (wealth, sex, power, fame, sociality) is an absurd road to happiness, only the wisdom of pure knowledge and a calm acceptance of "what is" can still the turbulent waters of frustrated desire. Through contemplation of things in themselves rather than objects of desire, the individual can find release from the will and come to a place of peace and acceptance.

For Schopenhauer, genius was a description of the man (he did not think women capable of it) who has come to an awareness of the object as it is in the clearest light, not distorted by personal desire or revulsion. Useful pursuits toward this goal included philosophy, science, and even art. Schopenhauer viewed art as the representation of objective truth through intuition, a direct contemplation of the eternal and universal, rather than through empirical research (science) or logical analysis (philosophy). His views on religion were more complicated. He saw most religion (as previously noted) as a naive and perverted "metaphysics of the masses," seeking to make sense of their lives and escape death. However, he also saw a higher potential for religion, if it were to reflect the deeper truth of the futility of Earthly happiness and the need to reduce the subjective, willful "I" of personal desire. He saw some potential in Christianity for this but found its best representation in Buddhism, which promised no paradise after death for believers but placed reduction of the will at the center of all its philosophy and practices. In other words, Schopenhauer replaced the terms "heaven" and "nirvana" with the word "genius," emphasizing the philosopher's preoccupation with thought over theology and emotional experience.

Of unique concern regarding this text's focus on concepts of mental health was Schopenhauer's derogatory attitude toward women. He saw them, as so many did at the time, as innately inferior to men. He not only described women as inferior to men physically, spiritually, morally, and intellectually but blamed them for many of the failings of men. He took the classic Christian view of woman as the "temptress," drawing young men away from their rightful path of spiritual, moral, and intellectual growth and seducing them toward physical lust, materialism, and worldly pursuits. To Schopenhauer, women constituted a nearly separate species, dragging men closer to will and away from genius. In his view, the less men had to do with them the better.

Not only did this reflect the zeitgeist of the age (sadly true of much of the world), but this attitude would continue in the world of philosophy and psychology well into the twentieth century. Obviously, it has continued to persist in various cultures throughout the world up to the present time. It is hard to assess just how misogynistic attitudes affected the self-concept and mental well-being of women in the nineteenth century. As noted earlier in the context of racism, recent research has certainly found that being a member of an oppressed group is associated with having to deal with more stressors than the dominant group, which puts them at higher risk for a variety of mental and physical health problems (David & Derthick,

2018). These authors discuss the findings from a body of research supporting the idea that being a member of an oppressed group negatively impacts both individual and group self-esteem and is linked to a number of negative health outcomes, including poor life satisfaction, depression, anxiety, general distress, suicidal ideation, poor school performance, and drug and alcohol abuse. It can be assumed that the oppressive regard and treatment of women negatively impacts their perceived and actual well-being. It can also be assumed that there is a self-fulfilling prophecy on affect, where the cultural attitude of female inferiority would lead many women to underperform or not even try to perform in areas in which they are told (explicitly or implicitly) they are not the equal of men. Of course, the outright denial of equal access to those areas would impact real and perceived performance as well. This was a particularly intense problem in the nineteenth century, which was more overtly and powerfully misogynistic than the twentieth and twenty-first, at least in the West, and may well have resulted in many of the mental health problems, such as hysteria, that were associated with women at the time.

Returning to the topic of nineteenth-century philosophy, while Hegel, Schopenhauer, and others developed Kant's ideas about idealism, there were some who pursued Kant's insistence that the external world is known only through our senses and our ideas – in other words, relativity. They were the precursors to twentieth century existentialism, and two of the best known were Kierkegaard and Nietzsche. They had a powerful impact on how we approach the search for truth about anything, including concepts of mental health and mental illness. Søren Kierkegaard (1813–1855) was a Danish philosopher, social critic, and theologian who is commonly considered the first existentialist (Marino, 2004). In his religious writings he stressed the importance of emotional, individual experiences through faith. He downplayed the importance of empiricism or objectivity when it comes to spiritual issues or the real lives of human beings. He differentiated subjective truth from objective truth and cared more about what people felt and did than what they knew. His religious faith led him to conclude that human reasoning and logic were poor tools to comprehend truth, which is primarily reached through subjective experience, often through trials and suffering. His writings focused on the primacy of the individual, struggling to find truth, grace, and salvation in a world beset with obstacles to that purpose, not the least of which was an arid philosophy of pure logic and objective fact finding. No evidence would be enough to justify belief in God or romantic love, yet these are objects worthy of human commitment.

This basic question, whether one should believe in something that could not be proven just because it seems like a good idea or is in some way essential to human happiness or well-being, became the central issue of existentialism. The collective answer was no, we have to accept the world as it is, with no evidence for the existence of God, with all truth being relativistic, and thus the call is for people to accept these painful realities and find a way to live in such a world. The existentialists concluded that the only ultimate truth was what the individual created for him- or herself, accepting truth's conditionality, and finding a place of meaning, purpose, and fulfillment (or not) with that subjective relativity. Some were more hopeful about that process (William James, John Dewey, Victor Frankl) and some were not (Friedrich Nietzsche, Jean-Paul Sartre, Ludwig Wittgenstein). It is to Nietzsche that we turn for the last word on nineteenth-century philosophy.

Friedrich Wilhelm Nietzsche was born in 1884 and died at the turn of the century in 1900 and thus provides a fitting end to this century of thought (Aiken, 1954; Durant, 1926; Millon, 2004). He began his career as a philologist, studying Greek and Roman texts. He was the youngest ever assigned the chair of classical philology at the University of Basel. He was just twenty-four years old. He had to resign ten years later because of health problems that plagued him throughout most of his life. He turned to philosophy and produced most of his work over the next ten years before suffering a mental collapse and what some might call a nervous breakdown at the age of 44. He had experienced a series of professional and personal failures, with his books barely selling, being denied multiple professorships, and repeatedly being romantically rejected by the love of his life, Lou Andreas-Salome. He is thought to have contracted syphilis at some point and became an opium addict. He lived most of the rest of his life with either his mother or his sister. It was his sister, Elisabeth, who edited many of his unpublished works after his death and twisted his thought to support her German nationalistic and anti-Semitic beliefs. It was asserted by many during the twentieth century that he was the intellectual and spiritual father of Nazism, but later scholarship has found this to be untrue and reedited his writings to support his original intentions.

One of Nietzsche's main concerns throughout his life was the question of religious faith. At one point, he was on a path to become a minister, like his father, but the more he studied, the more he came to the conclusion that people had created God, not the other way around. He was strongly influenced by Schopenhauer but took the thinker's ideas about the centrality of the human will and its role in creating the known world to their logical conclusions. He wrote on several occasions that "God is dead," by which he meant that Western secular civilization was moving beyond faith and had entered a period of profound cynicism, to the point of nihilism. In a world without faith, the world as it *should be* does not exist, leading inevitably to hopelessness and despair. Nietzsche saw this as a historical moment of deep crisis and called for self-reflection and the need for the moral strength to master the crisis and accept that the main driver of the human soul was the "will to power."

Perhaps it was Nietzsche's failures to attain his desired ends in life that led him to this conclusion, but he attacked Schopenhauer's amorphous "will" combined with idealistic musings about God, as well as the utilitarian's focus on the possibility of happiness and pleasure. Instead, he saw the core human drive as a raw desire to exert one's power in the world, with everything else being secondary to or rationalizations for that. He saw as necessary and heroic the emergence of the Übermensch (overman) who rejects the faith and values of his father, rises above traditional notions of good and evil, creates his own values, and exerts his own will to create a new world for himself. He expressed contempt for the common herd and the democratic ideal of egalitarianism. He saw this as an invitation to conformity and mediocrity. Will Durant (1926) proposed that Nietzsche's loss of his minister father's faith led him to conclude that life was empty and meaningless, and then his obsession with strength, driven by his own weaknesses, led him to exalt power as the only real value in life. In other words, it was his failures in life, without faith to bolster his spirits, that caused Nietzsche to be obsessed with the idea of power.

It is important to point out that the promotion of will and power to the highest moral virtues was also a direct consequence of the emergence of the theory of evolution. Simply put, if survival is the ultimate goal of existence, and success in that endeavor goes to the fittest, then the only real virtue provided by nature (the real world) is to be fitter than one's competitors. Putting aside the evolutionary advantages of love, cooperation, and altruism, many thinkers of the nineteenth century (Nietzsche and Spencer were the most prominent) focused on the competitive side of the coin in the evolutionary game. Strength, speed, aggression, and intelligence became the hallmarks of evolutionary success. Kindness, generosity, and caring for the weak were symptoms of a decadent and degenerate culture, slipping into decay after enjoying a bloom of success, which had been driven by the more competitive forces. Such a culture would soon be overtaken and destroyed by younger, more aggressive cultures, as the Greeks and the Romans had experienced. Nietzsche saw this pattern occurring repeatedly through history and called for a renewal of the aggressive spirit in Western society. This led him to champion the emergence of the German state and the easy assumption that he would have supported Nazism if he had still been alive for it.

One interesting part of his philosophy was Nietzsche's interest in the arts. He had dabbled in poetry in his early 20s and was a fair pianist. He was a friend of Richard Wagner at one point and saw in the arts the highest expression of the human spirit. In his view, if the real world could provide the necessary spiritual and moral balm for human existence, the only antidote for complete despair rests in the esthetic. Artistic creation and contemplation are the only experience of moral justification for the world and both individual and collective human existence. For Nietzsche, the extreme pessimism of the nihilists was a sign of decay (the luxury of wallowing in the emptiness of negativity) and optimism a sign of naive superficiality (refusing or unable to see the truth of reality). Therefore, the tragic embrace of reality is the response of the strong, who can face the horror of reality, seek an intense and legitimate experience of life, and experience an ennobling of that experience through the arts.

This conglomeration of impulses – his adoration of the heroic individual and culture, his belief in the cyclical nature of history through periods of evolutionary growth and decay, and his faith in the arts to ennoble both the foundational amorality and meaningless of life and need of humanity to find value and meaning anyway – led to one of his greatest works, *The Birth of Tragedy*. In that book, Nietzsche used the mythology of Ancient Greece to form a meaningful story about the patterns of human personality and the trends of history. In some ways it served as a counterpoint to his concerns about the underlying absurdity and meaninglessness of life. It was his antidote to nihilism and pessimism, if you will.

To do this, Nietzsche focused on the stories of two Greek gods, Dionysus and Apollo. He saw Dionysus as representing the emotional, instinctual, and energetic side of life. Interestingly, he saw this aligned with the aggressive will and the dynamic rise of culture. Apollo he saw as representing the thoughtful, refined, and aesthetic side of life and therefor aligned with the decay of society. This put him at odds with many in the West who interpreted the intellectual, self-controlled aspects of society along with the "high arts" as reflective of progress; culture on the ascendant. The more impulsive, emotionally driven elements of psychology and culture they thought of as "primitive" signs of an inferior culture: childlike and immature. Ironically, it appears that although Nietzsche wished to be Dionysian, he was really more Apollonian in nature and likely experienced a great deal of self-inflicted suffering as a result.

In any case, this approach to historical and personality interpretation was quite novel and, after an initial phase of intense criticism, would become highly influential in the twentieth century. Sigmund Freud and Carl Jung borrowed heavily from Greek and other mythologies to understand human nature, and Jung in particular was fascinated by Nietzsche and heavily influenced by his work (Bishop, 1995). Jung agreed with Nietzsche's basic conceptualization and saw Western culture as overly rigid and Apollonian, thus energizing a compensatory alternative, the Dionysian. Jung called this process (the idea that any extreme dynamically leading to its alternate) enantiodromia, and thus Nietzsche's concept of the Dionysian superman as the natural result, or correction, for Western culture's overemphasis on the calm, rational, self-denying Apollonian ideal. Nietzsche did not live to see the horrors of the First and Second World Wars. If he had, he may have softened his affinity for the amoral, instinctual life of power. Jung did live through these historical experiences and became quite wary of unleashing Dionysian energies in the world. Despite their reservations, Jung, along with Freud and the general thrust of psychotherapy in the twentieth century, would generally encourage their clients to soften the superego bonds to Apollonian rationality and self-control and to enjoy a more spontaneous, emotional, self-interested approach to life. The Gestalt call of the 1960s to "lose your mind and come to your senses" was the natural result of this movement, first propagated by Nietzsche nearly a hundred years earlier. While Nietzsche's life was no calling card for the utility of his philosophy of life, that philosophy itself has colored the Western approach to mental health ever since, pitting the emotional against the rational, the audacious against the cautious, and the transcendent against the mundane.

CONCLUSION

By the end of the Modern Age, in the early part of the twentieth century, the professional fields of psychology and psychiatry were set but far from settled. Psychiatry was split between, on the one hand, its empirical, medical model (concerned with diagnostic categorization and the neurological underpinnings of mental illness) and, on the other hand, its revolutionary new subfield of psychoanalysis, based on an intuitive, dynamic model, concerned with the unconscious mind, early childhood development, and inherent conflicts within the psyche. This split would continue well into the twentieth century, when the rise of psychotropic medication and academic, psychology-based psychotherapy would lead to the hegemony of the medical model in the psychiatric world. Conversely, psychology had emerged as an academic field but was also splitting apart between those who sought to understand the normal, everyday workings of the human mind and those who dared to tread in the field of psychiatry, exploring mental illness, including its definitions, roots, and treatments.

While these professional developments were occurring, the nineteenth century saw the emergence of a number of powerful ideas and movements that would impact how people understood both mental health and mental illness. The theory of evolution exploded into consciousness, challenging traditional concepts of human nature. Are we "made in the image of God," morally fallen but spiritual in nature, seeking for restoration of our religious birthright to "sit at the right hand of God"? Or instead, are we evolved animals, not fundamentally different from other primates, driven by our biological drives, self-creating our moral values, and at our supposed best, working together cooperatively to survive and enjoy our lives more? The philosophers of the time weighed in, often seeking to defend the Christian view, admitting that it could not be empirically validated but was nonetheless a valuable part of human life. In other cases, the philosophers took a harder line, proclaiming the end of all religious faith, asserting the need to embrace the subjective contingency of all human knowledge, and either lamenting or actually celebrating the idea of the "good life" being about finding individual meaning and purpose, and putting forth all one's energies to get what one wants in life, with morality being a relativistic concern.

While these professional and philosophical changes were occurring, there were also powerful political and cultural movements happening that transformed the field of our concern, especially in regard to concepts of mental health. The modern, industrial age led to the empowerment of women, minorities, the working class, and the poor in ways that were truly revolutionary. These groups began to organize, fight back against being ignored and/or dominated by mainstream society, and enlist the aid of democratic governments to "level the playing field" of life, protect their interests, and eventually (mainly in the twentieth century) fund their needs (education, physical health care, mental health care, housing, food, etc.). This progressive movement, at odds with traditional hierarchies in society, changed the self-concept of huge masses of people, along with their conception of individual and collective happiness and well-being. It set the stage for twentieth-century liberation movements, with their accompanying concepts of self-esteem and self-efficacy. By the 1960s, people would be saying "the personal is political," embodying the attitude that individual aspirations and happiness could not be separated in a meaningful way from collective and government action. Whether one feels sympathy for the drive to allow all adults to vote or is repelled by the abuses of the eugenics movement, the nineteenth century established the idea that personal well-being is connected to group advocacy and government policy and action.

Together, these changes would accelerate in the twentieth century. The fields of psychology and psychiatry would transform and be joined by a slew of new academic disciplines related to human wellness, such as sociology and women's studies. Concepts of mental health would increasingly extend to liberation movements, multicultural concerns, and even psychopharmacology. The battle between biological, evolutionary, and experiential models of mental health and mental illness would take on new dimensions and intensity. There would be debates about the normalcy of issues ranging from antisocial behavior to homosexuality and gender identification. The discussion regarding the fundamental issue of what is true and if there is any such thing as objective truth would go to new extremes. The twentieth century would become a battleground for competing models of mental health and mental illness, both in academia and on the streets, and that is where we will go next.

CHAPTER 8

THE POSTMODERN ERA

As the world entered the postmodern era, early in the twentieth century, a number of historical events were transforming the modern world. The First World War was a horrific event, tearing apart the political, economic, and social fabric of Europe. Millions died, empires were destroyed, and psychological thinkers like Freud and Jung seriously questioned their positive, hopeful views of human nature. A new breed of philosophers, like Sartre and Foucault, pushed the idea that truth was largely a matter of who held power to control a narrative and that ultimately, what was real was subjective and relativistic, rather than objective and empirical. People began to question many of the institutions, values, and beliefs that had previously given them meaning and stability in a changing world. Society was changing so fast that people began talking of generation gaps, "lost" generations, yearning for the "good old days," and seeking escape from the stress through drugs, cults, radical political movements, and self-help books. Looking back seemed preferable to looking forward, with fears of nuclear war, pollution, global climate change, and a social landscape that was increasingly unfamiliar and unpredictable. Despite this, many remained hopeful, focusing on the positive aspects of the changes around them, including a more egalitarian attitude about people, respect for and even celebration of diversity, the breakup of the colonial system, an appreciation for the blessings of modern science, growing wealth, and, ultimately, hope that humanity could address its problems and move forward on a trajectory of progress and enlightenment. This is the Postmodern age, and the questions regarding mental health and mental illness present a fascinating story.

THE STORY OF PHILOSOPHY – PART ONE

The story of philosophy in the twentieth century begins with modernism. This may sound strange, considering the title of this chapter is "The Postmodern Age," but the first part of the twentieth century was still dominated by the modernist perspective. Postmodern philosophy would come later and become dominant by the end of the century. At the beginning of the century, the Western world was amazed by the material progress that had been occurring over the last 50 years. The industrial revolution was transforming how people worked and how they lived. The invention of the internal combustion engine, the electric motor, the electric light, the telephone, and a wide range of medical technologies had changed people's lives. By the middle of the twentieth century, these and many other inventions had transformed society. In the mid-nineteenth century, the large majority of people lived on small farms, half their children died before reaching adulthood, they rarely traveled more than 50 miles away from where they were born, and they were deeply embedded in the culture of that 50-mile circle. By the mid-twentieth century, nearly half of Americans lived in cities, the large majority had jobs in companies, the population was swelling, and they could get on a train, into their car, or even on a plane and travel as far from their home as they liked. During this revolutionary period, people looked around and realized that the world of science and technology was right – not morally right but effective. It understood the real world, could manipulate that world, and had brought blessings barely imagined in the past. The musings of the Romantics in the nineteenth century seemed weak and out of touch. You think we can't know what is real? You think emotion is stronger and more important than reason? I'll laugh as I drive to the supermarket to pick up some homogenized milk and go back to watch *I Love Lucy* on my new television. Human progress wasn't just a dream; it was materially real.

Academic philosophy shifted from the Romantics and the German idealists to analytic philosophy. Its focus was not on the big ideas like morality, ethics, social order, or how to live a fulfilling, meaningful life. Led by a new generation of philosophers including Ludwig Wittgenstein and Bertrand Russell, its interest was formal logic and conceptual analysis. The goal was conceptual clarity, especially in regard to known facts, not fanciful ideas about ultimate truth. Because of this, for the first time in the history of philosophy, the work began to merge with mathematics, asserting that the way language was used in most philosophy was vague, tautological, and, in the end, basically nonsense. Any conclusions in the areas of ethics, aesthetics, and theology were unprovable and thus reflected nothing but personal opinion. This approach, referred to as logical positivism, asserted that philosophy, as an academic science, actually has a very limited role. It should provide the intellectual tools to clarify thinking not divert into areas where such clarity is ultimately impossible.

This philosophy held little interest for the wider public. Philosophy would no longer be about people's emotions, souls, or dreams – it was about properly describing the workings of the mental machine. This was not a particularly exciting idea for the public, nor could the mathematics-laced papers be easily understood beyond a tight circle of academics. The primary dynamic that had wide influence was how this new philosophy *reflected* societal change during the first half of the twentieth century. The modern narrative of material and intellectual progress, based on rational and empirical analysis, extended to the arts, sciences, and even architecture. The idea was to strip away the emotions and dreams from life and focus exclusively on its utilitarian essence. Things and, by extension, people were valuable only for what they could do or produce. Modern dance stripped away the formalistic displays of ballet to expose the raw foundation of movement. Modern music explored atonality to create a direct presentation of ideas, ones that were more intellectual than emotional. It became an exploration of form rather than an appeal to the senses. Modern architecture stripped buildings of all artifice to reveal pure utilitarian design with basic, geometric forms. Painting and sculpture dropped any pretense of human aspiration in order to explore basic color, shape, and material presence. At its core, the Modern movement was about humanity emerging as machines, serving a utilitarian purpose but having no soul. We can explore and understand its constituent parts, its essence (the thing-in-itself), but any reflection of emotion, what it means in the context of human dreams and need for beauty and deeper meaning, was considered the frothy indulgence of an earlier age. The factory is real and produces real things. The airy dreams of the

Romantics could not be measured, cannot be logically validated, and thus do not really matter.

It did not take long for this approach to life to hit a harsh wall. The cold, grey block buildings that sprang up across the communist world, as well as the West, inspired little love or comfort. Few people wanted to become a "company man" in a stiff black suit, with a narrow tie and a crew-cut hairstyle. Few women felt satisfied living in a square suburban house, in a preplanned neighborhood, cooking frozen dinners and "keeping up with the Joneses." Few people wanted to hear atonal music. Modernism quickly shifted from being a sign of human progress to being part of a modern nightmare. The cold emptiness of modern culture, with no morality or soul, inspired a deep reaction. In some places, especially those with severe economic problems, it energized a return to the societies' cultural roots. This was the case in Germany in the 1930s. In a desperate state, following the loss of WWI, the German people turned to the National Socialist Party, which promised it could save the country by embracing an idyllic image of premodern German culture. In America and much of Europe, modernism lasted longer but met its demise when millions in the post–WWII generation (baby boomers) rejected their modernist parents and dove into the emotional, more humanistic depths of sex, drugs, and rock-n-roll.

In the final accounting, modernism failed because most people did not want to be machines and did not want to live like ones. They wanted their lives to mean something, their emotions and dreams to matter, and they wanted to be surrounded by a cultural world that reflected that. They wanted beauty and excitement. They wanted natural environments, not cold concrete. Although there were obviously other factors involved, the demise of communism reflected this reality. Most people don't want to be cogs in the machine of the state. They typically prefer the messiness and "frothy nonsense" of human emotions, dreams, and aspirations. There will always be a certain element in the human character that recognizes and embraces the cool, machinelike efficiency and utilitarianism of modernism, but the human spirit always seems to cry out for more.

THE STORY OF PSYCHOLOGY

As the twentieth century was entering its second decade, the field of academic psychology was a few decades old and going through a dramatic change. In the nineteenth century, the field had mainly been focused on trying to figure out how the mind processes information to create consciousness and carry on its normal, day-to-day mental duties. Whether one supported the structuralism of Wilhelm Wundt or the functionalism of William James, the primary issues involved normal, everyday psychological functioning rather than human happiness or mental illness. As a consequence, those developments did not easily translate into interventions to either increase mental health or alleviate mental disorders. By the early twentieth century, this was changing. More and more, psychologists were addressing the *problems* of living, with an eye toward how to create change to improve people's lives. This approach, initially termed "applied psychology" and later relabeled "clinical psychology," was first promoted by Lightner Witmer (1867–1956), who studied under Wilhelm Wundt and became the head of the psychology department at the University of Pennsylvania. He began to work with children with learning problems, opened the first psychological clinic in 1896, and established the first journal in clinical psychology in 1907 (Hunt, 1993; Leahey, 2013).

Behaviorism

Another early psychologist who took a serious interest in learning theory and working with children was Edward Thorndike (1874–1949). His work on the learning process and behavioral analysis was directly applicable to the psychology of education. His focus on the law of cause and effect influenced the development of behavioral theory, which not only became a field of its own in psychology but was particularly useful in the school setting, where teachers are understandably focused on overt student behavior, and parents tend to find a behavioral approach in the school more acceptable than other, more controversial and intrapsychically oriented theories in psychology. Educational psychology was slow to catch on, but it gained momentum, and the role of applied psychology in the field of education has been profound and sustained. By the mid twentieth century, this approach would crystalize into what we now call school psychology. In 1954, the American Psychological Association held the Thayer Conference, at which the roles, functions, and required training would be laid out for school psychologists. At the time of the conference, there were only about a thousand school psychologists. As of 2007, there were approximately 76,000 school psychologists in the world (Jimerson, Stewart, Skokut, Cardenas, & Malone, 2009). By 2014, approximately a third of the 106,500 licensed psychologists in America worked in schools (American Psychiatric Association, 2014).

Applied psychology was not just for schools. Over the course of the twentieth century, principles of psychological functioning and change would be utilized in a wide variety of subfields. These included such areas as psychopathology (clinical), counseling, criminality (forensic), sports, organization, business management, and advertising, to name a few. What made much of this possible was the fact that a new core theory of psychological functioning and change emerged in the first half of the twentieth century. It challenged Freud's psychoanalysis for legitimacy and had the distinct advantages of being considered more scientific, academic, and easily understandable and was thus more acceptable to the public. That theory was behaviorism.

We have already introduced Thorndike, a psychologist of such profound intelligence and dedication who, over the course of his career, wrote 50 books and 450 articles, on subjects ranging from educational psychology and learning theory (as mentioned) to social psychology, industrial psychology, and language acquisition. He was initially fascinated by James's ideas, but as a graduate student, he chose to do research on the intelligent behavior of chickens! He noticed that the chickens in his study were able to learn and solve problems. Obviously, the chickens were not thinking through their challenges in deep, philosophical ways. Instead, a much simpler process had to be occurring. Thorndike called it "connectionism" and postulated two basic principles of learning. The first he called the "law of effect," which stated that organisms will do more of what leads to pleasure or success and less of what leads to unhappiness or failure. Some stimulus–response connections will weaken and others will strengthen based on the organism's satisfaction with the outcome. Finding paths through mazes that lead to corn are reinforcing for the chickens to continue following those paths. The other law he called the "law of exercise," which stipulates that cause–effect connections strengthen with repetition and the level of reward associated with them. Do something a lot while getting a good reward and organisms will form a very strong connection to that behavior. Pretty simple stuff, but it was being studied in a laboratory, had the legitimacy of academic and scientific status, and could be applied in a wide variety of settings. In fact, much of its power derives from its simplicity. Anyone can understand the basic principles, making it nonmysterious and easy to accept. In contrast, psychoanalysis relied on the concept of an unconscious mind with a will, values, and beliefs of its own that contradict the conscious attitudes of the conscious mind. Do I really, secretly want to sleep with my mother and kill my father? Where is that found in a laboratory? Prove it is true. You can't, but you can provide rewards for your children to get them to do their homework and clean up their rooms more often. That is science people can get behind!

While Thorndike (along with Ivan Pavlov) provided the basic theory, it took a more charismatic character to sell it to other psychologists and the general public. John Watson (1878–1958) rose from humble beginnings as the son of a violent, unsavory, dirt-farming father who abandoned his family when John was 13 (Hunt, 1993; Millon, 2004). John often got into trouble as a child, was violent himself, and was famously emotionally cold his entire life. After a rough start, he aggressively rose to the top of his field, becoming the chair of psychology at John Hopkins University. He launched the behaviorist movement then became caught up in an extramarital affair with a student, which led to his getting fired from the university. He then had a successful second career, applying his behavioral principles in the private sector with a major advertising firm. This combination of applications, one being academic and the other practical and economic, helped establish behaviorism as both empirically sound and practically useful. In his extensive animal research, Watson had established the power of behavioral methods of behavior change. In his writing, he aggressively rejected the notion of underlying mental processes in behavior and championed the idea that behaviorism was the only legitimate subject for the entire field of psychology.

> Psychology as the behaviorist views it is a purely objective experimental branch of natural science. Its theoretical goal is the prediction and control of behavior. Introspection forms no essential part of its methods, nor is the scientific value of its data dependent on the readiness with which they lend themselves to interpretation in terms of consciousness.
>
> (Watson, 1913, p. 158)

The work of Watson was not confined to behavior itself, though. He asserted that emotional patterns could be behaviorally shaped as well. In 1919, he started a research project that would become one of the most famous experiments in the history of psychology. He conditioned a one-year-old boy to develop a phobia of rats then generalized that fear to include other furry objects such as rabbits and even wool. Setting aside the obvious ethical problems of traumatizing a young child in the interest of psychological research, Watson's findings regarding "Little Albert" were profoundly influential and gave credence to his belief that behavioral conditioning was the underlying force driving all human cognition and emotion not just overt behavior.

One of the hallmarks of behavioral theory is that the core value of human behavior is seen as adaptability. In other words, it is not concerned with morality per se but rather with what *works*. However it is accomplished, behaviorism says little about what *should* be reinforced other than that moral beliefs themselves are rewarded or punished, leading to their increase or decrease, just like overt behavior. Behaviorism proposed that because values and beliefs are simply another behavioral product, they did not mean anything beyond their adaptive utility to a group that chooses to promote them and thus reinforce their existence in others.

In regard to mental health, therefore, the basic idea is that beliefs, values, and behavior that adaptively align with powers of reinforcement (parents, friends, social leaders, teachers, politicians, therapists, etc.) will lead to success for the individual. He or she will do well professionally and socially. This should lead to a sense of happiness and well-being. If a person's beliefs, values, and behavior are out of alignment with "the powers that be," then the result is conflict and failure, which engenders feelings of shame, guilt, and self-loathing. This can be extended to problems we associate with mental illness. For instance, drugs and alcohol tend to be intrinsically rewarding and thus easily lead to addiction. Other behaviors, like developing a successful career, are much slower to become rewarding, and thus it is hard to get up in the morning to go to law school, but it is easy to stay up the night before, drinking with friends.

Even less self-evidently behavioral problems like depression can be explained in behavioral terms. Depression is an unpleasant state and thus acts as an adaptive, endemic warning system, telling people that how they are behaving is not working well. In behavioral terms, it is a form of negative reinforcement to motivate people to engage in more adaptive behavior or, conversely, a form of punishment to motivate them to stop engaging in maladaptive behavior. One can also look at this from a developmental perspective, postulating that depressive attitudes and emotions were likely reinforced in the depressed person's childhood. Being happy, positive, and hopeful may have been discouraged as naive and childish. This would be particularly true if an influential social learning model, such as a parent, was also depressed.

But that is not where the story ends. B.F. Skinner was a behaviorist who did not just describe a science or technology. He also proposed a utopian society, designed along behavioral lines of course (Skinner, 1948). The main components of Skinner's ideal society include behavioral engineering to assure mutual cooperation, efficiency, and continual experimental improvement. The community would be strongly hierarchal, with a committee of "planners" who make policy and are chosen by the "managers" not the "workers." It would be egalitarian and seek to avoid many of the common problems of human society, such as cults of personality, corruption, and management that is not in the interest of the general community. The aim is to create a society that is simple, self-sufficient, strongly focused on everyone working toward the well-being of the community, and organized along behavioral lines – meaning that there are clear, consistent processes of operant conditioning to keep everyone working smoothly together toward the same goals and, presumably, happy.

Not surprisingly, Skinner's behavioral utopia met with a great deal of criticism. It was negatively compared to two similar novels from around the same time, Aldous Huxley's *Brave New World* (1931) and George Orwell's *Nineteen Eighty-Four* (1949), which were both dystopian stories of similar authoritarian, programmed societies. Most critics felt that Skinner failed to recognize the problems associated with such a society. A typical response was that of Harvey Gamble Jr., who was primarily concerned with the lack of human freedom and thus dignity in Skinner's vision. Gamble described the Walden Two community as a "perfectly efficient anthill" (1999, p. 3). This criticism of Skinner's utopian society mirrors criticisms of behaviorism generally. Critics say that it promotes behavioral technology to increase the adaptive operational efficiency of people within society but fails to account for any other human values except adaption and efficiency. It appears to be just as at home in totalitarian societies as democratic ones. Skinner himself had humanitarian impulses and no interest in creating totalitarian states. It just wasn't clear how his model would effectively avoid that, except that the planners would be part of a committee, they would have term limits, and they would be chosen by the managers. These "protections" would still be vulnerable to all the human foibles present in any other human-run system but without a truly democratic process.

Before moving on to psychoanalysis, however, we need to explore a late addition to behavioral theory. By the 1960s, a great deal of work was being done to understand the processes of cognition. Behaviorism had become the primary focus of academic psychology from the 1920s through the 1950s, but there was a rising level of criticism aimed at it, mainly based on how limited it was in understanding the full range of human psychology. It was obvious that there was a more complex cognitive process going on than was explained by behaviorism. This criticism became quite pronounced and publicly persuasive when Noam Chomsky joined the chorus of rebuttals (2008). The result was a revolution in academic research, exploring such cognitive processes as attention, memory, perception, problem solving, creativity, and language use. While little of this work was directly connected to issues of mental health and wellness – it was developing models of normal mental functioning – the findings were quickly integrated into a new model and practice of psychotherapy called cognitive-behavioral therapy (CBT).

This is important for our topic not to explore how CBT works therapeutically but in looking at how it conceptualized mental health and mental illness. Basically, the idea is that beliefs and ways of thinking can lead to people being more or less effective in their lives and feeling better. One of the primary factors in this is *realism*. Do a person's beliefs reflect reality? To the extent they do, that person will be more likely to make decisions and take actions that are effective and achieve personal success. This should translate into a greater sense of well-being. Another factor is *dysfunctionality*. Many beliefs are not grossly unrealistic but are distorted and lead to poor functioning and unhappiness. For instance, if a person believes that *everyone* must love him or it proves he is an unlovable person, then he is doomed to unhappiness. That thought could be replaced with one that is more realistic and functional, such as, "as long as at least one or two people love me, that would show that I am lovable." This replacement belief is more likely to lead to better relational outcomes as well as a sense of self-worth and happiness. Thus, in the cognitive-behavioral model, the emphasis is identifying realistic and adaptive thoughts, beliefs, and behaviors. The more a person experiences these thoughts and translates them into effective action, the better off he or she will be in life. Mental illness – especially depression and anxiety – arises from the combination of unrealistic and maladaptive patterns of thought and behavior (Beck, Rush, Shaw, & Emery, 1979).

Thanks to John Watson, B.F. Skinner, and the cognitive psychologists, academics, especially in America, reveled in the idea that psychology was now a "real science," and behaviorism, now closely associated with cognitive psychology, became the dominant model for the next 40 years. It was closely aligned with modernist philosophy and its focus on the utilitarian ideal of an efficient and adaptive society. In both its theory and practice as a therapy, the cognitive-behavioral model strongly promoted a conception of mental health as being based on effective, adaptive behavior, motivated by realistic, functional thought processes. It has remained to this day a central pillar of psychology, despite the challenges posed by other theories of human emotion, motivation, and, subsequently, behavior.

Psychoanalysis

The main model that behaviorism challenged was psychoanalysis (the word applies to both the theory and the clinical practice), which, because of Sigmund Freud's background as a medical doctor, had become entrenched in the medical field of psychiatry. Psychoanalysis became and remained the dominant model of mental health and mental illness in the field of psychiatry until the 1960s, when the success of psychotropic medications began to erode its standing. By the 1980s, the reemergence of the physical brain as the etiological foundation of mental illness signaled the end of psychoanalysis in psychiatry, and it became an independent model, with its own adherents and schools of training as a subfield of psychotherapy, but it lost a great deal of influence in the realm of conceptualizing mental health and mental illness, especially in the medical world.

Before that happened, however, psychoanalysis developed so far beyond its Freudian roots that it ended up being retitled *psychodynamic* and inspired many offshoots, including Anna Freud's *ego psychology*, Alfred Adler's *individual psychology*, Carl Jung's *analytical psychology*, John Bowlby's *attachment theory*, and Heinz Kohut's *self psychology*, just to name a few. From the very beginning of Freud's success and gathering of adherents to his theory, there were dissenters (Alexander & Selesnick, 1966; Ellenberger, 1970; Mitchell & Black, 1995). This is not surprising, given that the theory was revolutionary yet had almost no empirical research support for its suppositions. Its basis of knowledge came primarily from interpretations of patients' dreams and behavior, proposing that the true meaning of both was often hidden or even reversed from what it appeared to be. It was up to the psychoanalyst, working from Freud's theories, to figure out what they *really* meant. This can easily become a form of tautological thinking. Because the truth is hidden, the theory has to inform the observer what is true, explaining all in light of that theory. This circular reasoning was maddening to those not already inclined to believe in it and all too easy to adjust if the analyst had a criticism of one aspect of the theory and wanted to develop it in another direction.

As discussed in the last chapter, Sigmund Freud's model of the psyche included the id, the superego, and the ego. Neurosis results when the ego is unable to achieve an adequate compromise between these parts of the psyche, which should allow for some drive satisfaction, moderated through internalized morals but channeled through the ego defenses. For the neurotic, these compromises lead to the partial suppression of forbidden impulses, deeply uncomfortable feelings, and poor functioning in life. Neurotics continue to punish themselves for their impulses, whether they are consciously aware of them, act out on them, or not. The result is anxiety, guilt, lack of adequate work or play, and generally poor life satisfaction. The psyche is at war with itself, and nobody is really winning.

Even psychologically healthy people need to find ways to protect the ego from undue suffering from its internal conflicts with the id and superego as well as from its external conflicts with an often uncooperative environment. These ego defenses remain largely unconscious and can be relatively benign or even helpful in regard to some functioning but can be debilitating in their more primitive forms. If someone is engaging in *isolation of affect*, he or she does not consciously choose to allow disturbing ideas into consciousness only in intellectualized form; they just do it, but this does not preclude relatively healthy and effective functioning. On the other hand, if a person is engaging in *denial*, he or she is precluding from conscious awareness important aspects of reality that may be vital to consider when choosing an effective response. These factors make ego defenses both immensely important and difficult to identify and modify.

While Sigmund Freud had certainly introduced the topic of ego defenses, his daughter, Anna Freud (1895–1982), went further, describing and explaining them in much more detail (Freud, 1992/1936). Under Anna Freud's influence, psychoanalysis shifted from searching for the id, revealed in hidden forms, to unearthing the defenses, as they held the key to neurotic psychological functioning and its corollary, mental health. Her efforts were so successful that many of the ego defenses she identified entered the public lexicon, and people started talking casually about denial, reaction formation, projection, and even sublimation. Over time, psychoanalysts discovered the common ways that people's defenses became organized as personality styles, such as the narcissistic, the borderline, the obsessive-compulsive, etc. (Johnson, 1994).

The general public began to think about their own mental health in new ways. Anna Freud and others helped undermine the criticisms of Freud as wishing to unleash people's ids in an orgy of self-indulgent hedonism. This was never really true, although he did want to change people's conception of the id from it being demonistic to a biologically natural repository of instinctual wishes and energy. To some extent, this criticism was inevitable, since from most religious perspectives, id drives are often associated with sin and selfishness. Freud's nonmoralistic attitude about it and his desire for the id to be integrated in the personality, not repressed or completely (if that were even possible) removed, placed him in direct conflict with the dominant religious perspective of Western culture. He was branded a degenerate hedonist, and the entire enterprise of psychotherapy, from that point on, has been colored (from inside and outside the field) with that perception. Again, ego psychology softened the attack by emphasizing the importance of developing stronger, more effective ego defenses, part of whose job is to control the id and *not* let it run roughshod over the psyche.

Even before Anna Freud built on her father's basic conceptual model of the psyche, there were other challenges to Freudian orthodoxy. Alfred Adler (1870– 1937) parted from Freud on a number of issues. He thought Freud was wrong about the importance of childhood sexuality. Instead, Adler thought the primary issues of childhood are superiority and power striving. He felt that children naturally had fears of weakness and inferiority in relation to the adult world and that these could easily be made worse if the child has an unusual number of challenges to overcome, such as chronic illness, disability, and maltreatment by parents. Children could easily develop an *inferiority complex* and experience ongoing difficulty feeling strong, competent, and equal to others. The resulting compensatory efforts, both conscious and unconscious, could combine with other aspects of personality and behavior to become a *style of life*. In neurotic individuals, this would include pathological struggles for power and success, while in more healthy personalities, it would manifest as a striving for self-improvement and a concern for the welfare of others. These issues all dovetailed with Adler's concerns about social justice, leading him to emphasize the responsibility of psychoanalysis to actively promote human equality and dignity (Adler, 1992/1927).

Another heretical follower of Freud was Carl Jung (1875–1961). He had already established himself as a respected psychiatrist, especially through his work with patients with dementia praecox (what we now call schizophrenia), when he joined Freud's movement in 1907. Jung was far too independent a thinker to stay in the good graces of Freud for very long. He, like Adler, deemphasized Freud's sexual focus on libido and sought to expand it into a more holistic, psychic/biological energy. He also expanded on the theory of the unconscious mind, asserting that it was not only the repository of individual drives and memories but had a universal or collective level lying deeper than then individual unconscious (Samuels, 1985). Jung's theory of the *collective unconscious* suggested that Kant's ideas about predispositions of the mind (how people naturally take in, organize, and interpret information) did not go far enough and that all humans carry with them conceptual patterns passed down from our ancestral history.

> This psychic life is the mind of our ancient ancestors, the way in which they thought and felt, the way in which they conceived of life and the world, of god and human beings. The existence of these historical layers is presumably the source of the belief in reincarnations and in the memories of past lives.
>
> (1939, p. 24)

Jung felt that the collective unconscious included various archetypes, or particular forms of human experience. Some of these have become well known, including the Animus, the Anima, the Wise Old Man, and the Shadow. His concept of the collective unconscious met with a great deal of skepticism in the psychiatric community but was more influential in the general community, especially among artists and religious thinkers. The famous mythologist Joseph Campbell was impressed by Jung's ideas and felt he had tapped into a great truth about the dynamic of the human psyche and its propensity to independently develop surprisingly similar religious beliefs. Jung inspired a small but dedicated following of psychotherapists, and his theories have continued to live on in the subfields of Jungian psychology and archetypal psychology. Both psychotherapy clients and the lay public who attend lectures and workshops based on his ideas have been influenced in their perception of the kind of personal growth they can seek for a life that is richer and deeper as they plumb the depths of their psyches through their therapy, writing, and art.

Another stream of dissent from Freud's original work were the closely related concepts of object-relations theory and attachment theory. Melanie Klein may have been the first psychoanalyst to shift from Freud's concept of the infant battling the mother for resources, thus beginning a psychologically necessary individuation from her, to one of internalizing aspects of the mother so that the growing child integrates those aspects into a core sense of self. In other words, infants are seen as "wired" for human interaction. The object relations theorists (Fairbairn and Winnicott among them) took this a step further and asserted that infants are "wired" for this interaction to be loving and harmonious and that a mother who is properly *attuned* to her child's needs will provide what is necessary for healthy psychological development. It is not the child's fault if this development goes astray. It is the failure of the primary caregiver to provide *good enough* parenting. This shifted the focus from the individual ego to the interrelational self.

John Bowlby drew on this idea to describe the attachment process. He asserted that infants naturally seek attachment to others, that emotional security stems from confidence in the availability and competence of the primary caregiver, and that the patterns set down in infancy continue into adulthood (Karen, 1998). These patterns tended to coalesce around a relatively small number of characteristic styles, ranging from *secure* to *disorganized*. The overall approach of object relations and attachment led psychodynamic psychology to consider infants as naturally being born in a state of basic mental health but easily diverted by bad parenting into a neurotic state of maladaptive internal self-concept, poor relations with others, and emotional suffering. It provides a blueprint for how to provide better psychological development for youngsters and work through, if necessary, the difficulties of a disturbed internalized object and attachment style.

The last outgrowth of psychodynamic psychology we will touch on was the development of self-psychology. As the years passed after Freud's death in 1933, more and more of his original theorizing was criticized and dropped from many therapists' thinking and practice. The emphasis had changed from the individual with a psyche consisting of ego, id, and superego, trying to wrest resources from a resistant world, to one of a holistic self, in constant interaction with a world that shapes the experience of self-identity, sometimes for good and sometimes for ill. Child-rearing practices reflect the values and beliefs of a given culture and lead to different, not necessarily better or worse, self-experiences. Where Freud focused on the problem of conflict, Heinz Kohut (1923–1981) reflected more on alienation.

He insisted that children should be raised in an environment that supports the development of their *feeling human* and *connected* to a human community. The key, then, is the importance of *self-objects* (people, objects, and activities) that become internalized and complete the self. To the extent that self-objects are empathetically attuned to the individual, he or she will develop a core sense of self that is cohesive, vigorous, and harmonious. If not, the self is experienced as divided, weak, and conflicted. This leads to depression, anxiety, and generally poor life functioning. This model deemphasizes the roles of the id, superego, and ego of the individual and instead amplifies the importance of empathetic caregiving to aid the development of mental health.

Humanistic Psychology

While these developments were occurring in the field of psychoanalysis, a third approach to mental health and mental illness was growing in psychology. Sometimes referred to as the "third force," humanistic psychology emerged as an alternative to the highly technical and mysterious psychoanalysis and the overly simplistic and inhumane behaviorism. Compared to the other two approaches, humanistic psychology is the most hopeful, positive, and holistic approach to understanding human nature. It focuses on the inherent goodness of the psyche and desire for *self-actualization*. Human evil and suffering are seen as distortions of our natural inclination to feel connected to others, fit in well with society, get our basic needs met through cooperation with others, feel happy and at peace, and make the most of our talents and abilities in life.

Humanistic psychology's roots are in phenomenology and existentialism, philosophical approaches that emphasize the holistic, subjective self in its experience of life, seeking meaning and fulfillment. The original humanistic psychologists felt that psychoanalysis was too focused on artificially splitting the psyche into separate parts and obsessed with a very negative, conflictual concept of human nature. They were more interested in the positive, creative aspects of life. They believed that humans seek wholeness, peace, and even self-transcendence. They emphasized the capacities for free will and self-improvement. Rather than helpless victims of their own internal conflicts (psychoanalysis) or systems of punishment and reward (behaviorism), the humanists saw people as integrated beings able to direct their own lives. In this view, we may not be able to control many external circumstances, but we can choose how we respond to them, maintaining hope, meaning, and purpose in even the most difficult of circumstances. This was the position of Victor Frankl (1905–1997), a Viennese psychoanalyst who was interred in a Nazi concentration camp and placed in a position of medical care for other inmates. In his famous book, *Man's Search for Meaning*, Frankl noted that those prisoners who were able to maintain a sense of hope, purpose, and meaning had better outcomes than those who had psychologically given up (1959). This paralleled Nietzsche' belief that "he who has a why to live can bear almost any how" (Nietzsche, 2020). This simple but profound principle became the basis for Frankl's approach to philosophy and psychotherapy after WWII. His response to behaviorism was that "between stimulus and response there is a space. In that space is our power to choose our response.

In our response lies our growth and our freedom" (Frankl, 2020). This became the basis for his sense of mental health, that we base our actions and ultimate happiness on our attitude about life, what we think is important, our goals and values. He saw happiness not as a proper goal of life but as the natural consequence of pursuing our goals. Frankl's sense of the importance of meaning led him to be more aligned with Kierkegaard's will to meaning than Adler's will to power or Freud's will to pleasure. Turning tragedy into triumph was, for Frankl, not about exerting one's power or seeking pleasure but about living out the highest potential of found meaning in our life situations.

Another heavyweight in humanistic psychology was Abraham Maslow (1908–1970). Like Frankl, he faced serious difficulties in his life. He was born in poverty, grew up with a schizophrenic mother, and, from the age of nine, lived in a non-Jewish neighborhood, which, being Jewish himself, he described as like being the only African American in an all-white school. As a child, he was shy, lonely, neurotic, and often depressed. He began his career in psychology as a behaviorist but soon found the approach limiting and inadequate to fully explain human nature. He helped form the American Association for Humanistic Psychology, along with such luminaries as Erich Fromm, Gordon Allport, Karen Horney, and Carl Rogers. He felt, like the others, that the basic, innate nature of the human psyche was healthy and health seeking. Rather than overcoming neuroses, he saw mental health as pursuing higher-order goals.

In that spirit, he developed a theory of motivation with two forms. The first was related to meeting basic, biological and social needs. The second included the higher, more aspirational needs. This *hierarchy of needs* was his best-known and most enduring contribution to psychology and provided a more detailed map for self-actualization. Psychological wellness was associated with having met (adequately) the lower level needs and spending one's time and energy in pursuit of the higher-level ones. While he conducted little empirical research, Maslow did study people he thought were self-actualized. He found that they had a number of qualities in common. They tended to be open-minded, flexible in their thinking, empathetic toward others, civic minded, generous, spiritual, creative, energetic, authentic, self-accepting, decisive, insightful, wise, and not strongly bound to a particular culture. The last quality appears to be related to the fact that they tend to see all people as equal and recognize the values and failings in various cultures, so they tend to take a universalist perspective on human nature, including spirituality.

Gestalt Psychology and Systems Theory

The final perspective in our all-too-brief history of twentieth-century psychology, as it regards mental health and mental illness, is Gestalt psychology and its later transmutation, Gestalt therapy. Gestalt psychology emerged as a reaction to structuralism, which conceived of human mentation as derived from the splicing together of different elements of perception through the process of association. Gestaltists took issue with this, feeling that the best way to understand human mentation was in how it created organized, structured wholes. While the movement started as a rather technical debate regarding the formation of consciousness, it quickly extended to the consideration of personality. The psychoanalysts had broken down personality into a dizzying variety of subparts and processes. Humanistic psychologists drew on Gestalt principles to support their holistic understanding of personality. Even psychotherapists took notice. Fritz Perls, who started his career as a psychoanalyst, worked with Kurt Goldstein, a neurologist who applied the principles of Gestalt psychology to his understanding of the brain and organistic functioning. His wife, Laura Perls, had been a Gestalt psychologist before becoming a psychoanalyst. Together, they developed Gestalt therapy. Without getting into the specific techniques and practices of the therapy, the philosophical foundation of the approach includes not only Gestalt theory but existential phenomenology, systems theory, and field theory. As such, it was the first model of psychology and subsequent therapy that drew on all the theories mentioned in the introduction to this book as an organizing force for its understanding of the human personality.

Some of the guiding principles in Gestalt therapy, in this regard, are awareness, process, intersubjective relationship, a field-based conception of reality, and the paradoxical theory of change (Perls, 1972; Woldt & Toman, 2005). Awareness refers to the phenomenological importance of a person increasing his or her conscious awareness of everything going on, both inside and outside themselves. Observation and exploration help reduce the bias of presuppositions. We all carry with us assumptions about ourselves, others, and the world in general that may or may not reflect the real world very well. Openness to and experience of a greater amount of internal and external reality is valued as a road to truth. Process refers to the fact that nothing in nature is static. Everything is in a process of change, including people's personalities and their lives. Various phenomena interact on multiple levels, affecting each other in complex, dynamic ways, leading to hard-to-predict changes. These interactions include the relational dynamics between people. Person A meets Person B – the *contact* changes both A and B, leading to a new relationship state between them. There is no such thing as Person A existing in isolation, without being influenced by or influencing others in dynamic interplay.

Thus, the focus in Gestalt is not so much individual people, in and of themselves, but the point of contact and interactional dynamics between the individual and the world, including other people. This means that all phenomena, including human lives, exist in a *field* consisting of the individual and everything else in his or her environment. In a person's subjective experience, there will be foreground (those aspects that are particularly prescient) and background (still impactful but not a focus of immediate awareness). The main job of Gestalt therapy is not to *change* clients but to lead them to greater awareness of themselves and the field of their lived experience. The idea is that much of human suffering stems from limited or distorted awareness of oneself and the field of existence. For instance, if one is focused too much on having been mistreated in childhood, he may be limiting his awareness of potential sources of positive treatment from others (part of the field but thrust into the background because the foreground is dominated by the awareness of others who mistreat him). Thus, mental illness is seen as arising from limitations and distortions of the experiential field, and mental health arises from greater awareness of and a level of acceptance of more of the field.

This dovetails well with systems theory, which posits that the world operates through multilayered, complex interactions of various elements, which are best (and perhaps only) understood in reference to the whole. When thinking about individuals, one needs to consider various parts and levels of the system, including (internally) the nervous system, the whole biological body, and the mind and (externally) the immediate social system, extended family, cultural groupings, and humanity as a whole. Psychological wellness thus becomes an emergent quality when there is optimal systemic functioning, both internally and externally. Mental illness is a signal that something is not operating well, at some level or levels of the overall system.

This growing interest in systems over parts led the field of psychology, in the second half of the twentieth century, to widen its perspective about mental health and mental illness beyond its earlier focus on the individual to a greater appreciation of both the individual as a "system" and the functional or dysfunction dynamics of individuals within "systems." This included the expansion of clinical work to couples, families, groups, and even entire organizations. In theoretical work, it has energized interest in such professional areas as evolutionary psychology, social psychology, and cultural psychology. Each of these subfields tends to deemphasize individual pathology in preference for understanding the interactional dynamics of self-in-environment.

The Impact of Psychology in the Twentieth Century

Whether the focus is on the individual or the collective, it is clear that the academic and applied fields of psychology have been enormously successful in the twentieth century. The increase in college programs (both undergraduate and graduate), jobs, and customers of psychological services has been enormous. It is quite difficult to track these changes, especially as there was relatively little social research going on a hundred years ago. However, a recent survey conducted by the American Psychological Association found that almost half of American households had someone seek mental health treatment within the last year and that the percentage would be higher if more families had insurance that covered mental health care (Chamberlin, 2004). A more recent study found significant increases in the utilization of mental health care since the 2004 survey was conducted (Olfson, Wang, Wall, Marcus, & Blanco, 2019). This reflects the fact that more people than before are looking to the field of psychology to understand whether they are mentally healthy and seeking professional help for their psychological problems. We also know that there has been a large increase in the number of people impacted by professional psychology through a variety of different subfields, including health psychology, educational psychology, environmental psychology, performance psychology, and social work, just to name a few (Hunt, 1993).

It is therefore safe to say that the concepts from psychoanalysis, behaviorism, and humanistic psychology discussed so far have strongly influenced how many people think about their mental health and deciding if they are mentally ill. Part of this influence has been the impact of a trend toward "lowering the bar" of what constitutes mental illness or at least a good reason to go to therapy or take psychotropic medications. Previously, the concept of mental illness was reserved mainly for extreme cases of psychosis, suicidal behavior, and various types of severe mental breakdown, leading to such functional impairment that the person required hospitalization. With the emergence of the public face of psychology, widely available outpatient mental health care, and psychotropic medication in the twentieth century, a much higher percentage of people are now identified as having a mental disorder and possibly benefiting from professional care. And while clinical psychology has certainly had something to say about mental illness, the story of the conceptual approach to mental illness is still more reflective of psychiatry than psychology, and that is the next part of our chapter.

THE STORY OF PSYCHIATRY

At the beginning of the twentieth century, the field of psychiatry was based primarily in the asylum. Unlike academic psychologists, medical doctors trained and worked in the psychiatric hospitals, seeking to understand and treat the patients who were there. Because the main conduit of treatment was very expensive, long-term, residential care, they found themselves working primarily with the severely mentally ill. People with routine life issues, such as moderate levels of anxiety and depression, relationship problems, existential angst, and neurosis rarely found themselves committed to an asylum and were still being treated by general practitioners who knew little about psychology or through some form of home-based care, such as consuming large quantities of "patent medicines," often laced with alcohol, cocaine, or opioids. At the beginning of the twentieth century, psychiatry was just beginning to develop organized nosologies of mental illness and still knew very little about how to treat them.

Long-term placement in asylums, although they had become more humane, still did little to alleviate most severe mental illness (Shorter, 1997). There had been some progress in the development of various drugs to alleviate immediate suffering and symptoms. These included various kinds of opioids, alkaloid sedatives, and bromines. They could calm an agitated patient in the throes of mania and provide much-needed sleep. They reduced the need for physical restraints, but sadly, this practice gained the nickname "chemical straitjacket." They made the asylum a calmer, more humane place, but they did not cure. Psychiatry was still desperate for an understanding of mental illness that could lead to effective therapies, and in the meantime, the patients were piling up into hospitals throughout America and Europe, with Milledgeville State Hospital in Georgia alone housing more than 8,000 suffering souls. This situation fed a public sense that mental illness was horrific, because of the severe consequences (one could end up in an asylum), because it was mysterious, and because it seemed to be untreatable.

At the same time psychiatry was moribund, with rising patient loads and little to offer them beyond sedatives and other treatments of dubious quality, Freud's psychoanalysis had established itself as the outpatient treatment of choice. This created a bizarre bifurcation of the field. On the one hand, there was medically based psychiatry, focusing on the idea of mental illness as a number of discrete, biologically based disorders, with the treatment based on hospitalization and physiologically based interventions, including sedating medications, psychosurgery, medically induced coma, and electroshock therapy. On the other hand, there was psychoanalysis, which conceptualized mental illness as psychologically based, fundamentally continuous and dimensional rather than dichotomous in nature, and treated through psychosocial interventions (psychotherapy) rather than biological ones. This deep internal conflict within the field could not maintain itself for very long. This was particularly true in regard to the disagreement about the basic nature of mental illness. As just noted, mainstream psychiatry conceptualized mental illness through the lens of medical science. It was a brain-based phenomenon and part of the responsibility of medical science to identify the different discrete mental disorders because, as in the rest of medical science, they (the disorders) must reflect different etiology, type of dysfunction, course, outcome, and effective treatments. In medical science, influenza is different than pneumonia, calling for different treatment, based on what is known about the different diseases. Psychiatrists wanted to approach mental illness the same way. It was inevitable that the field would eventually reject psychoanalysis, and by the 1970s, it had.

This expulsion of psychoanalysis from psychiatry did not happen overnight. In the first half of the twentieth century, it existed alongside medical psychiatry in an odd sort of detente. Psychoanalysts were still medically trained and prominent in the world of psychiatry. They continued to conceptualize mental illness as arising from disturbed psychological development and treat patients with long-term psychotherapy. More medically oriented psychiatrists conceptualized mental illness through the medical model, sought to understand the biological roots of pathology, and supported biological treatments, noting that psychotherapy seemed to be ineffective with severe mental illness. Often, these practitioners worked in the same settings, belonged to the same professional organizations, and attended the same conferences. As the century progressed into the 1950s and 1960s, however, a profound revolution occurred that spelled the end for this uncomfortable coexistence, raising the medical model to full prominence and pushing the psychoanalytic model entirely into the camp of academic, clinical psychology (Scull, 2015).

That revolution was biochemical in nature. It was the discovery of drugs that, for the first time, actually reduced the symptoms of severe mental illness. As early as 1917, patients with neurosyphilis (a medical disease that caused psychotic symptoms) were being successfully treated through a process of repeatedly inducing a malarial fever then curing the fever with quinine (Shorter, 1997). This exciting finding led to an attempt to duplicate the results with other psychotics, but it did not work. The development of penicillin finally ended the scourge of neurosyphilis but offered nothing for other causes of severe psychiatric symptoms. By the 1950s, other medical interventions had been attempted, including ECT, chemically induced coma, and psychosurgery, but these drastic treatments were highly controversial, expensive, had dangerous side effects, and were often not very effective. Psychiatry was still dedicated to a medical model of mental illness but could not back it up with effective biological treatments and thus left the field vulnerable to criticism of the biological approach to understanding mental illness.

That changed through two historical developments: genetic studies and effective psychotropic medications. The first of these developments, genetic studies, began with the work of Gregor Mendel, who founded the modern science of genetics in the late nineteenth century. Prior to that time, psychiatrists had postulated a biological basis for mental illness, but their assertions were vague, with no fundamental science to support their theories. By the early twentieth century, researchers such as those at Emil Kraepelin's German Research Institute for Psychiatry in Germany were helping to scientifically establish the connection between genetics and psychiatric disorders.

They quickly realized that one did not need to have extensive knowledge of brain functioning to establish evidence for the inheritance of psychological and psychiatric factors. Early statistical studies had been unable to separate the influence of genes and environment, but it was discovered that you could do so by conducting twin studies and adoption studies. Twin studies are able to establish the genetic loading for a given characteristic based on the different concordance rates of monozygotic versus dizygotic twins. If a characteristic is genetically based, monozygotic twins will have a significantly higher concordance rate than dizygotic twins. In regard to the impact of environment on any given trait, if children are separated at birth and adopted by different families, than presumably, you can factor out shared environment for the prevalence of the trait. Various studies have found around a 50% concordance rate for schizophrenia in monozygotic twins but only a 15% concordance rate for dizygotic ones (McGuffin, 1994). Especially given that the risk of schizophrenia is about 1% in the general population, this is dramatic evidence for a genetic, biological basis for schizophrenia. There was still the question, however, of the impact of both children being raised in the same family. That is where adoption studies become important. A series of such studies found that schizophrenia was ten times more common in biological relatives of adoptees with schizophrenia than in the biological relatives of the control group members. It was also more common in biological siblings of the adoptees than in second-degree relations (Kety, 1988). Similar concordance rates have been found in connection with bipolar disorder. More recent research has found lower but still significant genetic linkages with a wide variety of psychological traits, including general intelligence, hypomania, depression, alcoholism, and even personality traits such as neuroticism, openness to experience, extraversion, agreeableness, and conscientiousness, some of which have been found to correlate with various mental disorders (Lo et al., 2017). All of this has become common knowledge, and few psychology students these days debate the idea that there is at least *some* connection between genetic inheritance, psychological traits, and mental illness.

This was not always the case. When this kind of research was first being presented to professional bodies, it caused a storm of protest from the psychoanalysts, who dominated psychiatry in the first half of the twentieth century. The turning point can be traced to the 1950 First World Congress of Psychiatry, when a major paper was presented that discussed the biological inheritance of schizophrenia (Shorter, 1997). It caused such upset that the chairman refused to read any of the written comments that had been sent in to criticize the paper. A number of papers were presented in that international gathering that would establish the idea that psychiatry believed the physical brain and genetic inheritance were the primary causes of mental illness.

Adding fuel to the fire, the next few years would see the development of a number of medications that, for the first time, significantly reduced the symptoms of depression, anxiety, psychosis, and mania. What was particularly important was that they did not do so, as previous medications had done, by simply sedating the sufferer. They reduced the psychiatric symptoms, seeming to target the actual biochemical basis of the disorder. Some were discovered by accident when researchers were studying the effects of a new compound and noticed that one of the side effects might be of interest to psychiatrists. Increasingly over the decades, research has become more focused, as we learn more about neurological functioning as it relates to mental illness (mainly the activity of a small number of neurotransmitters at this point) and get better at developing drugs that can impact that functioning. As a result, there has been an explosion of psychotropic medication usage. When these drugs were first being developed in the early 1950s, a small number of hospitalized patients with severe mental illness were taking them. As of 2016, it was estimated that 40 million (nearly 1 in 6) American adults were taking psychotropic medications (Miller, 2016).

While we do not have space to fully explore these developments in the genetics of mental illness or the proliferation of psychotropic medications, the point here is to discuss what these developments meant in regard to both the public and professional conceptions of mental health and mental illness. First of all, the shift in psychiatry in the twentieth century, from a psychoanalysis-based to a biologically based profession, reflected a profound change in conception. Psychoanalysis, as well as the other related psychological theories (behavioral and humanistic) focus on the psychosocial causes of mental health and mental illness. Their theoretical models provide little room for biological influence on the psyche. In the nineteenth century, psychiatry was decidedly biological in its conception of mental illness, pushed harder in that direction by the development of evolutionary theory. The emergence of psychoanalysis at the turn of the new century changed that, and for the next half century, psychiatry lived in a hybrid world. But the percentage of psychiatrists who self-identify as psychoanalysts has plummeted to less than 5%, and despite regular attempts to rectify psychoanalytic thought with biological psychiatry (Fonogy, 2003), most people are wondering if it still has any relevancy in the field anymore (Paris, 2017).

It is important to note a couple of dynamics in this overall process. The first was that when evolutionary theory came on the scene, it led to the eugenics movement. As previously discussed, this movement was driven by a racist belief in white superiority to other "races" and an inhumane desire to "purify" society by restricting breeding of people with undesirable traits. This movement reached its zenith in Nazi Germany, an extreme manifestation that led directly to a reactionary rejection of biologically based psychology for approximately the next 40 years. This meant that after WWII, the idea of a biological basis for psychiatry had to live on the margins, haunted by accusations of Nazism. As previously noted, the success of psychotropic medications in the 1950s began to relegitimize a biological approach to understanding mental illness but only in the medical schools not the psychology departments.

A second factor in the expulsion (or exodus?) of psychoanalysis from psychiatry was the rise of clinically oriented psychological theories *outside* of psychiatry. Behaviorism, cognitive behaviorism, and humanism all emerged as psychological theories with direct, clinical application. As previously noted, they emerged through the world of academic psychology not psychiatry. As such, they served as an *alternative* to psychoanalysis. Also, as psychoanalysis evolved beyond the original theories and practice of Freud, it slipped out of the bounds of medical psychiatry and was increasingly thought about, taught, and practiced in the world of academic and clinical psychology. This created a situation in which other psychological theories offered an alternative to psychoanalysis and thus weakened its position at the same time that they began to align with and eventually integrate with psychoanalysis. By the end of the twentieth century, there was a bifurcated world, with the psychological (nurture) world of academic and clinical psychology on the one hand and the biological (nature) world of psychiatry on the other.

While these dynamics were unfolding, another profound event occurred that would change the professional and public perception of mental illness in profound ways. In 1952, the American Psychiatric Association published the first *Diagnostic and Statistical Manual of Mental Disorders* (DSM). The initial drive for the creation of a classification system for mental illness in the United States was the need for statistical information for the 1840 census. It included a single designation for insanity. Soon after, the American Statistical Association complained that the information gathered was of little use and full of errors, such as the fact that many towns listed all African Americans as insane. A few years later, in 1844, the Association of Medical Superintendents of American Institutions for the Insane was formed, and after a few name changes, it became the American Psychiatric Association (APA) in 1921. This organization, along with the National Commission on Mental Hygiene, developed a new guide for asylums, which included 22 mental disorders.

World War II provided a new impetus for the classification of mental illness with the first large-scale involvement of psychiatrists in a war, participating in the selection, assessment, and treatment of soldiers. A committee headed by Brigadier General William Menninger (of the famous Menninger Clinic) developed a new classification system called Medical 203. This became the basis for the first DSM, which sought to standardize the confusing mix of different classification systems then in use. The APA revised Medical 203, sent it out for approval by its members, and published DSM-I in 1952. It included 106 mental disorders, organized in several categories, including personality disorders and neuroses. It was heavily influenced by the work of Adolf Meyer, who proposed that mental illnesses were "reactions" to biopsychosocial stressors. This was in opposition to those who saw mental illness as principally biological and was more in line with Freudian ideas about the primary importance of psychosocial stressors' impact on early childhood development. This helped psychoanalysts to remain prominent in American psychiatry and the APA. The DSM was revised in 1968. While it expanded the number of mental disorders to 182, the basic underlying concept was the same. It dropped Meyer's term "reaction" but kept the term "neurosis," signifying its adherence to the idea of most mental illness reflecting unconscious conflicts and maladaptive reactions to life stressors. This psychodynamic conceptualization meant that every case was unique and the symptoms separating different categories and disorders were not clearly specified, and thus it lacked reliability as a diagnostic instrument.

A watershed moment occurred in 1970, when a gay rights group protested at the annual APA conference in San Francisco. They claimed that homosexuality should not be considered a mental disorder. Other protesters broadened that specific concern and questioned the legitimacy of psychiatric diagnosis in general. By 1974, the APA had dropped homosexuality as a psychiatric disorder from the DSM, but it was replaced with a new category, "sexual orientation disturbance." Before discussing the development of DSM-III, we need to explore the movement that led to the dropping of homosexuality as a mental disorder and spurred wholesale changes to the APA's classification system.

If 1950 had been the seminal year for the transcendence of the biological concept of mental illness, then 1960 played the same role in the emergence of what would become known as antipsychiatry. That was the year that Thomas Szasz released *The Myth of Mental Illness*. As a psychoanalyst who worked in psychiatric facilities, Szasz was an industry insider who attacked the foundations of his own chosen field. He claimed that the very concept of mental illness was socially constructed. Rather than an ontological reality, waiting to be discovered and understood, he argued that it was a culturally inspired label that people put on others who they find disturbing. The central issue was not empiricism, seeking to "carve nature at the joints," but rather of social power – who gets to decide what beliefs, experiences, and behavior gets labeled "mad" or "sane"?

Almost overnight, Szasz became the patron saint of those who either took a rebellious stand against the profession, practices, and assumptions of psychiatry and/or embraced a postmodern, relativistic perspective on truth. His views fit a vision of epistemology that said that empiricism was grossly limited, especially in the field of human psychology, because the subject matter is hopelessly subjective. Humans are the object of their own study. There is no outside position possible to take when it comes to studying human psychology. Every researcher's own preexisting beliefs, values, and cultural perspective form the semi- to completely unconscious basis for their judgments about others. This reflects a situation in which profession of psychiatry is itself a subculture, with its own traditions, assumptions, and power dynamics. The concept of mental illness serves the interests of the profession, but does it have any reality outside that need?

If there was any suspicion that Szasz was a lone wolf, howling in a vacuum, it was quickly dispelled when a whole series of books flew out of the publishing houses in the 1960s, assailing both the beliefs and the practices of psychiatry. In 1960, R.D. Laing wrote *The Divided Self*. In 1961, Michel Foucault released *Madness and Civilization*. In the same year, Erving Goffman published *Asylums*. Then, in 1962, Ken Kesey released *One Flew Over the Cuckoo's Nest*. Together, these books painted psychiatry as a professional monolith, ignoring the subjective reality of its "customers" in service of the beliefs of the psychiatrists, their subculture, and the wider, dominant culture.

That was the backdrop of the APA convention protests of 1970 and the dropping of homosexuality as a mental disorder in 1974. It was becoming clear to the APA that it had to move away from a theoretically driven classification system toward something more empirical and thus reliable and scientifically valid. The result was DSM-III, published in 1980. The primary figure in this revision was Robert Spitzer, who chaired the task force to rework the DSM. Under his direction, the task force wanted to bring the DSM into closer alignment with the *International Statistical Classification of Diseases and Related Health Problems* (ICD), which was published by the World Health Organization and was used in other parts of the world, especially Europe. More generally, the task force wanted to improve the validity and reliability of psychiatric diagnosis in response to the criticisms of psychiatry that were being raised by many both inside and outside the field. The idea was to rely on criteria for different mental disorders that was established through empirical research rather than psychodynamic theory. This meant that the focus switched from presumed, underlying causes to reportable or observable signs and symptoms of mental illness. This constituted a fundamental restructuring and reconceptualization of mental illness from the APA's perspective. The theoretical neutrality and symptomatic specificity included in the new DSM led to its removing some disorders that were in DSM-II and adding many more, bringing the new total to 265 separate disorders.

DSM-III was published in 1980 and changed the way people thought about mental illness. It did this in two ways. The first was the aforementioned shift away from a psychodynamic theory of causation toward a more atheoretical description of symptoms. The new DSM would rely on empirical research, which in turn was relying more on phenomena that are observable and measurable and disregards those that are not. This meant that the new DSM was more reliable in its application but open to a new round of criticism regarding the validity of its underlying conceptualization of mental illness and subsequent categorization of the disorders themselves.

The second way it changed the way people thought was through the consequences of its success. By switching to a symptom-based system, supported by research, the DSM quickly became an essential tool for a fast-growing group of mental health professionals in America and, increasingly, throughout the world. The DSM-I was not widely used, and hardly anyone even knew of its existence outside the world of inpatient psychiatry in the United States. The DSM-III quickly became *the* standard for diagnosing mental illness. If a psychiatrist, psychologist, clinical social worker, or licensed psychotherapist in America wanted to be reimbursed by a third-party payer for their work, they had to produce a diagnosis from the DSM. It became the foundation for clinical training in psychodiagnosis in medical schools, colleges, and private schools that prepared mental health professionals for practice.

The success of DSM-III (and its newer editions, DSM-III-R, DSM-IV, DSM-IV-TR, and DSM-5) brought the fields of psychiatry and psychology (especially clinical psychology) closer together. Despite ongoing controversies about etiology and diagnosis, the two worlds had found a meeting place that seemed to solidify the professionalism of both. Psychiatry would provide the diagnoses and medical treatment (hospitals and medicine), and psychology would provide the conceptual depth and psychotherapy. Both would agree on the basic categorization and descriptions of mental illness through the DSM.

By the end of the century, on the surface at least, there appeared to be a détente in place. Psychiatry would increasingly focus on the biological underpinnings of mental illness, while psychology focused on the behavioral dynamics of human development and functioning. However, below the surface (and sometimes right in your face), everything was not so calm. The antipsychiatry movement that began in the early 1960s did not go away. The criticisms of the newer editions of the DSM did not go away. And even before the publication and success of DSM-III, profoundly different visions of mental health and mental illness were emerging, challenging the official professional views of psychiatry and clinical psychology. The story of the countercultural reaction to mainstream psychiatry, psychology, and Western culture in general is next.

THE STORY OF CULTURAL CHANGE

It was no coincidence that the antipsychiatry movement began just as the Western world was moving into a period of intense cultural rebellion. We have already discussed the cultural rebellion that occurred at the end of the Middle Ages in the West, as the ancient authorities of monarchy and the organized religion were being questioned, transformed, and, in some cases, completely overthrown. That process continued through the Enlightenment and the Modern Age. The 1960s represented the initial spark of still another period of transformation – one we are still too close to historically to fully understand in terms of its final consequences for both Western and world culture. The First and Second World Wars had essentially destroyed the informal system of European colonial powers controlling much of the world. The horrific extremes of Nazism ended any sense of moral or intellectual legitimacy for antisemitism and racism and, by extension, sexism, ethnic superiority, and authoritarianism. Part of the fallout was an increasing sense that hierarchies of all sorts could no longer be trusted, centralized power was dangerous, and science and technology did not automatically lead to social progress. The modernist movement was increasingly seen as a cold and empty shell that did not honor or even acknowledge the depths of human nature. Its psychological handmaiden, behaviorism, could not make a clear value judgment between adapting to totalitarianism and desperately fighting for human freedom. It seemed the human spirit was not necessarily good, and it certainly could not be trusted in regard to people or institutions in positions of power. The modernist philosophical and psychological responses to the problem were hopelessly inadequate or made the problem worse.

Thus, a new romantic humanism emerged and provided a value shift in support of the powerless, the outsiders, the young, the poor, and the disadvantaged. It would be "the people's" revolution. "Don't let others tell you who you are, what you should think and feel, and how you should behave. Do not let them call you crazy. Seek your own sanity in an insane world." The new bravery was to self-conceptualize and self-create. Thoughts are things, and by imagining a reality of beauty and love, you can bring it into existence in your life. Take control of your body (sexual revolution, birth control, legal abortion), take control of your mind (recreational drugs, self-help books, personal psychotherapy), take control of your society (political revolutions and emancipation movements, including civil rights, women's rights, native rights, and gay rights), and ultimately take control of your soul (alternative religions, New Age, human potential movement).

This was the foundation of change in the Western world as it moved into a postmodern perspective. It was initially sparked by the Enlightenment but then reenergized by the failures of Western civilization in the Modern age and finally unleased in the postmodern revolution of the 1960s. While America was the epi-center of this change, it played out around the world, shaped by the unique sit-uations in different places. Much of Africa threw off the shackles of colonialism and struggled to develop responsible, effective self-rule. Latin America was going through a similar process. Much of Europe was, to some extent, reflective of the American situation, with a youth culture demanding power and freedom (in many ways the same thing) and leading a humanistic revolt against the traditional moral, economic, social, and political authorities of the time.

How was this reflected in how people approached the conceptualization of mental health and mental illness? We have already looked at the beginning of the antipsychiatry movement. Now we will take a wider perspective, taking in both the academic and clinical world of psychology as well as the general culture of the West. In regard to the academic world of psychology, we have explored the three main approaches to understanding human nature, including mental health and mental illness. These included the cognitive-behavioral model, the humanistic model, and the psychodynamic model. Of those models, two of the three could easily be interpreted as maintaining a dogmatic, authoritarian attitude about psy-chology. The early days of the behavioral approach were marked by attempts to and a celebration of manipulating human behavior and thought to serve the end of creating a better modernist society. While its proponents saw this in benevo-lent terms, overcoming the societal problems of the modern world (Skinner, 1948), others saw such a vision in harsher terms, with a dictatorial individual or group controlling the population with an iron fist, and crushing individual freedom to maintain power and seek its own ends. A manipulative psychology, valuing adap-tive conformity over human freedom, was not a particularly attractive idea in the revolutionary 1960s.

Psychoanalysis had not painted itself in much better colors. There was the image of the analyst, wreathed in mysterious clouds of secret knowledge, sitting in austere silence behind the client, who lay prostrate and exposed on the couch. He knew you better than you knew yourself. He would reveal your deepest neuroses and, through a wizard-like power of transformation, heal them. The dynamics of superiority and manipulation were obvious and paralleled, in their own way, those of behaviorism. This image was softened with the evolution of psychoanalysis into psychodynamic psychology. The therapist moved in front of the client (establishing a more egalitarian relationship), was more transparent and forthcoming about what she was thinking, and utilized less obtuse and thus more accessible concepts with which she worked. However, this was a late development, and the previously estab-lished image of psychoanalysis was still fully intact in the '60s. The third approach, humanism, was the one that correlated better with the new spirit of the times.

It is safe to say that no human revolution is without its problems, and human-ism is no exception. The humanistic euphoria of the mid-1960s was quickly tem-pered by problems, many of which were connected to issues with drug abuse, political and social protest, and what became known as the *human potential movement*. Typically, this term refers to the rather narrow range of intellectual and humanistic interests related directly to the expansion of human capacities for psychological and spiritual well-being. However, it has also been linked to a much wider variety of interests and activities, including the hippie movement, New Ageism, democ-racy movements, drug legalization, civil rights, vegetarianism, environmentalism, self-help publishing, and the rise of all manner of therapies for the "worried well" to improve their lives, ranging from yoga and art classes to couples, family, and new forms of individual psychotherapy. Whatever labels we put on this movement, many in the West were on the path to reject traditional authorities, feel better about themselves, and perhaps change the world.

They were responding to both the failures and opportunities of the modern world, often, ironically, at the same time. For instance, it was the modern belief in human equality and freedom that helped fuel the drive for group rights for Blacks, Hispanics, women, homosexuals, Native Americans, transgender people, and oth-ers. It was the painful reality that the modern *promise* of equality was not being fulfilled that inspired social and political action in the '60s and '70s. If Thomas Jefferson's assertion that every individual has a right to life, liberty, and happiness was meant seriously, then why was it that so many in America did *not* have an equal opportunity to go to college, get a good job, buy a home where they wished, or become president of the United States? On the individual level, why couldn't they choose what drugs they consumed to feel happy? Why couldn't they marry whomever they loved, whether they are the same gender or not? Why couldn't they choose whatever religion they want (or no religion at all) and not face social, cultural, and political retribution? Why should they be denied access to the avenues of power and mainstream society because of their ethnic or cultural background?

If a primary source of personal happiness and psychological well-being is a sense of respect, equality, and inclusion in society, then these twentieth-century progressive questions are *directly* connected to the fundamental issues of this text. Mental health is, at least partly, an extension of social and cultural health. The experienced well-being of the individual is linked to that person's cultural status in the place and time that they live. Throughout the Western world, millions chal-lenged the status quo that kept them marginalized and sought a way to greater well-being and, by extension, mental health, by flattening the hierarchies of their localities and demanding full equality.

Postmodernism establishes the conceptual foundation for such movements through the idea that the foundational *truths* of modernism have no epistemological legitimacy. They are simply the subjective opinions of groups of people in a given place and time. The time-honored beliefs in white, Western, male, straight, Chris-tian superiority are self-aggrandizing myths with no greater claim for truth than any others. The same is true for the claim of Western cultural superiority in general. This new truth became a war cry for emancipationists of all stripes. Flushed with newfound self-respect, groups around the world fought against the oppressive truisms of the past and demanded that historically dominant groups give up their hegemony not just because they are forced to but because it is the *right* thing to do, based on this new approach to truth itself.

Of course, many in these movements were not opposed to the modern world, they simply wanted it to do what it promised, providing material wealth, democratic government, equal opportunity, and technological advances to make life better for everyone. In other words, many were not revolutionaries but evolutionaries. They wanted to be free to live their lives as they saw fit. They also wanted to pursue happiness through personal self-improvement, through psychotherapy, healthy lifestyles, professional development, and political action. Men went to workshops and learned to cry. Women went to feminist groups and learned to take control of their own lives. Blacks gathered support and ran for political office. Members of all marginalized groups went to college to become high-level professionals. Mental health took on the look of a cultural revolution not just as a fulfillment of postmodernism but often as a fulfillment of modernism.

The response to this movement toward *personal growth* and the cultural changes it reflected was swift and firm. Many in Western society saw what was happening and felt threatened, angered, and disgusted. They were concerned about the rise of the power of democratic governments to exert direct power over their lives, supplanting their *traditional values* with those of a new liberalism. They were shocked by the violence and upheaval of emancipation movements. They were members of dominant groups that found themselves assailed and marginalized. They yearned for a return to a previous age, when life was simpler, relatable, and the odds were more in their favor. They desired strong leaders who promised to bring back stability and the values they believed in. What, specifically, were they reacting to? In America, the original call to increased civil rights led to federal intervention in the local right to pass and enforce laws pertaining to individual freedoms (Jim Crow); there were deadly riots in cities in response to the assassination of Martin Luther King Jr.; young people were indulging in street drugs and "free sex"; violent crime was rising quickly; cities were growing while rural populations were shrinking; radical political groups were setting off bombs, taking up arms in public, and threatening to overthrow democratic governments in favor of Marxist ones.

In 1969, Richard Nixon appealed to the *silent majority* of Americans who were deeply disturbed by the counterculture and wanted a return to traditional values. His perception was that the changes that were occurring (especially in regard to opposition to American involvement in the Vietnam War) reflected the views of a minority of Americans but had been artificially amplified by academic and cultural elites. His reference to a silent majority was part of a political strategy to increase polarization, drawing traditional Democrats into the Republican voting bloc (Chafe, 2009). The result was a landslide victory in the presidential election of 1972 – he won 49 out of 50 states. A large group of citizens has continued to exert itself culturally and politically, supporting conservative issues, including the right to life (antiabortion), small government, antiunionization, "hawkish" foreign policy, individual gun rights, and strong execution of the "war on drugs." This highly heterogeneous cultural group has supported the presidencies of Ronald Reagan, George W. Bush, and Donald Trump. One of the primary issues it has championed is the idea of a strong sense of national identity and self-interest, or what we typically call *nationalism*. Postmodern counterculturalists saw nationalism as a regressive force and speak to the universal brotherhood of all people, while nationalists see their central identity as based on membership in a particular nation-state.

Many within the nationalist movement see nation-state identity as linked to the ethnic, racial, religious, and cultural groups they recognize as the legitimate founders and core of their respective nations. In America, this is typically identified as Caucasian, Protestant Christian, and rural. They speak of *real* Americans *taking back* their country from usurpers. This movement is not unique to America and has experienced strong recent backing in a variety of countries, including Germany, Italy, England, France, Russia, Greece, Serbia, Poland, China, The Netherlands, and Israel. There have also been regional movements toward nationalistic sovereignty involving the Middle East, South America, and Africa. These movements have been energized by various dynamics in the past, including American and European colonialism, as well as more recent and ongoing Western intervention in their internal affairs. More recently, they have been reignited by the rise of globalism, a force that has, in part, been a natural consequence of changes related to international travel and trade and in part a purposeful development of international organizations (United Nations, NATO, etc.) and agreements (NAFTA, etc.).

Many have discussed the ways the world is changing and found them mostly positive but also problematical. As Thomas Freidman famously wrote, the Earth is indeed becoming flat (2005). Thanks to a number of developments but mostly the internet, opportunities for commerce, collaboration, and personal connection have expanded exponentially around the globe. A person living in Nigeria may find better-paying employment with a company based in America but hiring call-center employees living in Africa. If he is an academic, he can work together with fellow researchers around the world, and they can all access the information they need to advance their project with Google. If he is lonely, he can fall in love with a woman in Kiev with a completely different ethnic, racial, religious, and cultural background. In many ways, his life is better, and one would assume, his mental health is too. On the other hand, the same technology that has enriched his life may be impacting his neighbor in different ways. She may find this connection to the rest of the world quite threatening. She sees her own culture becoming inundated by ideas, beliefs, and practices that are directly opposed to her own. She may feel increasingly alienated and unmoored in a virtual and McDonaldized world. She may become radicalized, feeling an existential threat to herself and her people, and decide to fight back through the best tool that humans have always had to combat an overwhelming foe – terrorism.

Thus, globalization is both an exciting outgrowth of universalism to those who welcome it and a horror to those who don't. Either way, the forces of universalism, egalitarianism, and globalization all create change. And change is scary – not "a kid jumped out from behind a tree" kind of scary, but a "you are destroying and replacing everything I loved and valued in the world" kind of scary. This means changes to the basic self-conception of nearly every person on the planet. Some are so threatened by these changes that they build survival bunkers in their backyards, join white nationalist militias, or move to another part of the world and join groups like ISIS. Others are more accepting and empathetic, especially those in groups that find themselves on the right side of the equation, but may still be nervous, wondering what is happening, how fast it is occurring, and what things may look like in the future.

This begs the question of whether we are living in a world that is changing so fast that it naturally breeds a special brand of disorientation, disturbance, and resistance. In the nineteenth century, a group of textile workers in England reacted to the industrial changes in their professional field. A single factory worker operating a large sewing machine could replace dozens of handloom weavers. Not only that, but the rise of textile factories threatened traditional rural life as people moved to the cities where the factories were located, and the workers themselves faced difficult, dehumanizing, and often dangerous working conditions in those factories. The result was the Luddite movement, and some of its more extreme members engaged in terrorism, breaking into factories and destroying the machines (Sale, 1995). There was no clear leadership or national organization. It was an organic uprising and as inevitable in its ultimate failure as antiglobalization forces are today.

Long-term, historical change cannot be stopped by protest. Change is scary and threatening, especially for those who stand to be directly hurt by it, but it marches on. The point here is that while many are benefiting, both materially and psychologically, from the postmodern, world-flattening changes in the world, many do not feel that way. They yearn for a return to the "good old days." They envelop themselves in myths of a golden age and see the world as disintegrating into a chaos of relativity. It is important to remember that this is not just a dilemma for social conservatives. There was a powerful force within the 1960s counterculture that was not yearning for a progressive movement to postmodernism but instead a return to a preindustrial world. They dreamed of a simpler time when the individual freedom and honor they sought could be found in the world of small towns, self-sufficient rural life, and thus the increased valuation of each life, with its potential for greatness on a small scale. Both liberals and conservatives dreamed of being Hobbits.

The Lord of the Rings is one of the best-selling individually authored books of all time, with more than 150 million in sales. First published in 1954 by J.R.R. Tolkien, the book was not only a great literary success of its own, it has spawned an avalanche of fantasy books, comics, movies, and video games. The story is set in a mythical land, Middle Earth, and is essentially a premodern morality tale. It revolves around the heroic actions of four Hobbits who overthrow a demonic force that threatens to overwhelm Middle Earth and plunge it into an age of darkness, at least partly through a process of hyperindustrialization. The story was based in part on Tolkien's love of Norse and Germanic mythology but influenced strongly by his Catholic faith and life experiences growing up in an industrial city (Birmingham) but moving to the English countryside, as well as having lived through two world wars. Clearly, Tolkien had no great love for the modern, industrialized world. He did have deep love for basic human goodness and decency, which he found to be stronger in the simple folk who lived in small towns and on farms in rural areas.

The Lord of the Rings became the novel of choice of the "me generation" of baby boomers. While some were involved in revolutionary movements, most just wanted to live happier, more fulfilling lives than the world of their parents seemed capable of providing. *The Lord of the Rings* provided the fantasy of a humble Hobbit heroically saving the world from the forces of evil, including modern industrialization. The question is how that generation chose to fulfill that fantasy. Some joined communes to fulfill the fantasy of small, self-sufficient communities – rejecting the urban and suburban life of the modern world. Most lived "normal" lives but reached out for the immediate pleasures of sex, drugs, and rock-n-roll. By the mid-70s, cultural critics like Tom Wolfe were pointing out the hedonistic narcissism that was being played out in this rebellion. And indeed, as the decade played out, the communes failed, the crime rate kept climbing, New Age spirituality either sputtered out or diverged into cults, drug and alcohol abuse became rampant, and almost all of the revolutionary fervor of the '60s devolved into a self-indulgent, cocaine-fueled disco fever.

It seemed that a perennial truth had been laid bare. Hedonistic self-indulgence is not a good road to mental health. On the one hand, many of the pursuits of the baby boomers seemed to make sense in terms of mental hygiene, including vegetarianism, yoga, jogging, spiritual practice, back-to-nature activities, meditation, and various psychotherapies. However, all too often, they seemed to lack the self-discipline to take the long road to well-being and lurched onto shortcuts to happiness that did not lead where they wanted. As the Buddha discovered a long time ago, pursuit of individual pleasure is as unfulfilling a path as extreme self-denial. The main problem likely lies in the fact that as biological beings, our basic drives literally drive us, through an uncomfortable need state, to pursue such pleasures. If we try to satiate them, they simply return a little while later. If we try to deny them completely, they continue to burn in us, and if they're not met at least somewhat, we die from hunger, thirst, or exposure. The baby boomers were a generation caught in a trap. Those who did not stay on the mainstream path (the silent majority) ran after nirvana without the culturally approved discipline of the ashram or church. The media of the modern world promised them effortless, immediate, consequence-free, never-ending pleasure, and sadly, this does not appear to exist.

In America, the 1980s was a period of transition, with many turning to the cultural nostalgia of the Reagan Revolution, with religio-poetic images of a shining city on a hill. Many of the hippies turned in their love beads for three-piece suits – they were now "30-somethings." The modern dream of a progressive cultural transformation and the postmodern dream of universal transformation were severely weakened. The idea that the government should use a transfer of wealth from the rich to the poor to equalize living conditions was a modern, progressive dream that many seriously doubted. The idea that the people would become more enlightened to their true spiritual potential, that this would happen around the world, and that people would no longer need or desire government to meet their needs was a postmodern dream that was looking increasingly naive. Both dreams suffered from their failures in the '60s and '70s. A series of assassinations (JFK, Robert Kennedy, Martin Luther King, jr., Malcolm X, Anwar Sadat), the failure to either stop or win the Vietnam War, the economic stagflation and demise of American heavy industry, and the failure to spark a more widespread human potential movement revolution all served to severely damage those dreams.

What replaced it was nostalgia for an earlier time. In a previous chapter, we briefly discussed the myth of the golden age (Heinberg, 1989). From time immemorial, people have seen themselves as living through a period of regression and decay. They dream of an imagined time in the past when things were better. Deep in the past, people lived in peace, harmony, and prosperity. Their lives were longer, they were stronger and wiser, and all of society lived closer to God. Then things went wrong. People became separated from God, and all of human society descended into a Fallen state. The problems of today exist because of this state, and our only hope is to bring ourselves back closer to God.

This story is nearly universal, with local adaptations, of course. In Ancient Greece, they described five Ages of Man, starting with the Golden Age and then regressing through the Silver, Bronze, Heroic, and finally the current state (at that time) of Iron. In the Golden Age, people did not have to work for their food, lived a long time, were good and noble, maintained a youthful appearance, and died peacefully. In the Christian tradition, Adam and Eve lived in the Garden of Eden, did not have to work, knew no guilt or shame, and walked with God. But they ate of the Tree of Good and Evil and thus became aware of and ashamed of their nakedness. Because of this sin, and to keep them from eating from the tree of Eternal Life and thus becoming like gods themselves, they were caste out, and cherubim with flaming swords were set at the entrance to Eden to keep them out. The concordant dream of all people raised in this myth is to someday return, in this life or the next, to a Golden Age of "re-ligion" with God. At the end of Ronald Reagan's political life, he described his Shining City: "it was a tall, proud city built upon rocks stronger than the oceans, wind-swept, God-blessed, and teeming with people of all kinds living in harmony and peace; a city with free ports that hummed with commerce and creativity" (Reagan, 1989).

For people of this faith, the goal is not one of progressing toward a human-based equality and brotherhood but instead a *return* to a time that was God based and thus better for all. From that perspective, liberal acceptance of homosexuality and false religions is not seen as progress at all but rather as signs of the further decay and decline of human society. People of this faith suffer to live in a society that pursues such an end. They see the universalist dream of the human potential movement as the hubris of the Iron Age, when moral truth is lost to a baseless relativity. People don't become better by developing and following manmade values. They do so by realigning themselves with *God's will*. Within that belief set, something one would call mental health is the result of submission of the human will to that of God. There can be no true peace and harmony any other way. In the Christian tradition, it was the hubris of Satan, unwilling to submit to the authority of God, that led to his rebellion and ultimately being cast down to Hell. Humanism parallels Satan's course, and it is no surprise that such a course would end with hedonistic self-indulgence, spiritual emptiness, and despair. For people of that faith, the San Francisco of the '60s and '70s was not a story of hopes dashed but the inevitable failure of a false dream and should stand as a warning, not an example.

What this all means, for our purposes, is that as we enter the twenty-first century, there is no single road to mental health. There is a religiously based road of atonement, a modern road of material progress, and a postmodern road of individual choice. These roads twist and turn, take strange detours, and often overlap each other in unexpected ways. Each individual finds his or her way along these roads, pursuing happiness and fulfillment in more or less satisfying ways. The large majority of people I have known find their own way to combine elements of all three in a personally unique way. And maybe that is the best description of where we are now as a culture. Fewer people are accepting a predetermined path or model of mental health, provided by a particular culture or religion, but rather are stitching together their own models, shaping their own roads, and going where they lead.

THE REST OF THE WORLD

As this chapter has unfolded, it has primarily been the story of the West. The twentieth century emerged as the American century, and most of the changes and movements related to mental health and mental illness took place in that country. Much of the rest of the world either adjusted to the influence of those changes or resisted them, with very few places impervious to their impact. One of the many dynamics of the *Earth is flat* phenomenon is that there are fewer and fewer places to hide from the influence of dominant cultural forms. We may be over the age of direct colonization, but the subtle but pernicious colonization by cultural influence is actually much more pervasive now than it was in the past.

In Latin America, the new self-governing republics struggled to find a way to incorporate various ethnic groups into a national community, a task made harder given their history of including some groups that had been seen through colonial eyes as being inferior to others (Meyer, 2017). This led to gross disparities between groups of attention to and perception of mental health problems. The medical and academic establishments tended to maintain attitudes and practices that were essentially holdovers from colonization. For instance, many psychiatrists and psychologists simply imported Western concepts, labels, and practices without consideration for the cultural dynamics of the various ethnic populations in their country. This was particularly difficult for tribal people who increasingly found themselves impacted by Western style modernization, which was highly disruptive of their traditional beliefs, values, and practices. To make matters worse, these people were not welcomed by the new national leaders as equals but rather as inferiors who constituted a threat to these same dominant, Westernized elites. Psychiatrists and psychologists often disregarded the racial, ethnic, and class differences between themselves and their patients. When indigenous people immigrated from the countryside to the cities, they were often seen as a social threat, and many ended up in institutions for the insane, based more on struggles to assimilate than on true mental illness. Of course, that is not the whole story, and there were some mental health professionals who took more understanding attitudes toward the poor and disenfranchised. A more empathetic attitude began to emerge in the second half of the twentieth century as liberalization movements took hold and Euro-elitist beliefs and practices were challenged and replaced. There was an increase in understanding that many of the psychological and behavioral problems that had been called mental illness and ascribed to inherent biology were in fact created (at least in part) by the social conditions that people were struggling to deal with.

The situation was somewhat different in much of Asia. The continent includes an amazing diversity of cultures, many of which have very strong roots and have been able to maintain their traditional ethnic and national identities. Despite that, colonization and Western influence had a major impact, as did the incursion of some Asian countries into other ethnic areas. This was particularly true of China and Japan. In some places, local cultural forces were strong enough to force at least a hybridization of the conceptualization and treatment of mental illness. Our last chapter included an example of that process in Tibet. In many areas, there was the emergence of a two-level approach, in which colonial forces held sway in major cities and established hospitals and asylums, but "folk practices" were maintained in the countryside, however marginalized by the colonial forces that opposed them (Ernst, 2017). This was not uncommon in various parts of the world impacted by colonization.

What was unique in the Asian experience was how many of the concepts and practices associated with mental health were imported to the West. Starting in the mid-nineteenth century, Westerners grew ever more fascinated by Eastern spiritual beliefs and practices, including Buddhism, Hinduism, yoga, and meditation. By the late twentieth century, the Western approach to mental health had strongly adopted many of these elements, initially in a process of protest against more traditional Western ideas and later as a fully integrated part of their theory and practice. As late as the 1960s, the study of Buddhism and practice of meditation were still "exotic" and controversial in America, discussed in regard to the revolutionary nature of the work going on at places like Esalen Institute and writers like Alan Watts. By the 1980s, that work had become part of the New Age movement and was becoming "mainstream." By the beginning of the twenty-first century, yoga and meditation (often separated from their religious foundations) had become standard practice in the world of psychology in schools, in counseling centers, and even in prisons. It has become so mainstream that *mindfulness*, a concept derived from Sati (a traditional element of Buddhism) is now a core element in various Western psychotherapies, especially those following the humanistic and cognitive-behavioral traditions. Seen as an adjunct to the talk-therapy part of the process of psychological healing, mindfulness-based meditation ironically balances the Western notion of actively changing disliked internal experiences with a Buddhist principle of radical acceptance of them.

Like Latin America and Asia, Africa also has a significant history of colonization. This means that it has its own story of various cultures being impacted in different ways by Western concepts of mental health and mental illness (Swartz, 2017). The main challenge here is that Westerners have tended to lump together all of Africa as one place with a homogenous culture, but of course this is not true, and the local histories are unique, complex, and yet often interwoven. The tribal traditions include many different conceptions of mental illness but are generally similar to those of many previous tribal societies, with an emphasis on malign spirits, possession, the impact of ancestors, and struggles to fit in with the expectations of one's culture. As in other colonized areas, the conception of mental illness as failing to fit in with the demands of one's culture becomes distorted when it switches to failing to fit in with the demands of a colonizing culture. For instance, it may have previously been considered normal to hear the voices of one's ancestors speaking out loud, but that experience attains the label of auditory hallucination from the Western psychiatric tradition. On the other hand, local beliefs about particular psychiatric afflictions were disregarded as "superstition" by Western doctors. Other racist misunderstandings abounded. For instance, many psychiatrists believed that the nervous systems of Black Africans were underdeveloped compared to whites, and thus they could not experience clinical depression. These doctors knew little about their patients' family backgrounds or the cultural context of their problems. They lacked, and did not appear interested in learning, the knowledge to make a more insightful and nuanced diagnosis. As a result, they would diagnose mania, which was then conceived as a "simpler" mental disorder, more likely in a "primitive" nervous system (Swartz, 2017).

Around the world, a similar pattern emerges. In areas that escaped direct colonization, local traditions survived with their culturally based understandings of mental health and mental illness intact but still influenced by Western ideas. In areas that were colonized, Western notions and practices were heavily imported, mostly for the benefit of the colonizers. To the extent they were utilized for the native population, they were implemented with little consideration of the unique psychology and culture of the patient. Western theory and practice tended to dominate areas of heaviest colonial influence, especially in large urban areas. In more rural areas, the local traditions remained more intact although usually influenced by the Western model. Thus, many hybrid models have emerged, with a wide variety of combinations of Western and native ideas.

This discussion of concepts of mental health and illness around the world begs the question of how much culture impacts these issues. Most of the theories, concepts, and research associated with mental illness come from industrialized Western countries, but almost 70% of humans live in non-Western countries (Triandis, 1996). Combined with the finding that cultural factors have at least a "moderate" impact on mental health (Draguns, 1997), this suggests that we need to take these factors seriously and not just rely on Western conceptions to guide our understanding of these issues. The problem, of course, as it has been explored throughout this book, is that the relationship between culture and mental health is extremely complex.

Take stress, for instance. It is a term everyone recognizes and understands as a problem. It is caused by life's difficulties and results in psychological and physical distress, right? Well, it is not that simple. There are multiple definitions of stress, with some emphasizing biological activity and some focusing more on psychological dynamics (Wiger & Harowski, 2003). Probably the easiest way to define stress is that it is the upsetting of homeostasis, or the state of balance in the body and mind. That covers an enormous range of phenomena, however, and it still leaves open the question of what any individual experiences as upsetting. For some, being late for work can be experienced as very stressful and emotionally upsetting. For others, it is at worst a petty annoyance and perhaps not stressful at all. Why would there be such a range of reaction to the same stressor? For one thing, there are cultural differences in the meaning placed on various experiences, such as lateness to work. In much of Latin America, timeliness for work appointments does not have the same meaning as it does in American and German business communities, where being even a few minutes late to a meeting could be interpreted as irresponsibility, not adequately valuing the meeting, or a lack of self-discipline. Thus, timeliness is a different stress factor in these respective cultures. The bottom line is that stress has less to do with the event itself than with the subjective experience of the person experiencing it, and culture is a powerful force in shaping that experience (Gurang & Roethel-Wendorf, 2009). In fact, cultural and ethnic differences are so important to stress appraisal and exposure to stressful events that multicultural models of stress have been proposed that direct us to consider the confluence of both conscious and unconscious factors that lead various people to assess the same situation quite differently (Hobfoll, 1989).

As the examples of colonization and stress reaction differences make clear, the impact of culture on concepts of mental health and mental illness is profound. The historical changes occurring throughout the Western world had both direct and indirect influences on the rest of the world in the twentieth century. Many groups found themselves incorporating the Western world's models of mental illness – some did so wholesale, while others managed to hold on to significant parts of their more traditional belief systems. And while some *concepts* of mental illness are universal, such as stress reaction, the details of how that looks for people in various cultures reflects the differences between those cultures.

THE STORY OF PHILOSOPHY – PART TWO

This consideration of differences in subjective experience when exposed to similar phenomena leads us to our last section of this chapter. A modernist, materialistic philosophy approached the world as an objective fact – to be explored, understood, and manipulated through empirical analysis and interventions. From that perspective, mental health and mental illness can be understood and controlled through biological and behavioral machinations. But what if the primary factor in how we respond to the world we live in is our *subjective* experience of it? Then that becomes the core variable for the reality of and our experience of mental health and mental illness.

People can and do argue endlessly over what different phenomena are and mean and how they should affect us. Nearly everyone thinks they are right and those who disagree with them are wrong. How do we find common ground to decide what is true? The empiricists asserted that there is a source of factual evidence that leads us logically to truth, but as we discussed in the last chapter, that surety started to unravel in the nineteenth century. Kant told us that we have preexisting modes of thought that filter and shape our thinking, making objective analysis all but impossible. Kierkegaard and Nietzsche took this argument further, emphasizing the importance of emotion and self-interest in our construction of reality. They created storylines about life, including the concepts of God and Superman, which they imbued with as much realism as stars and planets *because* they were so important to human psychology. They are a human reality.

The next step away from empiricism took the form of existentialism. Jean-Paul Sartre (1905–1980) is commonly considered the first true existentialist. He was particularly concerned with the idea of human freedom. He considered this the ultimate curse. If there is no creator, no preexisting purpose to life, no specified "human nature," then life is basically absurd, and each person is fully responsible for his or her own life. We can remain in the dark and act as though we have no choices and the world is preordered, or we can take the painful effort to wake up, accept the truth, and take responsibility for ourselves. Therefore, the highest values for Sartre were authenticity and responsibility. Accepting the truth that each of us is an animal, born into the world with no particular importance or reason for being, with the rest of the world largely indifferent to our existence, is a hard pill to swallow. It is an affront to our pride, leading us to pretend to greater importance than we really have. Thus, having the strength to be our authentic selves, not inflated pretend selves, is the only real heroic task we have. To face a meaningless world is to face the absurd, and the natural reaction of reflective human beings is anxiety, dread, and despair. What is the point of coming up with a reason to live when nature does not provide one and promises only death? This is the source of what we call "existential angst" and the reason Camus concluded that there is only one really serious philosophical issue, and that is suicide. That does not mean that the question of a purpose to life has no answer, but rather that it is up to each individual to answer it for him or herself. Sartre and Camus were both strong believers in the importance of human beings to find honor and purpose in existence and therefore were strongly opposed to totalitarianism, oppression, and injustice in all its forms. They were humanists who believed in fighting for a society that respects the human condition and provides the resources to build an authentic, honorable, and meaningful life (Durant, 1926; Millon, 2004).

Another force in twentieth-century philosophy closely associated with existentialism is postmodernism. Less a singular philosophy than a general intellectual stance, it asserts that there is no foundation for any particular truth. All truths are fundamentally unstable and arbitrary by nature. They exist, to the extent they do at all, only within a particular, subjective point of view. Postmodernists enjoy taking any established truth statement and deconstructing it – uncovering the assumptions underlying the assertion and exposing their inherent weaknesses and subjectivity. The logical result of this approach is radical relativity. From this epistemological position, any reality exists only in relation to another reality, which itself is only real in relation to another, and so on. The Gestalt psychologists understood this concept and used it to explain how the mind creates "whole" experiences from the various mental contents that are available. In other words, we seek integrated, whole perceptions of reality and use a creative process to get there.

What this means for mental health is that, from a postmodern perspective, we are the creators of our own psychology, often (in fact almost always) at an unconscious level. The truth we think we see is a holistic creation of subjectively experienced phenomena, pieced together through their relative relationships with each other. I and thou – this and that – power and weakness – black and white – rich and poor. We see reality through the contrasts that impress on our minds. We take factoids and create wholes. That does not mean the factoids don't exist, but they have little meaning until we give it to them, relative to other factoids and our own wants, needs, and preconceptions. Existentialism tells us how horrifically challenging it is to strip away our closely held beliefs and see our lives in the raw. Gestalt tells us how we put our beliefs together in the first place. Existentialist and Gestalt psychologies invite us to deconstruct our realities and build new ones that will serve us better, a truly postmodern enterprise. This enterprise is, in many ways, the foundation of a model of mental health and mental illness for the future. How that enterprise has been pursued moving into the twenty-first century is the topic of our next chapter.

CHAPTER 9

THE TWENTY-FIRST CENTURY

As of this writing, we are entering the third decade of the twenty-first century. Much has changed in the field of mental health since the end of the twentieth. The mental health field has grown, it has become more integrated with other professional fields, and it has become more professionalized in general. The battles between the behaviorists, the humanists, and the psychoanalysts are (mostly) behind us. The battles between the nature camp and the nurture camp are (mostly) over. The field has expanded beyond its focus on psychological problems and has become more engaged in the area of mental health and wellness. It has more fully embraced the populations it serves, providing them with a more equal footing in regard to how their challenges are conceptualized and addressed. It has taken a more multicultural perspective, thinking more about how mental health and illness are perceived and experienced cross-culturally. And finally, the world of neuroscience is emerging as a powerful force in how we understand the brain and its role in maintaining mental health or triggering mental illness. The key word here is "emergence." The various specialties in this wide-ranging field have lived so long in their own silos that it is still a challenge to get them to "talk together" in meaningful and productive ways to develop a holistic understanding of our topic.

MODELS OF MENTAL HEALTH

As just noted, the competing models of mental health have dropped their pitchforks and are much less combative than they used to be. That does not mean, however, that they have converged or do not still have major conceptual and practical conflicts with each other. Therefore, it still makes sense to describe them separately, in their current states, and explore the points of agreement and disagreement as they still exist. Although many academic subareas exist, these models can be organized within three primary approaches: the biological/medical model, the psychological model, and the social/cultural model. I will do my best not to be redundant, since they were first discussed in the previous chapter, but there may be some overlap as we focus on the most recent developments in each but have to reintroduce them. As always, in this text, we will limit our exploration of actual treatment and instead focus on their findings and conceptual foundations.

The Biological/Medical Model

As discussed before, the biological/medical model (I will use the term "medical model" here for ease of writing and reading), approaches mental illness in a similar way as it would physical illness. It sees mental disorders as discrete, ontological entities that have identifiable signs and symptoms, as primarily biological in etiology, varying significantly from normal functioning, and are most appropriately treated through biological interventions. Mental health is typically defined as the absence of mental illness and therefor the presence of normal psychological functioning. This opening description does not mean to suggest that all psychiatrists think about mental illness exclusively through that lens. What we are exploring is a model not the perspective of any particular doctor or health care system.

The model has developed from its early days as an informal subpart of the medical establishment in the premodern era. It emerged as a separate medical specialty in the modern era with the growth of the asylums and development of psychiatry as a separate professional track from general medicine. Psychiatrists were focused on identifying and treating severe mental illness. At first, there was almost no biological knowledge to assist in this work, and the emphasis was on direct observation and subsequent categorization of mental illness. This made sense because proper differentiation of illnesses can lead to discovering each illness's cause, course, and effective treatments. As noted in the last chapter, this pursuit led to a bifurcation of the psychiatric field between psychoanalysis and what we can now call medical psychiatry. By the end of the twentieth century, however, psychoanalysis had exited the psychiatric field and, in this chapter, will be considered a part of the psychological model. The field that we know as psychiatry is now firmly embedded in the medical model.

So, now that we are caught up, what is happening within this model in the twenty-first century? The first area to approach is the definition of mental illness. This is really quite tricky. We could define mental illness as significant deviation from mental health, but that leaves the question of what mental health is in and of itself. This is particularly problematical since mental health is at least partly defined within the context of a given culture, so various people will have different definitions. We could define mental illness in terms of psychological suffering, but that is problematical for a number of reasons. For one thing, not all mental illness includes a great deal of internal suffering. Some involves social deviance that may involve external criticism and punishment but not necessarily internal, psychological distress (antisocial personality). For another thing, not everyone reports or even experiences the same level of suffering when they have a mental illness. For instance, some people who are depressed experience more physical symptoms but report relatively little emotional suffering. Still another approach would be to define mental illness in terms of behavioral deviance. But again, this runs into the problem of cultural factors. Who is going to define deviance? What is deviant in one culture is not in another, so where is the discrete, ontological disease entity? Besides, where do you draw the line between eccentricity and mental illness? Is it even ontologically valid to equate not exhibiting approved behavior with something we would call mental illness? What if that behavior is a conscious choice to be different than others? That might reflect good self-esteem and the strength of character to not "follow the crowd." Is it different if the person feels *compelled* to behave differently than her peers? Now you have the same behavior but an entirely different etiology.

What we are left with is the *presence* of psychopathology but no real definition of what it is. At this point in history, we still have no medically recognized tests for mental illness. There is no blood test or brain scan that can identify a specific mental disorder. There are television advertisements for psychotropic medications that refer to a "brain imbalance," and although there is likely some truth to that, no specific imbalances have been identified (this is a bit of an overstatement that will be explained later). Different medications appear to impact various neurotransmitters in different ways, leading to somewhat different effects, but we are nowhere near able to test for abnormal neurotransmitter levels that will give us a diagnosis and thus a focused treatment protocol. We have things we call psychological tests, but for the most part, they are questionnaires, asking various questions about symptoms, so they are not a direct measurement of a disease process, only self-reported symptoms.

This is a problem. It turns out that psychiatry has created mental disorders based on mostly self-reported collections of symptoms and signs themselves not well-established, underlying, pathological, neurological, or even psychological processes that can be measured.

This raises a basic question regarding the true nature of mental disorders. Are they (or at least some of them) real, ontologically separate disease entities like the flu, or are they variable manifestations of problems involving a variety of psychological functions? These two ways of approaching mental illness are generally referred to as categorical and dimensional. Historically, the medical establishment has favored the categorical model, while academic psychology has favored the dimensional model. Many criticisms of the categorical model have been raised over the years leading up to the publication of DSM-5 (Kendell, 1975; First, 2003; Lewis, 2006). Some of these criticisms have been ontological in nature, but even when there is an ontological issue, much of the concern has been based on the fact that categorical systems like the DSM include too much overlap of symptoms (diagnostic co-occurrence or comorbidity) and lack of clear differentiation of categorical boundaries (Wideger & Samuel, 2005). It has often been found, both in day-to-day clinical practice and in controlled research, that patients can often meet criteria for multiple disorders because the symptoms overlap, and it is not clear which one should be diagnosed (Mineka, Watson, & Clark, 1998). This problem becomes even more pronounced when considering the possible diagnosing of multiple mental disorders over a person's lifetime, because an individual's psychological problems can easily change over time (Brown, Campbell, Lehman, Grisham, & Mancill, 2001). Did the person have one mental disorder in their 20s and then a different one in their 30s just because their symptoms changed? The expansion of the number of diagnoses to the DSM over the years has also contributed to the problem, as many of these "new disorders" have simply filled in gaps between other disorders. For instance, bipolar II was introduced as a mood disorder halfway between bipolar I and cyclothymia. Does this really represent the "discovery" of an already existing but previously undiscovered disease entity, or is it just a way to put a new label on a clinical presentation that doesn't quite fit an existing diagnostic category?

As a result of these questions and the core conceptual issues they raise, many have proposed that we take a more dimensional approach to understanding mental illness (Daker, 2018; Hagele et al., 2015). The basic idea is to identify the core *mechanisms or dynamics* of mental illness across nosological boundaries. This creates a number of challenges. First, it requires that we identify all the pertinent psychological functions (PF) or mechanisms. Like personality characteristics, there is no simple way to do this, and there are likely to be longstanding disagreements about how many PFs there are. Second, there will also be significant controversy regarding overlap of proposed PFs. For instance, does impulse control constitute one PF, or should it be broken down into multiple subfunctions, and what about overlap between impulse control and affect regulation? People who struggle to control their emotions are going to have trouble controlling their behavioral impulses as well because of the motivational influence of emotions on behavior. These and a number of other challenges to dimensional diagnosis have left it at the propositional level, and there exists, at the time of this writing, no comprehensive diagnostic system based on dimensional diagnosis.

So, with this controversy in mind, let us return to the ongoing history of the DSM. As discussed before, the identification and categorization of mental disorders has been a long history that culminated in the publication of the *Diagnostic and Statistical Manual* by the American Psychiatric Association. At the time of this writing, it is in its fifth edition. We discussed the earlier history of the DSM in the last chapter. Here, we will explore the changes present in the DSM-5 and the ongoing controversy regarding its conceptualization and categorization of mental illness. After the publication of DSM-III in 1980, not too much changed in the next three editions. A few diagnoses were dropped, a few were added, and ongoing research was integrated, but there was no substantial change to its underlying concepts or structure. DSM-5, published in 2013, was supposed to represent the first truly significant change since 1980. The writers of the new DSM recognized that "past science was not mature enough to yield fully validated diagnoses" (American Psychiatric Association, 2013, p. 5). They noted that recent research had revealed that an overly rigid categorical system fails to account for clinical experience and research findings that (1) the boundaries between many DSM categories are more fluid than previous editions of the DSM recognized and (2) there was too much overlap of diagnoses, meaning that many symptoms assigned to one diagnosis occurred in many other diagnoses as well. This led them to write, "DSM, like other medical disease classifications, should accommodate ways to introduce dimensional approaches to mental disorders, including dimensions that cut across current categories" (American Psychiatric Association, 2013, p. 5).

In maintaining the existing categorical system, however, the authors noted that they did not want to change the DSM too quickly, because (1) speculative findings did not belong in an official categorical system, (2) doctors and patients needed clear and concise descriptions of each mental disorder organized by explicit diagnostic criteria, and (3) they did not want to disrupt the mental health delivery system, which was used to having such explicit criteria (American Psychiatric Association, 2013). How, for example, was a third-party payer to decide whether or how much it should reimburse a mental health professional for services without an explicit diagnosis to consider? Did the patient really need treatment, and if so, what kind of and how much treatment would be appropriate for their mental health problem? Without a clear, categorical approach, the term "clinical necessity" can become hopelessly vague and subjective. On the other hand, if clinical experience and actual research findings indicate that a dimensional approach to diagnosis is more valid than a categorical one, how can we retain a system that we now know is fundamentally false? Rather than being honestly mistaken, we would be partic-ipating in a known falsehood, just because it is more professionally convenient. It is hard to imagine a situation more ethically compromised and compromising to clinicians who rely on the DSM for diagnostics.

That is a very strong accusation and one strenuously dismissed within the med-ical model. The critique of the accusation comes from three main directions. The first has to do with the challenges to professional application if we switch to a largely dimensional approach. As noted before, without a clear categorical system, based on observable or reportable symptoms, how can mental health professionals proceed with assessment, diagnosis, and treatment planning and get reimbursed for their services? This was a primary concern for the revision of DSM-5 and their first guiding principle was that the new edition was intended to be "a manual to be used by clinicians, and revisions must be feasible for routine clinical practice" (American Psychiatric Association, 2013, p. 7).

This is an important consideration. However, the topic of treating mental ill-ness is beyond the purview of this book. What we can look at is the other two main critiques of the dimensional approach. The first is the assertion that at least some mental disorders really *do* represent distinct disease entities with an established eti-ology in genetic inheritance and neurobiological processes, with reasonably consis-tent psychological signs and symptoms. The second is that many of those disorders that do not have as strong support for being distinct disease entities still represent clearly established and consistent *complexes* and still may have a neurobiological etiology. In regard to the first, there is a great deal of support from wide-rang-ing research, including twin studies, the identification of genetic risk factors and neural substrates, and the effectiveness of psychotropic medications to reduce cer-tain symptoms that all suggest a possible biological basis for some disorders, such as schizophrenia and bipolar disorder. While there is debate about the onset and course of these disorders being strongly impacted by environmental factors, there is little doubt that the primary etiology of *severe* psychosis and mania is biological and genetic and has the hallmarks of a disease process.

In regard to the second critique, the authors of DSM-5 recognized that recent research was increasingly critical of the validity of the current categorical system, especially because of high comorbidity rates and the clinical overuse of the *not otherwise specified* (NOS) criteria. While this strongly suggested that there was a lack of clear differentiation between categories, it did not necessarily contradict the idea that there were neurological underpinnings to the symptoms present. Progress was being made in understanding those underpinnings. For instance, a great deal of work is revealing the response of the human nervous system to acute threat (Hariri, Mattay, Tessitore, Fera, & Weinberger, 2003; LeDoux, 2000). Sensory stimuli reach the amygdala through different circuits, leading to increased output in the auto-nomic nervous system (the famous flight-or-fight response), as well as the hypotha-lamic-pituitary-adrenal (HPA) axis, associated with the release of stress hormones. This neurological process can be seen with fMRI and has been associated with at least 15 genes and neurotransmitters. Researchers have found that using fMRI to expose subjects to frightening stimuli, they can identify "high" reactors and "low" reactors. Not everyone who is a high reactor has an anxiety disorder, but those with an anxiety disorder are more likely to be high reactors. Thus, there appears to be an important biological substrate to problems with anxiety. What this means in general is that although there may be difficulties with the current categorical systems, there is a strong biological basis for many psychological problems, indicating an underlying disease process of some type, and thus a categorical system of some design is called for.

However, despite these advances in our knowledge of brain functioning, there is no diagnostic test for any specific mental illness, and researchers have not been able to link particular genes to particular disorders (Pliszka, 2016). One of the main possible reasons for this is that *disorders share symptoms*. In other words, it may well be that mental illness is heavily driven by biological factors, but the genes involved play complex roles that cross the categorical lines in our current system. For instance, there are likely multiple genes involved with a psychological function like impulse control, and this function is implicated in multiple mental disorders, ranging from substance abuse to attention deficit disorder to antisocial personality disorder.

Because of findings like this, the DSM decided to reorganize the categories to better align with the research on the relationships between disorder groups. Disorders that shared common symptoms and/or developmental onset were grouped together. This was designed to stimulate more research to identify the factors driving the "cross-cutting" of symptoms across diagnoses and categories – such as sensitivity to experiencing anxiety. It also dramatically increased its inclusion of conditions that were not officially included in the nosology but deserved further study. It also included some alternative ways to approach diagnosis and assessment that enhanced a dimensional approach, such as a trait-theory approach to personality disorders. Finally, it recognized the importance of cultural issues. However, it did so by emphasizing their impact on the *experience* and *expression* of mental disorders not on their foundational etiology. In other words, it retained the biological and thus universal emphasis on mental disorders (since we all share the same basic biology) while allowing more room for cultural variation for how disorders *appear* in different cultural contexts.

Overall, the authors of DSM-5 consciously considered it a "bridge" to a more dimensional approach to understanding mental illness, one that recognized that clinical reality and neurological research were both finding a strict categorical model did not fit how people experienced mental illness or how the brain really operates. It wanted to bring evolutionary change to the document – not moving faster than the research warranted or the professional field could handle. Not surprisingly, it was not moving fast enough or seemingly in the right direction for a lot of people. One of the first things that was criticized was the fact that 70% of the DSM-5 task force members had ties to the pharmaceutical industry, and they had all signed a nondisclosure agreement regarding their work on the new edition (Cosgrove, Bursztajn, Kupfer, & Regier, 2009). Beyond those issues with the ethical foundation of the work, many were concerned that it did not go nearly far enough toward dimensional diagnosis, did not acknowledge the impact of human experience, especially trauma and culture, in *creating or defining* mental illness, and retained the idea that breaking cultural norms itself could constitute a mental disorder.

Another issue was the DSM's basic definition of mental illness. The DSM-IV generically defined mental illness as a clinically significant behavioral or psychological syndrome or pattern that caused distress, impairment, or significantly increased risk of suffering death, pain, disability, or important loss of freedom. It signified that the syndrome or pattern must not be merely an expectable and culturally sanctioned response to a particular event and must be a manifestation of a behavioral, psychological, or biological dysfunction of the individual – not deviance or conflict with prevailing culture. DSM-5 changed the definition somewhat, saying that the syndrome must be "characterized by clinically significant disturbance in an individual's cognition, emotion regulation, or behavior that reflects a dysfunction in the psychological, biological, or developmental processes underlying mental functioning" (American Psychiatric Association, 2013, p. 20). While it retained the references to culturally sanctioned responses and the idea that social deviance itself was not a mental disorder, the references to regulation and biology clearly signaled a shift to a more neurological basis for mental illness. It was also notable that despite the retention of wording about social deviance not representing a disorder, the text itself continues to include symptoms and entire disorders that are directly connected to such deviancy.

For instance, conduct disorder was retained. This condition is a persistent pattern of behavior in which the basic rights of others or major age-appropriate societal norms or rules are violated. Examples include being aggressive toward people or animals, destruction of property, deceitfulness or theft, or serious violations of rules. It is not clear how any of these conditions requires that there be a *dysfunction* of psychological, biological, or developmental processes. The main difficulty is that the person is mean, selfish, and possibly violent and/or lacking in empathy toward others, but these last two are not required for the diagnosis. An adolescent could meet the criteria if he or she stays out past curfew, runs away from home, and starts fights at school or is truant. These reflect social norms and, according to the DSM's own definition of a mental disorder, should not qualify as symptoms unless they are caused by another mental disorder. It is quite likely – and, in most clinical experience, almost always the case – that this condition reflects problematical family and other environmental conditions. When these "symptoms" are present in a youth, there are typically severe problems at home: extreme poverty, parental mental illness, parental drug or alcohol abuse, physical or sexual abuse, severe neglect, etc. Rather than "diagnosing" the social context and seeing the youth's behavior as the disturbing but understandable result of his or her environment, the DSM calls for a diagnosis of the behavior, ignoring both its own rules and the common sense of looking at all behavior as occurring within the context of a larger social and cultural picture.

This does not mean that society has no right to establish and enforce rules of behavior and even underlying beliefs and impulses. It obviously does; that is why there are laws, prisons, churches, and families to do so. It is a primary function of culture to regulate the thoughts, feelings, and subsequent behavior of its members (Triandis, 1994). It is necessary for the smooth operation and thus the functionality of any society. The point here is that making the shift from behavior that breaks social rules and thus has negative consequences to calling it a mental disorder requires that an underlying disease process be identified. The medical model, by insisting that mental disorders are individually based disease entities, puts itself in the position of needing to understand and describe precisely *how* the neurobiological functioning of a person is malfunctioning in order to diagnose a mental disorder in such cases.

How is the medical model doing in its search for an understanding of the neurobiological underpinnings of psychopathology and linking that understanding to a subsequent nosology of mental illness? By almost all accounts, not well (Frances, 2009; Harrington, 2019). There is certainly a growing amount of information regarding the neurological basis of many psychological processes, as well as both genetics and epigenetics, but this explosion of knowledge has not translated into a clear biological understanding of any mental disorder or the identification of any biomarkers for mental disorders, and the entire enterprise is complicated by the fact that the same brain regions appear to be dysfunctional across various disorders (Pliszka, 2016). Harrington points out that not only have we not been able to isolate specific neurological dysfunctions for particular disorders, there have not been any significant improvements in the medical interventions for them either. Recent advances in psychotropic medication have consisted of incremental improvements to medications that have been around for decades, and their overall effectiveness continues to be weak compared to placebos in clinical trials (2019).

The situation in regard to the DSM is just as bad. The DSM-5 had promised to be a radical revision, establishing a biological basis for the nosology of mental illness, but it failed on that promise, and it was unwilling to fully commit to a more psychosocial, dimensional model. The result then was mostly a revising of chapters and categories, what Frances had previously referred to as "rearranging the furniture" (2009). The dream of a truly biological approach to understanding, categorizing, and then treating mental illness is still a long way off.

The Cultural Model

If the medical model does not have all the answers (yet), then we still need to look outside the individual body and brain to understand important aspects of mental health and mental illness. As noted before, throughout history, culture has been the main force defining what is crazy and what is sane. It continues to be, and the ability of people to adaptively "fit" and function in their cultural context is still a common approach to defining mental illness.

The initial question that needs to be answered here is, what is culture? Stephen Heine answers the question by pointing to two things: (1) information that is acquired from others through social learning that affects one's behavior and (2) a particular group of individuals existing within a shared context (2008). So culture is the group itself and the process by which it develops, enforces, and passes on shared beliefs, meanings, and practices. Obviously, this impacts all areas of the individual's life, from before birth until after death. Self-concept, socialization, spiritual beliefs and practices, love, sex, friendship, work, play, core beliefs about morality and justice, emotional experience and expression, and, of course, concepts of mental health and mental illness are all included.

Heine (2008) tells the story of a 14-year-old Japanese youth who took up residence in his family's kitchen, refusing to leave and not letting anyone else in. The garbage piled up, and his family had to eat elsewhere. They let him do this, and he apparently lived like this for quite some time as the family finally built another kitchen in the home. This condition is called *hikikomori* and affects as many as 1 in 10 Japanese males in their late teens to early 20s. It is an extreme form of social isolation. Many explanations have been offered for this syndrome, including parenting style, the extreme pressure of Japanese culture on youth, low birth rates in Japan leading to under socialization, etc. What we do know is that it did not exist in any significant numbers prior to the late twentieth century, is much more common in boys than in girls, and does not appear to be common in any other cultures. It also does not meet criteria for any mental disorder in the DSM, which refers to *cultural syndromes* but does not include any as recognized mental disorders and no longer provides a list of such syndromes in DSM-5.

The prominence of *hikikomori* in Japan raises the questions of what constitutes a mental disorder and to what extent they are universal versus specific within a cultural context. What is central to the cultural model is the idea that what matters most about any particular belief, feeling, or behavior is what it *means* to the social group of which the individual is a part. For instance, a 40-year-old woman, a mother of three children, working as an emergency room physician, living in suburban America, who drinks alcohol very heavily from Friday night through Sunday afternoon is likely to place – and have placed upon her – a very different meaning to her drinking behavior than a 21-year-old male who is attending college and living in a frat house. The concept of "boys will be boys" is quite different than "you are too old and have too many responsibilities to be acting like this." The difference is the culturally ascribed meaning attached to the same behavior being exhibited by different people. The young man and the middle-aged woman inhabit different subcultures with different rules, beliefs, and expectations. Adding to that example, such behavior from a young male today may elicit a different meaning than it did just 20 years ago. Culture changes over time. The relationships between subcultures change over time. Thus, the concepts of mental health and illness can be expected not only to be contingent on the meanings established by culture but to change as their underlying cultures change.

An example of this was a mental disorder referred to a couple of chapters ago. Neurasthenia was a condition first recognized in the early nineteenth century in North America. It was understood as a weakness of the nerves, leading to fatigue, anxiety, headaches, heart palpitations, high blood pressure, neuralgia, and depressed mood. It was thought to be a result of the exhaustion of the central nervous system and attributed primarily to the effects of modern civilization, especially urbanization and highly competitive work environments. The diagnosis does not exist in the current DSM. To the extent it still exists, it would likely be considered a *culture-bound* syndrome.

What happened to this disorder? And the larger question is, how is it, if mental illness is brain-based and genetically inherited, that mental disorders come and go over time and vary so much from culture to culture? The answer, from the cultural model's perspective, is that much of what we call human nature, including mental illness, is heavily mediated by cultural factors. This is reflected not just in what we consider culture-bound disorders, but also in the existence, experience, and course of more universal psychological problems.

Depression is perhaps the most universal of all psychological maladies. Many people around the world experience periods of time when they feel sad, down, hopeless, and lacking in energy. It impacts their work, their play, and their relationships. They lose interest in things that used to inspire them. They lose motivation and cognitive acuity and may even start thinking about suicide. Depending on how it is being measured, lifetime rates of depression in the United States are about 15% (Kessler et al., 2005). However, although it exists, depression rates in many other countries are far lower than those in the United States. In China, as recently as the mid-90s, the rates were one-fifth of those in America (Kessler et al., 1994). Historically, Chinese medicine has had little to say about anything resembling depression as we recognize it in the West. On the other hand, many people manifest depression less through emotional or cognitive symptoms but rather through somatic issues, including fatigue, sleep problems, and unexplained pain or weakness. Does this sound similar to the neurasthenia described a couple of paragraphs ago? When an anthropologist studied Chinese patients with this disorder, he found that 87% of them could be described as experiencing clinical depression (Kleinmann, 1982). So something related to depression may be universal (it has been found in every country studied), but how it manifests may be quite different in various cultural contexts.

One of the possible reasons for the difference in presentation of depression in various cultures is the meaning attached to various symptoms. In China, there is more of a stigma associated with having a psychological disorder than a physical one (Ryder, 2004). Other differences may include the possibility that some cultures may tend to focus on some symptoms and not others. Yet another one is that the cultural values and beliefs of a culture impact the actual rate of particular disorders (especially given the symptom profiles provided by the DSM) that reflect those values and beliefs. This could impact depression rates from culture to culture. For instance, in areas with more pronounced social anxiety concerns, such as East Asia, you could expect higher rates of social anxiety disorder, and that is what you find (Okazake, 1997). These kinds of differences emerge wherever you look. For instance, suicide rates are far higher in predominantly Christian cultures than in Muslim cultures, where suicide is especially condemned (Schmidtke, et al., as cited in Heine, 2008). Even schizophrenia, which has a strong biological basis and is found at similar rates around the world, has significant differences in presentation, with high rates of paranoia in England but low rates in India, while the pattern was reversed for catatonia (WHO, 1974). Together, these findings show that there are some types of mental illness that are universal, while others are more local, but nearly all can appear quite differently across cultures.

One way to approach the complicated topic of culture and psychopathology is to consider underlying psychological processes rather than specific mental disorders. One of the advantages of this approach is that it allows space for both cultural and neurobiological research, as it assumes a biological foundation for pathology as well as cultural variation in its expression. One of the primary psychological processes involved in maintaining mental health versus slipping into pathology is emotional regulation. All cultures provide norms for proper regulation of emotion, including the appropriate types (anger, joy, fear, disgust, etc.), levels, and social situations in which they may be experienced and expressed. These norms reflect various beliefs and values unique to each culture. For instance, in one society, it may be acceptable to become angry with one's parents, but in another, it is not. In that context, the universal, desired outcome of childhood development is not a particular profile of emotional expression but, instead, cultural emotional competence (Trommsdorff & Heikamp, 2013).

As a general rule, children need to learn how to inhibit their emotional reactions based on an internalization of societal rules as presented by primary caregivers; therefore, there will always be individual differences between members of a society, based partly on their individual neurobiological differences as well as their different caregiving experiences. Emotional regulation is culturally important in a wide variety of ways. It is a key to managing stress, getting one's needs met, and maintaining relationships, all within the context of a culture-based meaning system of self, other, social relations, and the world at large. It is also important to note that cognition is a central element of emotions. The emergence of any particular emotion reflects the conclusion of an analysis of current stimuli. That is, we decide what something means (is it funny, threatening, sexy, safe, etc.) and then experience an emotion related to that cognition. At the same time, emotion and cognition have a reciprocal relationship. Emotions are a central part of our continual assessment process regarding our inner and outer worlds. Those assessments are both personal and culturally mediated. In a closely related concept, there is the idea of emotional intelligence, which refers to the ability to recognize one's own emotions as well as others, differentiate various emotions, use emotionally based information to guide our thinking and behavior, and manage our emotions to adapt to various situations and reach our goals (Coleman, 2005). And of course, these processes are all culturally mediated.

What is particularly important for our purposes in this text is that cultural emotional competence and emotional intelligence are keys to mental health. They provide the tools to properly assess a variety of situations, be aware of how one is understanding and reacting to them, choose emotional expression that is adaptive, and maintain a variety of supportive relationships in one's life. Poor emotional regulation or competence has the opposite effect. The person makes significant mistakes in understanding what is going on, both inside and outside themselves, lacks self-awareness or adequate awareness of others, lacks control over their emotional expression, behaves in ways that are maladaptive, and struggles to form and maintain rewarding relations with others. This dovetails with a variety of pathological syndromes, including anxiety and mood disorders, substance use problems, personality disorders, and of course all sorts of behavioral problems that may or may not be identified as constituting mental illness.

Within a cultural context, one of the differences in emotional competence that can be found is between independence-oriented cultures and interdependence-oriented ones (Trommsdorff & Heikamp, 2013). Most Western cultures are independence-oriented and value autonomy and self-reflection.

Parents may encourage or at least allow their children to express negative emotions toward others, even authority figures. The highest value is authenticity. In much of Asia, interdependence is the norm, and the highest value is empathy. Therefore, parents teach their children that expressing negative emotions is socially undesirable and discourage it. As a result of this cultural difference, Westerners may find a greater sense of overall mental health and wellness when they feel they can be authentic and express their emotions freely, no matter if they are positive or negative. Conversely, Asians may feel a stronger sense of mental health when they are able to control their emotions, expressing mainly positive ones, thus valuing others and maintaining good, respectful relationships. The Asian personality may find the Western approach selfish and immature, while the Western personality may find the Asian approach inauthentic and manipulative. Both attitudes reflect a certain level of misunderstanding of the other, because both approaches are based on an appropriate value system and, when activated, sustain good mental health within a specific cultural context. It is also important to remember that this reflects large-scale group differences and not individuals who can be more or less independence oriented, no matter what culture they come from.

The idea of independence oriented versus interdependence oriented, with its corresponding Western personality and Asian personality, is obviously a grossly simplified concept. Reality is much more complex than that. There are many types of cultures and subcultures and many types of individual personalities within those cultures. Simplistic binaries tell us something, but they miss a lot and also tend to distort what is really going on. A more nuanced way to approach a cultural model of mental health would be to separate the *types* of influence culture has on mental health and illness (Rogers & Pilgrim, 2014). In this approach, one would consider *social causation*, in which social problems are a direct cause of psychological distress and thus mental illness. Linking the effects of racism and poverty to depression is an example of this. A second perspective is *societal response*, which explores how stigma and other negative cultural reactions to mental illness amplify the suffering and problems associated with mental illness. The impact of long-term institutional treatment on the patients and families of those with mental illness is also an example of this.

One of the many challenges in the cultural model is that it is nearly impossible to conduct controlled studies in this area. You can't gather a group of research subjects, randomly assign them different categories (Black, white, Asian, etc.), and then see how they respond to different societal situations such as poverty, migration, or discrimination. Virtually all research in this area is correlational. That means that we can never really know what factors *cause* other factors. To make matters even more complicated and unclear, there is always a combination of factors in play. You can't separate one factor – say, ethnicity – from all the other ones impacting a person's life, such as age, immigration status, socioeconomic status, physical health, gender, etc. The best you can do is measure the likelihood that someone is going to have mental health problems if certain conditions are present. Does being poor correlate with increased risk for depression, for instance? (The answer is yes, by the way.) Many researchers have found that a wide variety of social problems increase vulnerability to mental health problems (Fryers, Meizer, & Jenkins, 2003; Murali & Oyebode, 2004; Wilkinson & Pickett, 2009).

These findings point out two primary issues that are central to the cultural model. First, that social processes and institutions are important in regard to the formation, experience, expression, and consequences of both mental health and mental illness. This occurs in a variety of ways. On the one hand, being a member of a cultural group has many protective effects. Humans are social beings; we find comfort and support through our association and close relationships with others and collectively identify through various groupings, including ethnicity, religion, social status, profession, education, gender, nationhood, etc. These associations bolster our sense of self-identity and what we believe about ourselves, others, and the world in general. They provide feedback that can increase self-esteem and overall well-being. However, on the other hand, culture also includes dynamics that can lead to alienation, oppression, victimization, misunderstanding, and the creation or exacerbation of poor mental health. It is a double-edged sword, and culture has great power to both empower and disempower the human capacity for psychological well-being.

The second issue is that the DSM and the medical model themselves arise from a cultural perspective. They present themselves as value free, objective, and research based. However, this has been criticized as an intellectually disingenuous (Kiesler, 1999) and culturally blind perspective, focused primarily on what it *sees* as universal disease entities, identifiable by specific signs and symptoms, separate from the phenomenological experience of the patient (Scull, 2015). In general, the cultural model does not claim that mental illness has no biological component and typically does not even assert that there are not at least some psychological disorders that are universal. Instead, it asserts that culture is a powerful force that (1) creates certain unique disorders, (2) shapes the onset, experience, and course of others, and (3) is the psychological foundation of all conceptions of mental health and disorder. Therefore, any valid approach to the topic needs to keep cultural issues front and center as an organizing principle in understanding anybody's mental problems.

The Psychological Model

That is where the field of psychology kicks in – providing conceptually based meanings for the experiences of an individual life. With models of psychological functioning, focusing on individual development, as well as psychological wellness and pathology, the field of psychology provides foundational principles for how the human experience can move individual development in a healthy or unhealthy direction. We can revisit the major submodels of psychology, first introduced in the previous chapter, and see what they have to say about our subject matter in the twenty-first century. The major submodels of psychology can be generally organized as the psychodynamic, the cognitive-behavioral, and the humanistic. This organization has developed in response to how they have evolved along separate tracks in the twentieth century. Although they are now mainly associated with their respective psychotherapeutic treatments, each is based on a foundational philosophy about human nature and psychological functioning, especially as it reflects mental health and mental illness. Therefore, it makes sense for us to explore each one separately.

The Psychodynamic Submodel

The first to look at is the psychodynamic model. We will do a quick review and then discuss the more recent evolution of psychodynamic theory. Stemming from the original ideas of Sigmund Freud, this model has developed in interesting ways since he first saw patients late in the nineteenth century. In the last chapter, we discussed the revolution set off by the discovery of the unconscious mind, with Freud taking that idea and developing an extensive psychology around it, portraying the human psyche as structured in levels (unconscious, preconscious, conscious), and organized around basic functions (id, ego, superego). The human personality, as he saw it, was predisposed to experience high levels of internal (between the id and the superego) as well as external conflict (between the self and society); thus some level of neurosis was inevitable. According to early psychoanalytic theory, individuals are always at war within and outside themselves. The result is tension, anxiety, and a variety of ways in which people try to resolve the conflict. One way we deal with the internal conflict is to develop a number of ego defenses so that individuals can feel as if they are whole and unconflicted. Later theorists dropped the more controversial parts of the theory and focused on the more-or-less healthy ways that people develop a strong, stable, and socially connected sense of self. In recent decades, psychoanalysis has focused more on the importance of culture and interpersonal relationships to shape the human personality.

Feminist psychoanalysts have challenged the phallocentric nature of classic analytic thought, which valued masculine virtues, saw the female as "naturally" inferior to the male and psychologically suffering from the lack of a penis, and saw gays, lesbians, and transgender people all as experiencing a severe form of neurosis. Instead, healthy childhood development was reconceptualized as a process that calls for parental love, acceptance of children as they are, meeting the child's basic needs, and helping the child develop the internal resources to manage the challenges of life. The healthy self can be gay, straight, bi, or questioning. It can feel predominantly male, female, or mixed. It can live out a variety of lifestyles, believe in various religions (or none), and exist adaptively (or in rebellion) in many different societies.

The newer paradigm became *intersubjectivity* – referring to a process in which personality development is influenced by the relationship between the self and others – a reciprocal interaction rather than the classic idea of the unidirectional self struggling against the other. This evolution of psychoanalysis has extended to its consideration of culture as well. Moving beyond the conflict-based Freudian interpretations of culture (the individual is called on to develop in spite of culture and in perpetual conflict with it), modern psychoanalysts emphasize the prominence of culture in shaping the individual psyche. These considerations of the intersubjective perspective in both the individual and cultural domains has led modern theorists like Jessica Benjamin to explore a variety of issues, including why people submit to authority and enjoy it, the appeal of domination and submission, and the ongoing "war of the sexes" these dynamics perpetuate (1988), leading to new understanding of the power of *recognition and interpenetration* of self and other, the development of *mutual responsiveness and transformation*, and the emergence of *the third*, the relational matrix between self and other (2018).

In some ways, psychoanalysis has remained the same. It deeply honors and seeks to explore the hidden corners of the psyche, the "dark country" of what we are not aware of in ourselves and between ourselves and others. It recognizes that we are influenced by things inside us that our conscious self finds repugnant. It believes that in order to be whole, we need to increase our self-awareness. The dance of blaming others for what we ourselves create in our psyches and our lives gets us nowhere. To own ourselves, we need to know ourselves. It also retains important aspects of earlier parts of the overall theory, especially in regard to defense mechanisms, object relations, and attachment theory. Psychoanalysts are still interested in how people internalize aspects of primary caregivers to develop their own sense of self. They still look to the dynamics of early childhood to identify ongoing issues in present-day relationships. And they still look for the ways that people protect their own feelings by twisting reality to fit their wishes, dreams, and desires. The unconscious and early development are still the keys to unlocking the psyche (Summers & Barber, 2010).

In other ways, however, psychoanalytic theory has changed. Carl Jung developed the concept of the *collective unconscious* early in the twentieth century. By the twenty-first, his ideas were still embraced by many followers, and some still considered themselves Jungians. Others had made enough changes to his theories that it was now called archetypal or depth psychology. Led by James Hillman, this approach drew upon Jung but seeks to widen the scope of the psyche. It explores many myths and legends throughout history to identify and amplify the meaning-laden themes of human life. Expanding the idea of ego or even personality, Hillman unapologetically refers to the *soul* and sees it connected to the wider energies and images of human imagination from time immemorial. He invites people to rise from their self-conception (and professionals' conception) of pathology. Psychological problems can be ennobled through an association with mythological themes. He asserts there is a sense of soul in the suffering of psychopathology. There can be a richness and depth in emotional pain and the life difficulties of any person. Hillman wrote that "mythology is a psychology of antiquity – psychology is a mythology of modernity" (1979, p. 23) It was in this spirit that he approached human dreams as reflecting the presence of the underworld and death. He meant that the soul's foundation rests in the chthonic, earthly depths that are not reached through the arid, Apollonian heights of intellectual discourse so common in psychology. It is met through the images of the creative imagination. Images of darkness and death provoke an experience at the core of our being, and only by braving the entry and journeying through that darkness can the soul retrieve riches to enliven the human life.

Modern life has stripped us of much of that richness. It provides few guides or signposts for the journey, so modern man stands as a weak shadow of his potential self in a world stripped of depth. Hillman envisioned a psychology that could help people descend to that depth and reclaim its riches for themselves and for the world around them (1972). Beyond that, he proclaimed an image of the soul as embodied in the world. Individuals are a reflection of the soul of the world, both the natural world and the world of our making – the buildings, the cities, the governments, the economies, and the societies. If the world we live in is sick, how can we be well? If we are sick, is it not a reflection of the sickness of the world? Hillman imagined a psychology that took human suffering as a sign that we should change the world, not just ourselves. For us, we should enter our suffering and find out what it really is and what it wants. It is part of us, in some ways our most authentic self, and *through it*, we become more fully ourselves (Hillman, 1992).

The addition of intersubjectivity and depth psychology had the effect of moving psychodynamic theory in the direction of the humanist model. The humanist model was already strongly impacted by a postmodern approach to human wellness, recognizing that people create their sense of meaning and purpose through a transactional process of mutual influence. It was already dedicated to the notion that we are social beings who develop a sense of wellness at least partly through the quality of our relationships with others. It already acknowledged the importance of the outside world in supporting or hindering the development of a healthy, positive sense of self in relationship with that world. By dropping some of the hierarchal and outdated trappings of classical psychoanalysis and embracing a more constructionist model of reality, psychodynamic theory has begun to look much more humanistic in the twenty-first century.

The Cognitive-Behavioral Submodel

The next submodel of psychology to consider is behaviorism. The mythopoetic approach of Hillman and the depth psychologists could not stand in starker contrast to the cognitive-behavioral theorists of the twenty-first century. As described in the last chapter, behaviorism developed in the academic world as an empirical, scientific response to psychoanalysis. The human mind was considered a "black box," inaccessible to any direct measurement then available. The result was a theory focused on what was measurable. The theory went through three recognizable stages – behavioral conditioning, cognitive theory, and third wave. The first two were described in the previous chapter. Pavlov famously found that the dogs he was working with started salivating for food before the food was present or could be smelled if they received a stimulus signaling its impending arrival. This created a new stimulus–response relationship – it was conditioned, rather than natural, and thus is called classical conditioning. B.F. Skinner built on this idea and recognized that complex patterns of human behavior could be controlled through a process of rewards and punishments, that is, secondary to the direct stimulus–response relationship. The stimulus could operate through secondary means, like offering a raise to an employee if he or she works harder. This became known as *operant conditioning*. An extension of operant conditioning was offered when it was noted that humans do not always need direct rewards and punishments but often learn behavior through the influence of important people in their lives. They look up to and seek to emulate the beliefs and behavior of others and, conversely, may feel repelled by the beliefs and behavior of others who have been identified as abhorrent by admired or influential social forces. This is referred to as *social learning*.

As introduced in the last chapter, behaviorism's focus in relation to mental health and illness primarily is that it provided a basic understanding for the dynamics of human motivation and, by extension, provided a foundation for a proposed utopian society based on adaptive conformity. In regard to the first part, behaviorism as a theory is really value free. It posits a basic philosophy of human motivation based almost entirely on a system of rewards and punishments. It rejects the idea of underlying, unconscious processes or even conscious aspirations. Skinner claimed that there had been no progress in the science of human behavior up to his time and that references to mentation were spurious and unscientific, akin to asking about the goals and dreams of a computer or robot (1971). The technology of human behavior can be and is used in many different ways, for good or evil, and the theory of the technology itself has nothing to say about this except to insist that all pathological behavior is *reinforced* the same way as healthy behavior. In regard to the second part, it postulates that the individual and, by extension the human collective, works best when it operates on behavior principles, with beliefs grounded in reality, a clear and consistent system of rewards and punishments, and the ultimate values being efficiency and adaptation.

That extreme model of behavior was modified by the introduction of cognitive psychology. It was acknowledged that *something* was going on in the mind before it decided to *do* something. However, it still mainly focused on basic mental processes like memory and basic problem solving rather than bigger ideas like our deeper hopes and dreams. By the beginning of the twenty-first century, the cognitive-behavioral model no longer denied that such things were real (just because they could not be scientifically measured), but they held no substantial place in the model, which was now focused almost exclusively on the treatment of behavioral and mental health problems. Hardly anyone is writing about utopian cognitive-behavioral societies anymore; they just want to address clinical problems like depression and anxiety.

Having caught up to the twenty-first century, now we can explore the newest stage of the theory and how it relates to our central topic. The final piece of the cognitive-behavioral puzzle is what is typically called "third-wave CBT." The first wave (pure behaviorism) was combined with cognitive psychology in the 1970s to form the second wave. By the turn of the century, that wave was itself running into problems (Hayes, 2004). One difficulty was the fact that it turned out that changing cognition was not very effective in producing clinical progress. Another was that clinicians and researchers were increasingly doubtful that a modernist, mechanistic approach to human psychology was particularly valid or effective. What this means is that in both the behavioral and cognitive approaches, the assumption had been that human beings act like machines – elementary parts are put together in subsystems and linked to other subsystems, and then a predictable output can be achieved. Behaviorism had been developed on an animal model of functioning with very basic mentation. Cognitive psychology had been developed on a computer model of functioning with clear, consistent rules of data processing. The problem is that humans do not work in quite that simple, logical, consistent way, so the systemic assumptions of the CBT model were not leading to the effects that were predicted. This led to a reevaluation of the entire model.

The new model is more constructivist and postmodern. It turns out that the *context* of mental processes, interpersonal relationships, and external forces matter more than the elements of cognition themselves. This finding was reinforced as research began to emerge that found (1) psychotherapeutic treatments in general tend to have broad impacts and (2) psychopathology itself tends to have broad impacts (Lebow & Jenkins, 2018). This suggested that there was a significant overlap between disorders as well as between treatments. It began to make more sense to think in terms of general models of pathology and treatment approaches. Therapies that addressed a range of targeted problems with a range of interventions and that were flexible in how the treatment was provided to any particular client were found to be most effective (Lebow & Jenkins, 2018). An early example of this was Martha Linehan's dialectic behavior therapy (1993), which combined training in mindfulness-based meditation and coping skills training, alongside the more traditional cognitive-behavioral talk therapy. Other therapies followed suit, such as mindfulness-based cognitive therapy (Teasdale et al., 2002). They found that it is more effective to change cognitive functioning (context) than the form of thoughts themselves (mechanistic). This reflected the underlying reality that the human psyche could not be reduced to simple behavioral or even more complex cognitive processes. Mental health reflected a combination of behavioral, cognitive, and other psychological processes, acting in concert, within a particular context.

A more recent form of therapy to emerge from this sea-change in thinking in the cognitive-behavioral world was acceptance and commitment therapy (ACT) (Hayes, 2004). Hayes makes it clear that a lot of philosophical work went into the development of ACT. He refers to the new conceptual approach as *functional contextualism*. With this term, he emphasizes the idea that any thought or behavior needs to be understood not in and of itself but within the wider context of a person's entire life. Along those lines, what is concluded to be "true" must be based on an epistemology of pragmatism. Things are true to the extent they *work*, that is they are effective and resonate with other known truths. That is, things *become* true (both conceptually and practically) within a relational dynamic with other things. In the clinical realm, this means that it does not make sense and is thus impractical to consider a client's depressive thought ("nothing ever works out for me") as an isolated phenomenon to be changed, rather than one part of an entire way of thinking that exists within the context of everything else about the person's current situation and life history.

This contextualism demands that people consider all aspects and intersubjective dynamics of a particular "situation." An abbreviated list of these aspects would include the person's current physiological health, life history of mental and physical health issues, current work, financial and relationship status, and cultural issues. The resulting "truth" of the person is necessarily limited and subjectively defined. Nobody is aware of all contextual aspects of their immediate life situation – people attend to a narrow band of information. There is also the vast expanse of influences that people are not aware of but still impact them. They constitute the "water we swim in," and people are so used to it that they don't know they are in water.

The second part of this contextualism refers to intersubjective dynamics. Hayes alluded to this concept with what he called relational frame theory (RFT)

(2004). This model describes learning as a bidirectional process in which the formal properties of objects are cognized, related to by the receiver, abstracted, and those abstractions applied to other, seemingly similar objects. Thus, learning is an ongoing dynamic process of interaction between objects, the subjective analysis of the learner, and new objects. "Objects," in this context, refers to all internal and external stimuli that the human organism processes. An example Hayes uses is the evolution of understanding coin values by a child. The young child sees that a dime is physically smaller than a nickel and thus concludes the nickel is more valuable than the dime (big things > small things). As she grows and adds a new cognitive object to her thinking, she realizes that dimes are actually worth more than nickels (monetary value vs. physical size). She can then test this new understanding in the practical world to "see" if she can buy more candy with a dime than a nickel. The truth of that proposition is embedded in the culture in which she lives. Both a dime and a nickel are just round chunks of metal. Their monetary meaning is provided by a given economic culture.

So people interact with the world (and themselves) relationally and build up an experience of themselves and the world through this transactional process. This means, in part, that people all think they are "right" about their conception of reality because it corresponds to multiple sources of feedback. Someone can argue that another is "wrong" based on one source, but that other person has other sources of feedback, both internal and external, that tell them they are right. This makes attitude and behavioral change quite challenging – the original clinical problem that led to the change in philosophical direction. Patterns of cognition, and thus subsequent emotion and behavior, tend to be subjectively biased and self-reinforcing. It doesn't really matter if the pattern supports mental health or mental illness; people are just as rigid in their continuation of distorted, dysfunctional patterns of belief as they are in ones that promote wellness and success.

David Levy reviewed some of the most common ways that people engage in this process, many of which were discovered in social psychology research (2010). One way we do this is through the power of naming. Once we have a vocabulary for something, we assume it exists. This has been a criticism of many ideas in psychology, starting with some of the more controversial ideas of Sigmund Freud. Just because he was a prominent figure and came up with the term "Oedipal complex," does that mean that such a phenomenon actually exists? This is an easy one to question, but what about substance abuse or attention deficit disorder or even depression? How do we know such things really exist outside the power of language to convince us they do? What if we used terms like "substance use," "action oriented," or "melancholy" – would that change how we think about, feel about, experience, and respond to the same phenomena?

Another way we often misunderstand the world is confusing dichotomous variables with continuous ones. We often think about things that exist on a continuum (substance abuse, ADHD, and depression for instance) as if they are black and white – they exist in total or not at all. Every time we say that so-and-so "always" does this or "never" does that, we are probably engaging in that cognitive error. There are also a number of ways we maintain preexisting beliefs: we fit incoming data into them (assimilation bias), we only look for and see data that matches them (confirmation bias), we look backward after an event and think we knew it would happen all along (hindsight bias), and we even find our beliefs leading to behavior that leads to the expected result (self-fulfilling prophecy).

The human mind's ways of distorting reality are nearly endless (Levy, 2010). The stronger people's emotions are the more they believe our perception of the stimulus is accurate. People pay more attention to the initial, the most recent, and the most dramatic examples of things. People assume that causation is unidirectional when it is often bidirectional or multidirectional. People confuse correlation with causation. It has also been found that people have a tendency to minimize their responsibility for their own actions but exaggerate the personal responsibility of others (fundamental attribution error). There are also the imaginative ways people utilize personal memory. For instance, there is the common phenomenon of how people, when they enter substance abuse treatments like Alcoholics Anonymous, begin to reorganize their life memory to fit the prevailing myths of the treatment program (Hillman & Ventura, 1992). Overall, people tend to think that their perception of themselves and the world around them is like a hyper realistic painting, when in fact it is more like surrealism or, for the less cognitively organized, abstract impressionism.

Making matters even more complicated, these and other cognitive processes happen automatically, below the level of conscious awareness. Hayes calls this *cognitive fusion* and points out how it leaves people less in touch with the here and now of direct connection with themselves and the outside world. If I am creating a depressive life-view, I will typically take it as "real," not recognizing my own psyche at work or more reality-based, nondepressive aspects of the world around me. The answer then is *not* to confront the specific thoughts, feelings, or behavior that is present but rather to help people become consciously aware of the *process* by which they are pathologizing their own experience.

This is not dissimilar to Gestalt's view of the psyche as creating its own version of reality as a spontaneous emergent process of consciousness based on contextual analysis. Without getting too deep in the weeds regarding therapeutic technique, both ACT and Gestalt see psychological problems through the lens of contextualization and field theory and the way out of these problems as utilizing various tools to amplify self-awareness and thus increase the potential for thoughtful, value-based, organistic responses from a more integrated self. This can be done through a dialectic process – a therapeutic conversation whose aim is to bring awareness to and deconstruct the meaning and import of an otherwise automatic cognitive process. Hayes calls this *cognitive diffusion*. It can also be done through nonverbal activities such as *mindfulness* exercises. Its purpose is to increase contact, both within the self and between the inner and outer worlds, without judgment. A person's thoughts about the stimuli (cognitive, emotional, somatic) are simply other stimuli to be aware of. This breaks up the cognitive fusion, bringing awareness of the contextual subjectivity of the currently lived experience.

Of course, there is more to ACT than mindfulness, but it was particularly important to point out how its use reflects a revolutionary change in how the cognitive-behavioral model conceptualizes mental health and mental illness. By moving toward a more relativistic, postmodern perspective, the cognitive-behavioral world has taken significant steps toward the humanistic world, narrowing the distance between the two and creating the possibility for rapprochement and integration.

The Humanistic Submodel

But before we get there, we need to explore twenty-first-century humanistic psychology. As described in the previous chapter, this model focuses on the ideas that (1) human beings should be considered holistically, not as a collection of parts, (2) human beings have self-will and autonomy, (3) human beings have goals and values, and these are central to their nature, and (4) human beings naturally strive for well-being, superior functioning, community, and often spiritual growth (self-actualization). It is a philosophy more than an academic discipline and has its roots in existentialism and phenomenology. Its clinical manifestations were initially in existential and client-centered psychotherapy. It was central to the human potential movement of the twentieth century and the integration of various practices (Gestalt therapy, bodywork, yoga, and meditation) for personal growth. Its high valuation of spirituality helped distinguish it from the psychodynamic and cognitive-behavioral models and helped it easily work synergistically with various religious/philosophical systems, but it seems most at home within Buddhist or eclectic spiritual approaches.

By the end of the twentieth century, the human potential and related New Age movements had petered out. Many of humanistic psychology's early leaders, including Abraham Maslow, Carl Rogers, and Rollo May were gone, and it wasn't clear who would lead this movement into the new century. Culturally, there seemed to be a backlash against the positivity of the whole approach. In America, the idealism of the '60s was followed by the hedonism and subsequent alienation of the '70s. This "burnout" appears to have opened the door to a desire to return to the more "traditional" values of materialism, militarism, and nationalism, and thus the '80s found America in revolt from the humanistic '60s and '70s. Although there was a slew of self-help books on the shelves and lots of people were going to therapy, they seemed more concerned about healing their inner child, getting the love they needed, and recovering from being abducted by aliens than with saving the world. People were licking their wounds, and the humanistic movement began to appear naive, self-indulgent, and soft-headed. It was often seen as the playground of a bored and frustrated upper middle class, still desperately seeking meaning in a plastic-laden, suburban landscape.

So, in the late twentieth century, the humanistic enterprise was weakened and in a defensive posture. Where was humanistic psychology by the start of the twenty-first century? It had certainly not gone away. It had moved in two basic directions. In regard to the clinical side of the movement, begun by Carl Rogers 70 years ago, the core beliefs and values of humanistic psychotherapy have now evolved into (1) a basic foundation for psychotherapeutic practice and (2) the emergence of positive psychology, wellness, and the recovery movement. On the theoretical side, fathered by Abraham Maslow, it has fostered an increased interest in multicultural approaches to understanding mental health, an ongoing critique of a predominantly Western, medical modal approach to mental illness, and a dedication to a postmodern, relativistic epistemology. Its concerns have thus naturally grown beyond that of the health of the individual to the larger society and not just local society but encompassing all of humanity and the Earth itself.

First, there is the question of humanistic psychology becoming the foundation of therapeutic practice. It has become the norm that training programs, no matter what the stated theoretical, focus teach client-centered principles as the foundation of psychotherapeutic skills. In the 1950s, Carl Rogers was a maverick, asserting that it was not as important what therapists *did* but rather who they *were*. He believed that in order for clients to feel safe to delve deeply into the vulnerabilities of their psyches, the therapist should exhibit a set of personal characteristics that created a sense of safety and trust. He asserted that if this core condition was set, clients would naturally bring forth those elements of their soul that would energize them to move in a healthier direction in their lives. These conditions of safety and trust arose when the therapist was empathetic, supportive, authentic, exhibited unconditional positive regard for the client, and was able to establish a close but professional relationship. Techniques were secondary – the qualities of the therapist and the therapeutic relationship were primary. The large majority of future therapists are taught those principles in training programs today. The importance of this for our topic is that the focus on the interpersonal qualities of the therapist reflected the humanistic conception of mental health being a natural consequence of people feeling free to be fully themselves. Rather than relying on therapeutic "tricks," the humanistic therapist tries to establish the conditions for people to feel safe to be more open and feel good about themselves as they are.

Building on this principle, a major element of this client-centered approach is a deep respect for the value of the client as an equal human being, worthy of such respect. This attitude, quite different from the hierarchal perspective of the other two major models, became increasingly important over the decades after its development. Emancipation movements, for African Americans, Native Americans, homosexuals, Hispanic Americans, women, etc. all assert the basic equality of all people. Why not people seeking psychological services? For a hundred years, psychiatrists and then professional psychotherapists have all too often treated their patients/clients as weak and damaged, unable to define their own problems or identify their own solutions and having no real choice in their treatment. The doctor knows best. The growing internal revolt within the field of psychiatry itself in the 1960s helped spark the flame of a rebellion against psychiatric authority. The human potential movement shifted the onus of psychotherapy away from an emphasis on pathology to a journey toward higher functioning and wellness. Even the success of Alcoholics Anonymous was a factor, as it emphasized the importance of peer support, the lack of a need for an authoritative doctor for treatment, and the treatment itself being an ongoing process of recovery rather than a cure. This combination of factors resulted in a situation in which psychotherapy clients were looking for an egalitarian relationship with a real person who cared about them, treated them with respect, and valued their conception of their problems and the proper road to recovery. This situation fell neatly within the humanistic model and dramatically changed the general conception of mental illness. Rather than the person having a distinct mental illness, he or she could be seen as experiencing an unfortunate diversion from their natural state of wellness and that it can be restored if they can experience conditions of radical acceptance and support for who they are.

Not surprisingly, given this approach, the humanistic model has traditionally deemphasized diagnosis or a pathological view of human psychological problems. It has typically emphasized the positive characteristics of each client, trying to engage a natural impulse for personal growth. By the 1990s, the field of psychology was ready to pick up the humanistic threads of that movement and pursue a more positive, nonpathological approach to human nature. The result was positive psychology. When Martin Seligman became the president of the American Psychological Association in 1998, he chose it as the theme for his term. Back in 1967, Seligman had conducted important research on conditioning depression in dogs. He found, not surprisingly, that when the animals were exposed to electric shocks and had no chance to escape, they eventually stopped protesting, gave up, and passively accepted the shocks. What surprised him was that even when given a chance to escape, once the dogs had given up, they would not take it. Seligman termed this condition *learned helplessness*. The conditioned animals had to be forced to exit the cages of their torture. Seligman saw parallels with the attitudes of depressed human clients who struggled with a perceived lack of control (self-efficacy) in their lives (Peterson, Maier, & Seligman, 1995; Seligman, 1991). He became interested in how humans created conditions of psychological well-being, which he described as having five basic elements: *positive emotion, engagement in life, healthy relationships, a sense of meaning and purpose,* and *a sense of achievement* (Seligman, 2011).

Seligman has pointed out (2011) that he does not like the term happiness when thinking about positive psychology. Happiness is a very limited word, referring to a specific emotion, and has little to do with a deeper sense of well-being. Introverts report lower levels of happiness than extraverts, but that does not mean they do not have the same level of overall well-being – they just experience it differently. The term *positive emotion* is better suited for positive psychology because it refers to much more than being in a good mood, which is transitory and too individually variable. Seligman sees well-being as being linked to the five previously mentioned elements. In regard to positive emotion, it goes beyond feeling happy to include the whole range of emotional states that feel good, including calmness, joy, mirth, satisfaction, etc. You may notice that these states are connected to cognition. What and how we think about situations lead us to the emotions we experience during them.

Paul Granello also took note of this and made it a central part of his conception of wellness (2013). He approached cognition as encompassing everything the brain does, including memory, attention, association, language skills, overall personality, and emotions. He also took an evolutionary approach, asserting that our cognitive abilities developed through natural selection to enhance survival of the species (Seligman also takes an evolutionary perspective) by serving the need to accurately perceive and understand our environment and thus choose adaptive behavioral responses. Cognition serves to modulate stimuli, reach judgments regarding the meaning and importance of that stimuli, and organize it into stable categories or schemas. To the extent our cognitive processes "get it right," we may experience a sense of wellness, including a preponderance of positive emotions.

Seligman's second element of wellness is *engagement*. Seligman supported the findings of humanistic researchers like Maslow in concluding that people who experience a strong sense of well-being report it is directly connected to a felt experience of full engagement in life. This can be as intense for a monk, sitting in meditation in an ashram, as it is for an extreme athlete, skiing off a mountaintop, a mother playing with her baby in a living room, or an executive discussing the company's future plans in a board meeting. It is not about what one is doing or why; it is about putting all of one's attention, energy, and care into it. Disengagement is related to a sense of hopelessness and helplessness. One has given up and no longer cares. This is not the same as peaceful resignation – acceptance. With acceptance, one is still engaged in the process, even if parts of it are unpleasant. Disengagement means one has given up on the process and withdrawn. There is no sense of wellness in that, only numbness or despair.

The third element is *healthy relationships*. There is a tremendous amount of research addressing the importance of interpersonal relationships for people to feel good about themselves and their lives (Cacioppo & Patrick, 2008). We are fundamentally social creatures – being psychologically isolated is an unnatural state, and few can tolerate it for long without severe emotional disturbance. Even in prison, where you would think people would love to get away from each other, a common form of punishment is social isolation ("administrative segregation" in modern parlance). Extended time in such isolation is commonly associated with highly disturbed behavior, such as self-cutting, smearing feces, and enraged assaults on property and staff. That being said, interpersonal relationships can obviously be toxic and abusive. Sadly, humans need relationship with others so badly that they will typically choose to stay in unhealthy ones rather than be alone. That is why it is important for wellness that people have the skills (communication, empathy, self-love, etc.) to be able to form and maintain healthy, mutually respectful and supportive relationships.

The fourth element is a sense of *meaning and purpose*. By this, Seligman was referring to having a meaning for one's life and efforts beyond oneself or the immediate enjoyment of the activity. Watching old 1970s sitcoms can certainly be enjoyable (at least for me), but it hardly serves a higher purpose. Therefore, such an activity may temporarily boost my mood (happiness) but does not deeply enrich my life experience (well-being). Abraham Maslow, the godfather of positive psychology, found that self-actualizers always have a high purpose, beyond their self-centered interests, for their activities in life (1967). It can take many forms, including service to family, community, nation, or all of humanity. He found that such people spend relatively little time thinking about furthering their own interests, tend to be secure in their own individual needs being met, and thus spend much of their time and energy in the services of others.

The final element is *accomplishment*. Seligman realized that many people seek success for its own pleasure, not for other lofty goals. This also brings a sense of well-being. One can play basketball against another person, work hard to win, and feel very accomplished in victory without any higher meaning involved. Many psychologists would attribute this to an innate competitive drive. We want to outdo our peers – not just keep up with but surpass the Joneses. Such a drive would have great evolutionary power. On the one hand, we are social creatures and often seek out cooperation. Working together and even subverting our own selfish interests at times has obvious evolutionary advantages for the species. However, at the same time, we often feel compelled to excel in our lives, wanting desperately to *win* the game. This competitive drive can lead us to better survival skills with equally obvious evolutionary advantages. Being better than my neighbor at basketball may not help the species much, but being a better hunter might and could lead to more advantageous mate selection in the bargain.

So positive emotions (linked to cognition), full engagement in life, healthy relationships, higher meaning and purpose, and accomplishment were identified by Seligman as the basic elements of human wellness. What then are the main ways to secure these elements? This is where wellness counseling comes into play. Granello (2013) identified a number of ways to facilitate the development of these elements. He emphasized the importance of developing *flexible, realistic, and adaptive* beliefs and goals. In order to be able to do this, people need to have *metacognition*, the ability to think about thinking – being consciously aware of and adjusting one's beliefs in an ongoing process of critical (in the good sense of the word) self-reflection.

The second area he discussed was emotional regulation. This has become a major focus of clinical attention in the twenty-first century and is seen as a key part of healthy psychological functioning, adaptive behavior, and, of course, wellness (Bandura, Caprara, Barbaranelli, Gerbino, & Pastorelli, 2003). The ability to monitor, evaluate, and modify our emotion reactions, as well as those of others, is important to social functioning and other key areas of one's life. Granello (2013) identifies five categories of emotional regulation, including *situation selection* (choosing what we do to control potential emotional reactions), *situation modification* (manipulating the situation we are in to manage emotions), *attentional control* (directing our attention toward or away from particular triggers and emotions), *reappraisal* (changing how we are thinking about something to manage the emotion), and *response modulation* (the many ways we change our reactions to our emotions). As an example of how this works, let's say that Sue has been invited to go to a house party where she does not know many people. She decides to arrive late so lots of people will already be there to lessen her anxiety; she then chooses to stay in one area of the house so she can focus on a limited number of social interactions; she then focuses on aspects of the conversations that are pleasing and purposely ignores comments that may express criticism of her or her beliefs; she then thinks about how this insulting person has a generally bad attitude, so what he said does not feel so personal; and finally, she decides to ask the person who invited her to arrange future social encounters but only with certain people she met at the party that she liked. Together, these regulation skills contribute to a sense of social well-being in Sue's life, and if she had *not* been able to manifest them, the entire experience would have been much more negative, potentially contributing to a wide variety of problems.

A third area of wellness functioning is the physiological. One aspect of this involves the psychological benefits of physical fitness and exercise. The connection between exercise and psychological wellness was identified by the Ancient Greeks. Aristotle, Hippocrates, and others saw human happiness in holistic terms. The "good life" flowed from a balanced lifestyle that included equal measures of regular exercise and rest and relaxation. The Ancient world did not conceive of health as separated into physical and psychological spheres, as the modern, Cartesian world has. The ancient healing center of Asklepios at Epidaurus (approximately 500 BCE to 100 CE) was initially a religious center but developed into a place of holistic healing, with beautiful grounds, hot and cold baths, an amphitheater, stadiums, and a gymnasium. A combination of spiritual, social, medicinal, and physical (diet and exercise) treatment was prescribed for a wide variety of medical and psychological problems. Modern research has found exercise is linked to a wide variety of wellness attributes, including the reduction of depression and anxiety and the boosting of self-efficacy, energy, mood, positive emotions, and overall quality of life (Berger & Tobar, 2007).

One of the main psychological elements in the linkage of exercise and wellness is the concept of self-efficacy. There is a sense of accomplishment and self-mastery that emerges through a program of exercise that appears to generalize to other areas of a person's life (McAuley & Blissmer, 2000). There are also, of course, psychophysiological effects of exercise that enhance wellness, including the well-documented finding that exercise reduces anxiety and symptoms of stress (Raglin, 1997) as well as symptoms of depression (Dishman, Washburn, & Heath, 2004; Lox, Martin Ginis, & Petruzzello, 2006). Despite these findings, however, the relationship between physical activity and mental health is complicated and bidirectional, meaning that an increase in activity enhances a sense of wellness, which motivates an increase in activity and vice versa (Clow & Edmunds, 2014). A similar complex, bidirectional relationship is probably present in regard to other health-enhancing behaviors such as eating a healthy diet and increasing time spent in nature.

The last area of wellness functioning we will discuss is spirituality. As our text has explored, religion and mental health have been closely linked throughout history. In most societies, at most times in history, concepts regarding what is sane and insane have been regulated through religious beliefs, and the presumed causes of mental illness have been connected to religious belief as well. In the West, this linkage began to weaken during the Enlightenment and then was broken in the Modern Age with the rise of the academic and clinical fields of psychiatry and psychology. In other areas of the world, religiously based beliefs about mental health and illness have persisted, with some more and some less influenced by Western psychiatry and psychology. All that being said, there is a separate area of mental health that considers the *effects* of religious belief and practice on psychological well-being. This area of study is not concerned with the validity of such beliefs; it looks at them only in terms of their practical value.

Before looking at this research, we need to review the approach or attitude that modern psychology has had toward religion in general. At the beginning of the twentieth century, Sigmund Freud set the tone for psychiatry and psychology for the next 50 years. He believed that religious faith arose from a need for an authoritarian father figure, a need to project our darker impulses onto imagined entities, and that modern people who still held onto religious faith were, frankly, rather childish and neurotic. He felt that psychological maturity required that we identify the gods as projections of our own inner dynamics and conflicts and work them out for ourselves (Freud, 1950). Albert Ellis, representing the cognitive-behavioral field, was an avowed atheist and was particularly concerned about the power of religion to make people feel guilty or ashamed of their natural impulses, especially sexual ones (Ellis, 1958). As cognitive-behavioral theorists began to embrace acceptance and meditation in clinical practice, that subfield softened its attitude about religion as well. After the death of Sigmund Freud, psychoanalytic psychology became increasingly accepting of religious beliefs and, by the end of the twentieth century, had dropped Freud's antithesis to religion entirely, seeing it more in line with the other two subfields – neutral in terms of theology but ready to address problems it might be creating in a person's life (guilt and shame), as well as being supportive of its more positive aspects. The related field of depth psychology, emerging as it did from Jung's theories regarding archetypes and the collective unconscious, developed a unique relationship with religion. While it typically does not support a literal belief in God (not being hostile to such a belief, however), it has enthusiastically supported the idea that many gods and goddesses can be understood as representing different aspects and dynamics of the human psyche. With titles like *Gods in Everyman* (Bolen, 1989), archetypal psychologists looked to the stories from mythology to illuminate the inner lives of modern people, placing their struggles and dynamics in the perspective of universal forms of personality and culture.

Of the three major subfields of modern psychology, the humanistic model has always had the most benign attitude toward religion. Based on a foundation of honoring people's "truths" rather than refuting them, humanism has traditionally been more open to recognizing the positive qualities of religious faith in people's lives. In looking for strengths to build on for mental health, humanistic psychology actively looks for the ways spirituality helps people, both philosophically (providing a sense of hope, meaning, and purpose) and practically (the practice of religion being a source of social support). Interestingly, humanistic psychology has tended to be more supportive of non-Western religious faith and practice, at times enthusiastically endorsing Buddhism, Taoism, and Hinduism while remaining more suspect of Christianity, especially aspects of the faith that can be seen as self-judgmental and oppressive.

By the end of the twentieth century, led by humanistic psychology, the field of psychology had become much more open to exploring the positive aspects of religion and spirituality. Rather than declaring "God is dead," they instead seemed to be saying, "I don't know if God is dead or not, but if it works for you, that works for me." As noted before, this approach is supported by a great deal of research. In a comprehensive review of the literature, Bonelli and Koenig (2013) found that there was solid evidence for a positive relationship between mental health and religious involvement. Such involvement lowers the risk for depression, suicide, and substance abuse. There was some indication of lowered risk for stress-related disorders. However, there was not enough evidence to support the idea that religious involvement lowers the risk for schizophrenia or bipolar disorder. It may be that these disorders are more biologically based and therefore not as sensitive to environmental influences as some other psychological problems. In general, religiosity appears to be a strong factor in resilience to adverse environmental experiences (Kasen, Wickramaratne, Gameroff, & Weissman, 2012). In fact, there has been some research regarding the role of experiential trauma and the potential for personal growth. Dealing with adversity can help people develop a stronger sense of self, interpersonal relationships, and philosophy of life, and this is particularly true if they start with a religious worldview (Shaw, Joseph, & Linley, 2005; Tedeschi, Park, & Calhoun, 1997).

On the other hand, religiosity has also been associated with an increase in psychological problems. While most people find that their faith helps them deal with mental illness, a significant minority finds it makes things worse (Mohr, 2006). For instance, those who are highly religious and experience auditory hallucinations may be more inclined to believe they are from a demonic source, follow the commands of their voices, hurt themselves or others, and/or delay or refuse treatment (Birchwood & Chadwick, 1997; McCarthy-Jones, Waegeli, & Watkins, 2013; Moss, Fleck, & Strakowski, 2006). These issues present us with the difficult problem of sometimes having to differentiate spiritual and mental health problems, if that is even possible. To a large extent, this has to do with the preexisting beliefs of the person who is suffering. For many, struggling with sadness, loss, loneliness, lack of meaning, and even hearing voices is experienced and understood through the lens of their religious faith and even as an important part of their spiritual growth, producing wisdom, endurance, compassion, and a test of faith (Davidson et al., 2016).

This movement away from a problems-based perspective toward a strengths-based one is largely connected to the humanistic model of mental health. Humanistic psychology has always tended to focus on people's strengths, resources, aspirations, and potential for growth. However, the movement toward a user-focused concept of mental illness and its treatment has taken on a life of its own and become transtheoretical. It has been driven not so much by theories of mental illness but rather the practical realities of mental health care in the modern world. For a long time, such care has been provided through a hierarchal, problems-focused, medical model. A patient was diagnosed by a professional, and with that mental disorder identified, treatment was prescribed by and provided by the professional. The patient was a *passive recipient* of the assessment – which focused almost entirely on an identification of individual pathology and its treatment. The patient stopped being a human being and became an illness. Patients and their families felt depersonalized, objectified, disempowered, and manipulated. Any concerns they had about their professional treatment were brushed aside and seen as signs of "resistance" or confirmation of their pathology. This has obvious connections to the medical model and its contrast to the humanistic. At the same time though, clients were experiencing this basic problem in all areas of the mental health system and from a wide variety of professionals.

The result was a backlash – the mental health recovery movement (Gehart, 2012; Ralph & Corrigan, 2005). It started as a grassroots movement in the 1930s, driven by mental health consumers and their families, to protest how mental health care was being conceptualized and provided. It was not taken seriously at first, but by the 1980s, it was gaining traction with substance abuse counselors. They were influenced by the 12-step movement, which was not concerned with formal diagnoses and treatment by professionals. Instead, it relied on a description of the problem, a prescription for the problem, and treatment of the problem, all provided by the people with the problem. It was originally inspired by the medical establishment's failure to deal effectively with alcoholism and developed by two alcoholics who took it upon themselves to find a better way (Anonymous, 1939). The result was Alcoholics Anonymous (AA). The founders (Bill W. and "Doctor Bob") felt that the medical establishment did not understand the true nature of alcoholism (and, by extension, all additions). Rather than a medical illness to be cured, they saw it is a chronic condition tied to the person's personality characteristics (primarily an exaggerated sense of self-will) that called for a complete realignment of the person's values, the subversion of self-obsession to be replaced by a spiritual orientation, and an ongoing peer-based program to initiate and then continue supporting the personality changes that were required to stay abstinent. By the 1980s, so many people had "gotten sober" through AA that many had become professional substance abuse counselors and were a growing influence in the field.

Their success and influence in the field of substance abuse treatment led to the extension of their foundational principles to other areas of mental health treatment, including even that involving severe mental illness, such as schizophrenia and bipolar disorder. This dynamic was bolstered by the research work of the World Health Organization, which found that 28% of people diagnosed with severe mental illness experienced full recovery, and 52% experienced at least partial recovery, even when there was minimal psychiatric treatment available (WHO, 1974). Contrary to popular (and professional) opinion, people could recover a significant level of functionality, it did not require high levels of formal psychiatric intervention, and they could lead useful, fulfilling lives, especially with strong community support. With these two factors in place (the success of AA and empirical support from research), the recovery movement took hold in many countries in the 1990s (especially in Europe) and finally in the United States in the early 2000s. In 2002, the President's New Freedom Commission recommended that America move toward a recovery-oriented approach to mental health services.

Our focus, of course, is not about how this movement has changed treatment but rather the underlying conception of mental health and illness. The recovery paradigm utilizes a social model, emphasizing how different factors impact psychosocial functioning over diagnoses and symptoms to understand people (Gehart, 2012). That is not to say that it rejects the idea that there are discrete mental illnesses or that medication is not an effective intervention to consider. What it says is that people are not their diseases, and the focus should be on the whole person, including their beliefs, values, strengths, and life goals, no matter what their psychological struggles. It also emphasizes the importance of the person in the context of the wider world of their social relationships, communities, and cultures. As Gehart points out, this way of understanding people and their psychological struggles came naturally to couple and family therapists, who were used to thinking less about individual pathology in favor of exploring how a people are interacting with their environments and how that is impacting them. Therefore, reflecting its humanistic roots, the recovery focus emphasizes the identification and activation of people's hope, self-efficacy, meaning and purpose, and potential. This aligns with Seligman's sense of wellness and places people with mental health problems at the center of defining their own reality, placing their mental health concerns in the context of their whole life, and putting them in charge of their own recovery.

This takes us to the end of our discussion of the clinical aspects of humanistic psychology at the beginning of the twenty-first century and how they relate to the concept of mental health. To review, we looked at how humanistic psychology, in its clinical application, became a widely agreed upon foundation for therapeutic practice, as well as the emergence of positive psychology, wellness, and the recovery movement. Now we can explore the second part, pertaining to the more philosophical extensions of the humanistic model. To do so, we will focus on two main concepts: world concerns and more recent advances in postmodernism.

The term "world concerns" relates to how the humanistic model is being extended beyond *individual* wellness to larger cultural and even ecological issues. This extension to cultural issues makes sense as it relates to how humanistic psychology has always emphasized the importance of cultural dynamics in how people deal with their lives. The question of ecology may not be so obvious. The fact is that humans do not just live with each other, they also live in a natural environment. People rely on the health of the natural environment to provide food, water, air, and play. From the humanistic perspective, the health of the natural environment is linked to not only the physical health but also the mental health of people living in it (Pilisuk & Joy, 2015). We need an ecological system that can both sustain human life and do so for all people but can also be a source of beauty, recreation, and spiritual renewal. A variety of ecological problems impact wellness from the humanistic perspective, including deforestation, climate change, ozone depletion, waste disposal, genetic food engineering, availability of clean drinking water, soil pollution, the loss of wild animal habitat, etc. The problems are manifold, and they disproportionately affect people of color and people who are poor. Of course, the reasons for the problems are also manifold.

At one level, we are victims of our success. Dramatic advances in medical science and food production have fostered an expansion of the human population from approximately 1 billion at the turn of the twentieth century to almost 8 billion in 2020. In a modern, industrialized world, that means more pollution, more habitat loss, and more overall destruction of the natural world. While there are efforts to curb our destructive behavior, it is obviously not enough at this point. This is a disturbing truth and suggests not only that the generally increasing population is putting more pressure on the ecosystem but also that as more people are able to enter the middle to upper classes, they are in a position to have a standard of living that allows them to pollute more and otherwise impact the planet in negative ways. This puts humanistic psychology in an awkward position. On the one hand, it places a high value on individual development and wants people to escape poverty and enjoy a higher standard of living. However, on the other hand, if a worldwide rise in the material standard of living has the effect of accelerating damage to the ecosystem, which impacts worldwide wellness, how do we deal with that?

One way is to think of ecology in humanistic terms. Humans are part of the ecosystem, so its health reflects human health. They may no longer be able to afford to consider their own well-being outside the context of the overall ecosystem of which they are a part, at least not without allowing much more ecological damage as a result. By extension, if nature is central within the context of human life, and thus humanity benefits from its health, then it would be useful to think in terms of an "ecological self" (Pilisuk & Joy, 2015). People should also consider the negative effects of the modern obsessions with material wealth, nationalism, competition, and individualism. These values are promoted strongly, especially in the West, and they contribute to the ecological problem, as well as a variety of psychological problems, including depression, anxiety, stress, and substance abuse. However, it is also true that multiple studies have found that increased wealth *does* make people happier, partly because it helps them attain other resources (health care, housing, transportation, education) that are more direct drivers of life satisfaction (Senik, 2014). Even if wealth did not actually make people much happier, many people believe it does and will work hard to get it. One consequence of this is that while it is not clear how much the money itself makes people happy, the *success* that leads to earning it definitely does, which is a central tenet of Seligman's positive psychology. There is also the self-fulfilling prophecy that when a dominant cultural paradigm is materialism, then one is hard-pressed not to judge oneself and be judged by others in terms of one's wealth or income. It makes it a difficult balance for humanistic psychology to promote individual success and wellness on the one hand and the ecological self on the other. Perhaps the balance point is to promote *responsible economic growth* and support policies that compel wealthier groups to invest in responsible growth technologies, such as renewable energy and sustainable agriculture, in poorer, developing areas.

In a related vein, many in the world of depth psychology and elsewhere have equated the natural, material world with the feminine (Mother Nature, Demeter, etc.) and thus the masculine principle (Apollo, Judeo-Christian God, etc.) with the sky and with a wish to escape, dominate, or ultimately destroy the natural world (and by extension, the feminine) as it seeks to free itself from entrapment in its limited, material existence, and attain spiritual transcendence and freedom from death (Eisler, 1987). This is often interpreted as helping explain the ferocity of the Western assault on nature, with its moralistic fervor to wantonly exploit, pollute, and destroy the natural world. The modern world is largely the creation of and world of men, exalting their ability to build that world through sheer will and technology. Conversely, it has been the relative rise of feminine power, starting with its leading role in the progressive movement of the nineteenth century, at least in the Western world, that is trying to provide an alternative relationship to nature, one embracing a *partnership* model rather than a *dominator* one (Merchant, 1980).

These and other challenges and issues have led to the development of ecopsychology. This subfield studies the connections between human beings and the environment and tries to develop ways to expand the emotional connection between the two (Roszak, Gomes, & Kanner, 1995). Its central premise is that human beings evolved within the context of the natural world – we adapted to nature and thus are inextricably linked to it. Ecopsychologists are also aware that it is ongoing human choices that are driving the ecological problems we face, and we need to understand *why* people make those choices in order to develop motivational techniques and processes to move toward more sustainable practices. This field takes a bidirectional approach to the subject. On the one hand, it strongly values the natural environment and sees humans as having a unique responsibility to maintain and improve its overall health. It calls on people to raise their consciousness about the needs of the natural world and how it is suffering under our treatment. On the other hand, it also values human psychological well-being and sees it linked to the natural world, so it promotes the nurturance of emotional and spiritual ties to nature, and it celebrates cultures that have traditionally been supportive of nature. It even links aspects of psychopathology to a disconnection from nature (Shepard, 1982). Why do we continue to destroy the planet we live on? Even more importantly, why is it that so many of us do not change our attitudes and our ways now that we know what we are doing? Perhaps it boils down to greed, or perhaps it runs deeper, in our longstanding cultural belief in the need to control and dominate nature. Perhaps it is rooted in the Judeo-Christian theology that nature is aligned with the Devil; that the material world in all its manifestations (including our own bodies) is profane. From that perspective, the human goal is to reject and transcend the profane, not honor or love it. In that theology, there is no place for environmentalism. Love of nature is associated with material decadence, carnality, and secular humanism. In that theology and its associated religious culture, environmentalism is seen as profane and antireligious – especially to the extent that environmentalists appear to be worshiping nature.

Another area of interest for humanistic psychology is peace and war (Pilisuk, 2015). Naturally, it values states of relations that foster healthy human development. It views nearly all forms of violence as anathema to that value. It recognizes the long-standing human propensity to engage in warfare, even when the costs are high and the potential benefit seems low in comparison. This begs the question of whether cruelty, selfishness, and violence are central and universal aspects of human nature. Humanistic psychologists have long pondered this question and explored the psychological dynamics that appear to drive the impulse to engage in warfare (LeShan, 2002). These include concerns about sovereignty, anxiety over resources, exclusivity of values, overconcentration of power, wealth disparity, and myopic focus on the self, leading to narrow group identities and demonization of the "other" (Keen, 1986).

By and large, the humanistic tradition has avoided genderizing the problem of violence and aggression, but it is hard to imagine issues related to violence without considering the obvious fact that around the world, males are much more prone to engage in direct violence than women. From an historical perspective, the gods of war have been predominantly male: Ares, Anhur, Set, Maher, Belus, Perun, Idis, Valkyries, Juno, Mangala, Great Gish, Hadur, Chiyou, Futsunushi, Rongo, and Maru, to name a few. There are some goddesses of war, but they are few in number. Overall, being warlike and making war has been predominantly a male undertaking. Women, with a few cultural exceptions, are expected to support the men, honor and reward their warrior spirit, and help raise male children to be good warriors themselves. In fact, as noted earlier in this text, a common initiation rite for males in tribal societies has involved removing the young male initiates from their mothers (who ritualistically scream and cry, trying to hang on their beloved boys) to bring them into the adult world of men. To succeed in this, the initiates must endure a harrowing and painful initiation to test and temper their courage.

These initiations are mirrored in the modern world in the process by which males are often tested when they seek to enter the masculine worlds of street gangs, prisons, and the military.

Whether it is genderized or not, humanistic psychologists stand opposed to the use of violence against others. It directly impacts both the life of the victim and the humanity of the perpetrator. The sufferings of war are both ubiquitous and obvious; the death of children and other noncombatants; the destruction of infrastructure, including homes, fields, and entire cities; the wholesale disruption of economies, leading to poverty and starvation; the disruption of populations, leading to forced migrations; and the particular vulnerability of women and children to rape, slavery, and slaughter. The effects do not end when the war is over. The economic and cultural damage can take many years to heal. Landmines and chemical poisoning continue to maim and kill the innocents. Humanistic psychologists study the causes and effects of war, as well as working to avoid wars and help heal the damage during and after them.

They point out that although entire societies get caught up in a righteous fervor for war, in many instances, most of the soldiers must be drafted, and they tend to fight more out of loyalty to their fellow soldiers in their units than for their country or cause (Stouffer, 1965). War is promoted and maintained through propaganda and severe legal coercion. In most cases, there is an anti-war group within the population that seeks to avoid unnecessary conflict and bloodshed. They try to find peaceful resolutions to intergroup conflicts. That is the main interest in humanistic psychology. It values all human life and wants to build more peaceful, caring, and empathetic societies. That means promoting nonviolent ways for people to meet their objectives and resolve conflicts, partly by finding ways to change the conditions that drive much of the violence, including gross inequalities of wealth, position, and power (Pilisuk, 2015). The goal is to create a situation in which everyone can live in a world where war is seen as illegitimate and there are good opportunities for more people to create decent lives for themselves, live in harmony with others and nature, value diversity, and share a sense of meaning with others (Harmon, 1984).

Integrated Model

Compared to other models of mental illness, the twenty-first-century psychological model tends to take a more holistic approach. It already has to account for three significantly different approaches to psychological theory (psychodynamic, cognitive-behavioral, and humanistic). It also allows for more equal status between the biological, social, and developmental/experiential factors as causal agents of mental health, seeing them as *mediated* through psychological processes (Kinderman, 2005). Thus, it has been from within a larger psychological perspective that an integrated model has developed. Often referred to as the biopsychosocial model, it incorporates multiple factors in the maintenance or loss of mental health. Also, it eschews the medical model's reliance on categorical, diagnostic approaches to identifying mental illness. Instead, it looks at individuals as unique entities, each with his or her combination of biological attributes, cultural background, personal histories, and resulting strengths and weaknesses.

Despite its current home in the psychological model, the roots of the biopsy-chosocial model are in medical psychiatry. The godfather of the integrated model was Adolf Meyer (1866–1950). Briefly mentioned in the previous two chapters in regard to his role in the development of a psychodynamic understanding of mental illness at the beginning of the twentieth century and its influence on the eventual writing of the first DSM, Meyer proposed what he called ergasiology (psychobiology), which was basically a biopsychosocial model of mental illness (Alexander & Selesnick, 1966). He felt it was vital to gather as much information as possible about patients regarding the biological, social, and psychological factors related to their psychological problems. His dedication to building highly detailed case histories of his patients was legendary. He did this because he believed that most mental illness was the result of a *reaction* to stressful life events combined with biological factors.

By the 1970s, this concept was being strongly challenged within psychiatry by the biomedical wing of the field. This led George L. Engel (1913–1999), a psychiatrist at the University of Rochester (1977), to become deeply concerned about the state of the field of psychiatry at the time. He saw the field as a random mix of mostly unscientific philosophies, opinions, and "schools of thought," increasingly influenced by a biological point of view. He feared that this had led to endless tribalism, politics, and lack of clarity. The field was being pulled in different directions, partly because of the rise of both medical knowledge (the biomedical model) and competing psychosocial (psychodynamic) approaches to mental health, neither establishing a hegemony on the conceptualization or treatment of mental illness. He was acutely aware of the criticisms of medical psychiatry and acknowledged that a medical model of "diseases" was not adequate to truly understand mental illness. As he saw it, it simply made no sense to disregard the psychosocial issues that impacted their patients. How could there be a "real organic illness" outside of such a context? Engel noted that the field of psychiatry had apparently split into two camps. One took the position that psychiatry should no longer consider itself a medical science at all because mental illness is a purely cultural concept and outside the traditional medical concept of disease; the other maintained the medical model but saw the proper role of medicine as addressing only problems directly connected to brain dysfunction. Mental illness arising from such dysfunction would remain the exclusive domain of psychiatry. The problem Engel saw with the second approach was that if the main problem lay in how mental illness was being conceptualized within the medical model, then this approach was fatally flawed, and what was really needed was a new model.

The biomedical model assumes mental illness is fully explained by measurable biological factors. There is little room allowed for an understanding of psychological or sociological variables in the patient's psychiatric functioning. As such, it is reductionistic (complex phenomena arise from a single factor) and supports a mind–body dualism (the idea that the mind and the body are somehow distinct and separable). Engel challenged that model, first by pointing out that like any model, it is culturally derived and supported, at least in part by becoming dogma – meaning that the attitudes and beliefs of doctors are shaped by the model before they even start their training, and the training itself *assumes* the validity of the model without considering possible alternatives or its own foundation as a form of cultural adaptation. As dogma, the biomedical approach forces data to fit the model or be rejected out of hand. It becomes a form of circular reasoning. All behavior and reported psychological experiences that are problematical are either conceptualized within the biomedical model or they are excluded from the disease concept.

Part of the problem with this approach, as Engel asserts, and this writer would agree, that throughout history, mental illness has always been identified as behavioral, psychological, and social in nature. People behave in ways that disturb those around them, causing social and other functional problems. Sometimes this is combined with internal distress and sometimes not. In other words, mental illness had always been embedded in a sociocultural context. It was not until the concept of mind–body dualism developed in the West that it became common to separate the workings of the body (brain) from the behavioral and psychosocial. This artificial bifurcating of perspectives has had its successes, such as the development of effective psychotropic medications, but the exclusive focus on the body (biomedical) has significant difficulties. For instance, until we know more about the actual biochemical working of the brain, we must rely on the identification of *symptoms* to differentiate mental disorders without a direct linkage to identifiable physiological substrates or processes. Experiencing hallucinations is commonly considered a symptom of a mental illness called schizophrenia, but we don't know what specific biological dysfunction is *causing* the symptom. That means that in the biomedical model, the linkage is *assumed* but not proven. Also, the biomedical model excludes other factors from its consideration, so the range of psychological, social, and cultural factors that impact the onset and experience of hallucinations is disregarded. Adding to this difficulty is the fact that because we continue to rely on a combination of observed signs and self-reported symptoms, the *personal history* of the patient is paramount in that it determines how he or she exhibits signs and reports symptoms of mental illness. This both complicates the assumed connection between symptoms and underlying biological dysfunction and makes it essential that anyone attempting diagnosis be fully conversant with the patient's personal history, including an ability to analyze the patient's psychological, social, and cultural dynamics. However, these areas are already excluded from the biomedical model, so they are unlikely to be considered important within that approach.

These difficulties with the exclusively biomedical model led Engels to propose something different. The biopsychosocial or integrated model starts with an acceptance of biological factors in mental illness – based on the fact that all psychological phenomena have a physiological component. In other words, the integrated model asserts that in order to understand the causes and forms of the "problem," it is vital to acknowledge the biological aspect of all mental phenomena but to take into account the patient's individual psychology, social system, and cultural context. It also requires a consideration of the cultural factors determining the relationship between the "doctor" and the "patient." The boundary between health and illness is rarely fully clear, and it is impacted by social, cultural, and psychological considerations on the part of both the patient and the doctor. How does one or the other differentiate between mental illness and "normal problems in living"? What if the doctor and patient disagree? These questions reflect the vital factor of how a state of mental illness or lack thereof is conceptualized.

What if a patient says he is depressed and wants medication, but the doctor thinks the patient has a light case of "the blues" and should consider it a normal part of life? In the biomedical model, the doctor is the authority on mental illness and has made a diagnosis based on his or her training and experience. The doctor is right. In the integrated model, consideration is given to the psychosocial reality of the patient, so his or her conceptualization of their experience is an important factor in the overall understanding of the case. Perhaps the patient is right. On the other hand, if the doctor has enough evidence to conclude that the patient is in some way minimizing the symptoms and there really is evidence of a serious organic problem, then the doctor is right.

The experience of grief is an example of a situation in which it is difficult to differentiate illness from normality. It is a common human experience, linked to a specific and rational environmental stressor, and does not require or signify an organic dysfunction, yet it is related to significant psychological distress, possible life impairment, and sometimes a desire or need for professional help. A crucial question emerges regarding the patient's cultural context – what are the expectations or norms of the culture regarding the experience of and exhibited behavior associated with grief? Can we say that something we consider mental illness should include experience and behavior that is outside those norms? That would certainly be outside a biomedical definition unless it can be established that the experience or behavior is *caused* by a biological dysfunction, which certainly cannot be assumed when faced with a reaction to a very real life stressor.

It is important at this point to remember the difference between causation and correlation. With causation, one phenomenon is a direct force leading to the other phenomenon – A >> B. With correlation, there is a relationship between the two, but the form of that relationship is not necessarily clear – it could be bidirectional – A >> B and B >> A, or another factor C is causing both. Therefore, it cannot be assumed that any physiological dysfunction is causing mental symptoms. The symptoms may be causing the physiological dysfunction. By the same token, it cannot be assumed that just because a medical intervention (psychotropic medication, for instance) has a psychological effect, that it proves a biological etiology for the symptoms. The introduction of a medical intervention may have a psychological effect, no matter what the etiology of the problem. For instance, nearly anyone taking a stimulant medication would be able to concentrate better, but that does not prove they all have a biologically based attention deficit disorder. The integrated model recognizes and honors this difference, postulating first that we need to consider the reality that there is more than A (biology) at work, so the formulation is more like A + B + C = D, but also that D (symptoms) also impact the presence and dynamics of A, B, and C.

The switch from a unidirectional path of causation to a multidirectional pattern of correlation (or mutual causation, if you will) implies a more systemic way of thinking about the issue. It is holistic, rather than reductionistic. There are basic laws and principles that operate across the system and others that are unique to each level. Because all levels are linked, all interact and affect each other in various ways. That means that every event and object has its own qualities, but they affect and are affected by every other event and object. When it comes to mental health and mental illness, inheritance plays a role, as do endocrinology, neuroanatomy, epigenetics, developmental theories, evolutionary theory, family dynamics, education, psychodynamic theory, cognitive-behavioral theory, humanistic theory, local community dynamics, and various levels of cultural dynamics.

The point, then, in the integrated model is not to reject biology but rather to understand it within a hierarchy of other *levels* in the system that makes up a human being in the context of his or her entire life and psyche. This model has been extremely successful since its introduction in the mid-1970s. It has become a major model in the field of psychology, although, ironically, it has been less influential in psychiatry, the field it was attempting to affect (Pilgrim, 2002). It has served as a conceptual bridge between the various silos of academic and professional fields that have a stake in defining mental health and mental illness – a point that will be explored in much more detail in the next chapter.

It is not without its critics, however. For instance, it has been found that although it may be helpful to *understand* mental illness through the lens of systems theory, in clinical practice, people tend to fall back on more traditional, structural models, such as the categorical diagnoses offered in the DSM (Benning, 2015). It has also been argued that general systems theory is not an appropriate model for psychiatry, but it should be noted that von Bertalanffy himself successfully explored the applicability of his model for psychiatry (1969). He and others have concluded that it has a lot to offer, including the description of a hierarchy of multiple levels of causality in mental illness and the fact that, in order to truly understand mental illness, one must appreciate both the fluid nature of mental health and illness and the dynamic nature of the relationship between both individuals and their environments and also individuals and those who seek to understand and treat them. Despite its apparent relevance to mental illness, however, the model has not changed the biomedical course of psychiatry nearly as much as Engels had hoped.

As noted, the biopsychosocial model has strongly influenced the field of psychology but, like psychiatry, more at the conceptual level and not the applied one. The biggest problem it has is that while it provides a general conceptual model, that model demands the inclusion of so much information in any understanding of mental illness that it is very difficult to put it into practice. Just considering an introductory list of the necessary types of information about a person, ranging from epigenetics to culture, is daunting and beyond the knowledge base of any one assessor. It is no wonder that beyond an acknowledgment that there are multiple factors in any person's psychological functioning and the mutual influence of the person and their environment, most clinicians still follow a relatively linear model, including a very narrow range of information to assess a person's mental health or illness. What is needed is what Benning (2015) described as the "Herculean" task of creating an exhaustive epistemic encompassment of the field that would integrate the diverse etiological factors that contribute to mental wellness or illness.

THE CROSS-CULTURAL WORLD

As we move deeper into the twenty-first century, the issue of the cross-cultural validity of Western ideas about mental health and mental illness continues to foment. There has been growing concern that the DSM is a culturally grounded document, reflecting the values, beliefs, and practices of a particular tradition, and thus its relevance for people outside that culture is questionable at best. Before DSM-5, the APA had responded to the question of cultural issues by including a section in the DSM listing a number of culture-bound syndromes. Many found this inadequate because it did not respond to the fundamental issue of the direct interplay of culture and mental illness. From a constructivist perspective, the concept of mental illness is built up from the information available in the environment, combined with the active mind, which gives meaning and order to that information. In other words, human knowledge is the result of an active, collaborative process between the individual and the environment – it is not the passive acceptance of outside sources of "truth" (Raskin, 2002). From this perspective, mental health and mental illness are what the experiencer *thinks* they are, with the person's culture playing a vital role in the process. Culture does not just impact how mental illness is experienced but is central to how it *exists*. To assume that Western notions of mental illness are universal is seen, from the constructionist perspective, as a form of cultural elitism, causing one to see through blinders. Instead, many see the dynamic of culture itself as a key component in the underlying conception of mental illness, and thus it should be central part of any design of a diagnostic system (Mezzich, 2013).

The DSM-5 answered this criticism by asserting that mental disorders are defined *in relation to* cultural norms and that culture provides an *interpretive framework* that influences the expression and experience of the DSM diagnostic criteria. DSM-5 removed the listing of culture-bound syndromes that had included in previous editions but added a section called "Cultural Formulation" that includes tools for cultural assessment. It also proposed replacing the concept of culture-bound syndromes with three concepts: *cultural syndromes* (clusters of symptoms unique to a given culture), *cultural idiom of distress* (unique ways that different cultures experience and communicate psychological experiences), and *cultural explanations or perceived cause* (differences in attribution of causation of mental illness) (American Psychiatric Association, 2013).

These changes clearly did not satisfy those who took a more multicultural perspective. Many noted that the DSM claimed to be approaching its task with greater cultural sensitivity but in reality was delivering mixed messages as it continued to provide only diagnoses with Western culture-bound symptoms and increased its focus on neurobiology over contextualized distress (Bredstrom, 2017; Thorton, 2017). They point out that the manual remains strongly ethnocentric and takes a narrow understanding of culture, which it views as impacting the experience of mental illness but not defining it. This issue of defining mental illness through a cultural lens led to the development of competing taxonomic systems. These include the Chinese Classification of Mental Disorders, the Cuban Glossary of Psychiatry, and the Latin American Guide for Psychiatric Diagnosis (Mezzich, 2013). These systems do not represent complete departures from the Western view; instead, they are *adaptations* of the International Classification of Diseases (ICD), which is produced by the World Health Organization and is closely aligned with the DSM. They seek to retain what is universal in mental illness and then add what is unique and specific, reflecting a particular cultural reality. It is this balance that many are seeking to help bring a higher level of validity to a system that has become so internationally dominant in the field of mental health.

The other side of the equation from the relative exclusion of other cultures from the DSM taxonomy is the inclusion of a *culture of mental illness* implicit in the historical development of its taxonomy. This refers to both breadth and depth – meaning that over the years, a wider and wider net has been cast to identify more people as mentally ill by creating more disorders and also by making it easier to qualify for many of these disorders (Horowitz, 2002; Kutchins & Kirk, 1997). This increase in diagnostic categories has made a wider variety of psychological phenomena qualify as mental disorders. The lowering of the bar for the level of pathology needed to meet criteria for them has brought relatively normal levels of distress or dysfunction into the realm of mental illness. To complicate matters more, many of the disorders in the DSM do not even correspond to its own definition of mental illness.

Let's take a look at a DSM disorder that has issues in all three areas – expanding the list, lowering the bar, and not fitting the DSM definition of a mental disorder. The diagnosis is conduct disorder (CD). It is described as, "a repetitive and persistent pattern of behavior in which the basic rights of others or major age-appropriate societal norms or rules are violated (American Psychiatric Association, 2013, p. 469). Some of the behaviors listed are bullying others, starting fights, being cruel to people or animals, destroying property, breaking into houses, lying, stealing, being truant from school, running away from home, and breaking curfew. The person needs to have engaged in at least three of these behaviors for at least a year, and it has to have caused *clinically significant* impairment in social, academic, or occupational functioning. There is also a severity specifier, so the person can be diagnosed at the mild level – with only the minimum number of behaviors present and only mild harm or problems caused by them. So an adolescent can be diagnosed with a mental disorder if she has been lying to her parents, staying out late at night, and "partying" with her friends, drinking alcohol and smoking marijuana. On the surface of it, this may seem like a stretch. It certainly is behavior that will cause many parents and society at large a great deal of distress, but is it a mental disorder?

First, let's look at the question of *expanding the list* of disorders. The disorder first appeared in the DSM in its second edition, published in 1968. Ten years later, it was added to the ICD. Before that time, psychologists and psychiatrists were certainly aware of childhood behavior problems, but they were typically conceptualized in terms of developmental and risk factor issues, not psychiatric mental illness, unless a separate mental illness could be linked to the behavior. In fact, problematical behavior was typically not seen as a mental illness in and of itself. It could be seen as a *sign* of mental illness, but in both the biological and the psychoanalytic systems, there needed to be some underlying disease process at work to identify a mental illness. Thus, the addition of CD to the DSM and ICD reflects an expansion of the list, one that would have been highly questionable in previous incarnations of psychiatric nosology.

In regard to *lowering the bar*, we have already noted that CD can be diagnosed if the person has engaged in just three troublesome behavior types (lying, stealing, etc.) over the course of a year, with only mild problems associated with it (school suspension, friction with parents, etc.). This reflects the use of severity specifiers in the DSM. Many disorders are linked to the possibility of it being mild, moderate, or severe. On the one hand, this is connected to the idea of a dimensional approach to mental illness, and although it already existed in previous editions of the DSM, it is now supported by the DSM as reflecting its dedication to shifting its conception of mental illness in a more dimensional direction. However, the qualifiers do not describe different levels of a *life problem* but rather different severity levels of a *mental disorder*. In other words, the person is seen as having already crossed a threshold into the conceptual arena of mental illness and inclusion in a particular disorder. Thus, severity specifiers do not move us toward dimensional diagnosis. What they do is significantly expand the number of people who will qualify for a disorder and call into question the issue of pathologizing normality. Now that it is considered a mental disorder, CD is found to affect approximately 4% of adolescents, with significantly higher rates for males than females (American Psychiatric Association, 2013). Since there are currently about 40 million adolescents in America, that means that about 160,000 of them meet criteria for CD. That is a significant lowering of the bar for mental illness.

It can be assumed that throughout history, some children and adolescents (adults can also be diagnosed with CD, but it is rare) have engaged in inconsiderate, illegal, and violent behavior that has caused a lot of problems. It was also probably noticed that many, if not most, of these children seemed to grow out of these problems and become "well adjusted" by their mid-20s. This casual observation is supported by research. Property crime arrest rates (in America) peak in the mid-teens (about 4%) and then drop to 1% in the mid-20s and continue to drop to about .2% for people in their 60s and 70s (as cited in Siegel & Welsh, 2017). Assuming that not many of these adolescents get a significant level of psychological treatment after their arrests, it is likely that a number of maturational forces *naturally* come into play, including the development of the prefrontal cortex, increasing the ability to control impulses, delay gratification, and think through the consequences of behavior (Sapolsky, 2017), and dealing with the increased responsibilities of adulthood (Siegel & Welsh, 2017). This suggests that a significant amount of childhood acting-out behavior is a "phase of life" issue, driven by a large number of variables and not a distinct mental disorder.

Of course, some of the children and adolescents diagnosed with CD really do have significant problems that they are not likely to simply grow out of. They may have started exhibiting severe behavior problems at an unusually young age, may be engaged in behavior that is particularly cruel, vicious, and lacking in empathy, and they may have a variety of other psychological problems related to abuse, depression, or sociocultural problems. In fact, children diagnosed with CD have been found to have an average of 2.2 diagnoses, with higher scores on multiple symptoms, and worse relapse rates than children with other diagnoses (Lambert,

Wahler, Andrade, & Bickman, 2001). However, this pattern led Lambert and his associates to wonder if CD is more reflective of a global disability than a discrete mental disorder, especially as these youth had high rates of various psychosocial stressors and few coping skills. The authors wondered if CD was not an example of externalizing behavior as a primary coping mechanism rather than a mental disorder.

In fact, these developmental and environmental factors call into question the underlying assumptions of what we call a mental disorder and the role of culture in both creating and identifying such disorders. The DSM definition of a mental disorder is:

> a syndrome characterized by clinically significant disturbance in an individual's cognition, emotion regulation, or behavior that reflects a dysfunction in the psychological, biological, or developmental processes underlying mental functioning. Mental disorders are usually associated with significant distress or disability in social, occupational, or other important activities. An expectable or culturally approved response to a common stressor or loss is not a mental disorder. Socially deviant behavior and conflicts that are primarily between the individual and society are not mental disorders unless the deviance or conflict results form a dysfunction in the individual, as described above.
>
> (American Psychiatric Association, 2013, p. 20)

This indicates that a pattern of emotion, thought, or behavior is not a mental disorder *just* because it is socially deviant unless it is caused by some other dysfunction – psychological, biological, or developmental. DSM-5 notes the possibility of poor affect regulation and disinhibition as possible causal factors in CD and other "externalizing disorders." However, it also points out that, "the shared diathesis that constitutes the externalizing spectrum remains unknown" (American Psychiatric Association, 2013, p. 462). It also notes that CD is influenced by both genetic and environmental factors. In regard to the genetic and physiological risk factors, it refers to the fact that the disorder is more prevalent in children of parents with a wide variety of behavioral and/or psychological problems themselves. It also notes that structural and functional differences have been found in children diagnosed with CD versus those not diagnosed. The central question here is cause and effect. Is there a common genetic factor that is causing problems for the parents that is being passed on to their children (biological basis)? Or conversely, do the behavioral and psychological problems of the parents lead to behavior problems in their children (environmental basis)? The same issue is in play regarding brain functioning and structure. Do these children have preexisting neurological problems resulting in CD, or do the environmental stressors that result in development problems lead to abnormal neurological functioning? By calling these "genetic influences," the DSM assumes a one-way causal relationship, disregarding the interactive quality of environment and neurological functioning.

This entire conversation calls into question whether CD meets the DSM's own definition of a mental disorder. It has not been able to identify any particular psychological, biological, or developmental dysfunctions that cause the problematical behavior. It alludes to some possibilities but admits that no diathesis (constitutional predisposition) or biomarkers have been identified. This leaves the behaviors in question representing a conflict or deviancy from cultural norms, and possibly the expectable result of environmental stressors. The DSM-5's discussion of culture-related issues pertinent to CD is two sentences long. It notes that the diagnosis could be misapplied in cases where the pattern of behavior is "near-normative," such as in war zones and high-crime areas. This seems grossly inadequate given the complexity of cultural dynamics associated with interpersonal violence, crime, and socioeconomic disparities.

This issue is particularly important when we consider the differences in prevalence of CD based on gender, ethnicity, race, and socioeconomic groups. Boys are two to three times more likely to be diagnosed with CD than girls, particularly in adolescence (Moffitt, Caspi, Rutter, & Phil, 2001). It has also been found that minorities and low-socioeconomic youth are more likely to be diagnosed with CD (Proctor, Vosler, & Murty, 1992). Leaders in the field of criminality and juvenile delinquency, like Siegel and Welsh (2017), are more likely to address social and cultural factors that drive violent, rule-breaking behavior as individual ones. They discuss peer groups and relationships, family functioning, education, community conditions, exposure to violence, economic stresses, and racism as important factors in CD-like behavior.

A related line of reasoning is postulated in social control theory (Hirschi, 1969), which discusses delinquency in terms of a lack of interpersonal bonds, which leads the youth to not care about the wishes or expectations of other people or society in general. This idea can be considered as an organizing factor, subsuming the previous list of stressors and risk factors explored by Siegel and Welsh, and included in the DSM, considering how they could negatively impact a child's interpersonal bonding. Could it be then that there are important cultural considerations, especially in regard to subcultural groups that have intense stressors such as poverty and racism to contend with, to account for in a well-integrated conceptualization of CD and delinquency?

This is obviously not just an issue in America. Bao, Haas, and Xie looked at a variety of factors, including life strain, social control, social learning, gender, age, and family SES in regard to delinquent behavior in China (2016). Unlike most American studies, this one found a strong correlation between SES and delinquency. They noted that recent changes in Chinese culture, largely due to economic reforms creating a greater disparity of wealth and the one-child policy placing greater pressure on children to be financially successful, have placed a high level of strain on Chinese youth, especially those raised in low-SES families, and a sharp rise in delinquency. The primary factor appears to be the repeated strains that some Chinese youth experience in school, leading to weakened family bonds and poor internalization of conventional values and beliefs, which, in turn, lead to strengthened bonds with delinquent peers.

As in Western countries, there are much higher rates of delinquency among males versus females, despite recent increases in female delinquent behavior. It was asserted that this is because, also similar to Western countries, boys are encouraged to be active, assertive, dominant, fight with peers, are given more freedom outside the home, and have weaker bonds within the family. It was also noted that males experience more financial strain (expected to be the primary wealth producer) and violent interpersonal conflict (aggressive peers). In a pattern that is again similar to that in the West, delinquency peaks in mid-adolescence and drops significantly by late adolescence or early adulthood.

Mid-adolescence is a time when Chinese (like Western) youths begin to individuate from their immediate families (especially the males) and rely more on peer groups for identity and support. At the same time, though, social and academic demands are rising. If the strains and social learning dynamics are strong enough, combined with a lack of interest in or talent for school, then the situation is primed for delinquent behavior.

All of this has been exacerbated in China by recent economic and cultural changes that have undermined traditional beliefs, norms, and social controls. Not surprisingly, the sharpest increases in delinquency are seen in fast-growing urban areas experiencing the greatest impact of these economic and social changes. Slow-changing rural areas are experiencing much lower rates of delinquency (Bao & Haas, 2009). Interestingly, Bao et al. (2016) found that the link between parental attachment and delinquent friends was weak, but the link between school attachment and delinquency was strong. In other words, a positive relationship with school is a better insulator from delinquency than solid family relationships. This is different than what is found in America and may reflect the recently increased demands in China for a well-educated and skilled workforce. A good education is the primary road to financial success, and smaller families place more stress on fewer male children to be successful. Parental and cultural ambition, combined with struggles in school, lead these vulnerable adolescents to seek status, support, and success with delinquent peers and subsequent acting-out behavior.

These studies make it clear that in some ways, there are common roads to CD-type behavior in different cultures: being male, in mid-adolescence, with financial strains in the family, difficulties at school, and exposure to delinquent peers. However, there are also significant differences based on culture. Recent economic and cultural changes in China have affected the dynamics of delinquency, especially the stronger importance of school experiences and family demands for economic success. Of particular interest is the difference in the effect of poverty. Most studies in America have found little impact for SES on delinquency, but the Chinese have one. This may reflect the idea that countries that are less developed or are developing quickly experience a greater impact of class differences on delinquency than so-called advanced societies. It also suggests that any society that is experiencing an increase in wealth inequality can expect stronger pressures for delinquency among groups feeling like they are being left behind.

A final note on these reflections on CD and delinquency – the studies and textbooks just cited discuss delinquent behavior in great detail but give scant attention to CD as a mental disorder. The Siegel and Welsh text on juvenile delinquency (2017) mentions CD only two times, and the Chinese studies do not mention it at all. It appears that the research professionals in that field are overwhelmingly focused on sociological/cultural dynamics in youth behavior, not mental illness.

Part of what this reflects is the silo effect – different professional fields have a tendency to pursue their understanding of a subject within the theoretical, institutional, and relational bounds of their own discipline (Tett, 2015). They publish in the same journals, respond to each other's research, socialize within their own departments, and read the same articles and books. In an ironic twist of fate, it may be that the more knowledge we produce in academia, the more difficult it is to keep up with one's own field and the more specialized we become, despite our giving lip service to the importance of cross-discipline research and the ultimate value of integration. The implementation of the biopsychosocial model is suffering from this dynamic. Nearly everyone agrees that human behavior, and mental health and illness by extension, are the result of various factors, arising from the general areas of biology, sociology, and individual development. However, it is far easier to stay in our silos, safe within our tribes, and focus on a small part of the big picture. That has been the general theme of this chapter: how the approach to understanding human nature has continued to be isolated within competing groups of people with their own sets of beliefs and practices, talking mostly to each other.

Despite this, many researchers are exploring links between evolution, neurology, and group identity (Greene, 2013; Sapolsky, 2017). They are figuring out how our brains evolved for tribal life, identifying and bonding with a small group of people. Early humans needed to agree on most things, behave in common ways, and fight ferociously against enemies. The most important dynamic was identifying *us* and clearly identifying *them*. By definition, *we* are good and *they* are evil. We must be protected and they must be avoided or destroyed. This dynamic extends to beliefs, values, and morals. What we believe is right, because it is a group belief and we must be defended against outsiders, including outside ideas. Now that we are moderns and discussing an intellectual topic, one might think that those dynamics would no longer be active, but they are.

As first discussed in our Introduction, Thomas Kuhn famously asserted that scientific knowledge does not progress as smoothly is it sometimes appears, especially after the fact (1962). As a graduate student, he was reading about the history of science and was amazed to find that it does not proceed as a steady accumulation of discoveries, inventions, and subsequent adjustments to theory and knowledge. Instead, he noted that especially in the early stages of a science, the situation tends to reflect competing views of a given field, each of which has at least some foundation in valid forms of observation, method, and even results. They fight for their existence, and unfortunately, they also engage in research that tries to, "force nature into the conceptual boxes supplied by professional education" (p. 5). Conceptual boxes are what we call paradigms – a standard, accepted group of ideas or beliefs about a given phenomenon. Paradigms are resistant to change, as they serve the purposes of both individuals and groups to have a foundation of surety about the world, strong relational bonds with others in the group, and other important commitments based on the paradigm, such as jobs, grants, conferences, contracts, etc.

Another term for paradigms is memes. Richard Brodie (1996) describes them as the conceptual building blocks of culture, "infecting" groups of minds with ideas that impact their sense of self, others, and the world in general. The use of the term "infecting" is not accidental – Brodie sees the spread and impact of memes as directly relatable to the epidemiology of infectious diseases. He also sees them as having an equal potential for destructive force. Memes can have a positive impact (eating fruits and vegetables is good for me) but can just as easily be destructive (people who disagree with my political views are evil and must be stopped by any means necessary). Just like an airborne disease, they reflect something inserted into an environment, easily copied and spread, essentially amoral and irrational, and best understood at the group level.

He also sees the dynamics of memes through the lens of evolution. At their core, the truths of evolution are quite simple: things change over time, they change in reaction to what is going on around them, and things that succeed in replicating themselves survive, while things that don't don't. Things do not change to *improve* or *get better*, at least not in the way we typically think of these terms. That would be a moralistic projection onto a natural process, which is just as kind to intestinal parasites and cancer cells as it is to humanistic philosophers. All that really matters is replicability, and that requires fitness not goodness or even logical or philosophical correctness. What this means for human memes is that they serve no purpose other than their own survival, and they are typically driven by the human imperative of recognizing and responding to danger and opportunities. Human problems tend to be simple but ubiquitous – we need to find sustenance, avoid being killed, and procreate. That means we are highly sensitive to messages about threats to the food supply, potential human and nonhuman enemies of all kinds, and our own potential for attracting a mate. We are also quite sensitive to messages that offer solutions to these problems – get-rich-quick schemes, ways to destroy our enemies before they get us, and how to get a mate (sign me up for Coolsculpting!). These messages do not have to be accurate; they just have to push the right psychoevolutionary buttons. The point here is that those buttons were laid down by evolution in the basic way our brains/minds operate. That makes memes very powerful and hard to combat or change. As noted before, they shape how people think about themselves and the world around them, often by amplifying threats to perceived wellness. This has powerful implications for collective experiences of mental health and wellness in a world awash in negative memes and the insular tribes that support them.

CONCLUSION

Our story has now caught up to the present time. We have explored the variety of now-current viewpoints about mental health and mental illness. We find that they fit three broad approaches: the medical/biological, the psychological, and the cultural/sociological. It should not be surprising that these three approaches come from three very different and professionally separate places. The first is the province of the medical department, with its biologically focused research and professional role in the diagnosis and treatment of severe mental illness, often in a hospital setting. The second is based in the psychology departments of both traditional and professional schools. Its concerns range from normal functioning to clinical problems, but it has tended to focus on the individual and sometimes small groups or families but not so much the wider cultural context or biological underpinnings of mental health or illness. The third is based in the other social science departments. Rather than seeing individuals *impacted* by culture, they tend to see people as *embedded* in culture. This difference in emphasis is vital, as it is more likely to see mental illnesses as the creation of cultures, while psychologists and psychiatrists are more likely to see mental illnesses as individual and universal but influenced by cultural factors. Working in different places, talking mostly among themselves, these three groups have different perspectives, each with its own validity as well as blind spots.

As we entered the early part of the twenty-first century, this dynamic of competing models of mental illness was very much still in play. But as we noted, the competitive edge between them has been softening, and the emergence of the biopsychosocial model has introduced a new paradigm that has the potential to bridge the models. However, that model is really still in its infancy, and as Kuhn points out, new paradigms take time to establish themselves and unseat old ones. Institutions, like the ideas they represent, have inertia and often resist quite strenuously efforts at change. Also, as Brodie points out, paradigms (or memes, if you prefer his vocabulary) are driven by evolutionary "hot buttons" and, as often as not, are irrational and inaccurate but have tremendous power all the same.

What is required, then, is rapprochement between opposing forces and a slow, careful consideration of the wisdom of any new ideas or approaches to this (or any) topic. Referring to a resumption of harmonious relations, this term is historically appropriate. Before the atomization of scientific enquiry in the twentieth century, there was not nearly the hyperspecialization we have today. Learned people read and conversed across academic areas with regularity and ease. While there is the very real risk of being considered an intellectual dilettante if one is caught crossing professional boundaries, in the past, one would have been thought ignorant and insular if one did not take into account the knowledge of various disciplines related to one's central topic. The good news is that we are beginning to see an increase in the kind of healthy cross-fertilization, advocated here. Well-regarded academics such as Steven Pinker and Robert Sapolsky are producing work that brings together research from various quarters in order to draw a "big picture" of human nature.

So this chapter has brought us up to the current time and looked at how the major models have developed over the last few decades, especially in relation to each other. The next chapter will take us into the future and look at how rapprochement can occur so that various areas of human knowledge can coexist within a more holistic model and help us see the "big picture." Hopefully, this will place the future understanding of mental health and mental illness within a significantly larger context of human knowledge than is currently utilized.

CHAPTER 10

NOW AND INTO THE FUTURE

Our historical timeline has run its course. We are now, finally, at the current point in time, still relatively early in the twenty-first century. So where are we now and where are we headed? These questions are difficult to answer. It is always easier to see where people stood in the past, with some historical perspective, than to know where they are at the present moment. It is simply harder to consider context when you are standing in the middle of the lake you are trying to describe. It is even harder, and in fact grossly pretentious, to try and predict the future. Many have tried, and the vast majority have failed. That being said, we will do it anyway but, in so doing, try to be tentative, be more general than specific, and stay grounded in the realities of the current day.

THE CHALLENGE

In exploring the terrain of our project, I want to start with an observation – one that may be less true than I imagine. It appears to me that the field of mental health is far less revolutionary than it used to be. In the twentieth century, there were regular explosions of theory about mental health, starting with psychoanalysis and continuing through behaviorism and humanism. The shift toward a biopsychosocial model has been more evolutionary rather than revolutionary.

This appears to be a valid observation about old paradigms in relation to the ongoing work of developing the DSM. Before the DSM-5 was published, its developers were being warned about serious problems with the nosology that needed to be addressed. In 2009, at the American Psychiatric Association's Annual Meeting, various researchers presented their findings related to how the DSM was conceptualizing and thus organizing mental illness. Their work was published in 2011, two years before the release of DSM-5, and it does not appear that many of their concerns were integrated into the new manual. The authors agreed that the increase in reliability following the profound changes to DSM-III were not supported by an increase in validity (Regier, Narrow, Kuhl, & Kupfer, 2011). As noted before, subsequent editions have had major problems with comorbidity (people diagnosed with multiple disorders because the same symptoms appear in different diagnoses), lack of homogeneity within syndromes (people diagnosed with the same disorder exhibiting very different symptoms), and lack of logical consistency (for instance, a low level of psychotic symptoms would be diagnosed as a personality disorder, while a high level of symptoms would be diagnosed as a psychotic disorder). As discussed in the previous chapter, the DSM-5 reflects the APA apparently "moving the deckchairs around the *Titanic*" but not addressing the glaring need for full reevaluation of its approach to nosology. Steven Hyman points out that the most recent work in genetics and other related fields that will eventually explicate mental illness are still in a very early stage of development, there are no scientific tests for any mental illness, and there are significant structural problems that suggest the DSM nosology does not embody the basic need to reflect clinical reality (Hyman, 2011). He and the editors of the book agreed that the more we discover about the interplay of biology and mental illness, the more it looks like nature designed a mental system that is much more dimensional than categorical and includes multiple factors (both internal and external) impacting every facet of its functioning, including mental illness.

This certainly makes sense. It is hard to argue with the idea that human behavior is multidetermined, with biological, sociological, and developmental factors involved. In this chapter, we will begin by proclaiming that some form of a biopsychosocial model is the only reasonable starting point for a thorough understanding of mental health and mental illness moving into the future. However, there are a number of challenges involved. These challenges, as noted before, are twofold. First, there is the *resistance* to breaking down old paradigms and changing the institutions that were built around them. Second, there is the difficult task of somehow *integrating the immense array of information* from the various fields involved, both what we already know and the steady deluge of ongoing developments. The first challenge is already being met. There is very little overt resistance to the basic idea that mental health issues are complex phenomena that are multifactoral and multidimensional. Not everyone who supports that approach agrees with evolutionary theory, but that does not matter very much, because while there may be differences of opinion about *how* the human organism and human society got to the conditions they are in now, there can still be agreement on the current state of multifactoral complexity regarding mental health and mental illness.

So it appears that the shift of paradigm is already well underway and meeting less resistance with each passing decade. What is the main challenge? It turns out that the *level of complexity* itself is the main obstacle to fully developing biopsychosocial model and incorporating it into our basic understanding of mental health and a nosology of mental illness. For instance, we offered a very short list of related topics in the previous chapter. Now, to indicate how crazy this project really is, here is a list of related subject areas, drawn from a course catalog at Stanford University:

School of Earth, Energy and Environmental
    Earth Systems
    Environment and Resources
School of Engineering
    Bioengineering
School of Humanities and Sciences
    Anthropology
    Art History
    Biology
    Communication
    Comparative Literature
    Comparative Studies in Race and Ethnicity
    Economics
    Feminist, Gender, and Sexuality Studies
    History and Philosophy of Science

Sciences School of Medicine
    Biochemistry
    Developmental Biology
    Genetics
    Neurology
    Psychiatry

    Urban Studies
    Statistics
    Sociology
    Psychology
    Philosophy
    Humanities and Sciences
    Human Rights
    Global Studies

And remember, these are just the subject areas, not a list of specific courses, so saying one is interested in a biopsychosocial model of mental health presents profound difficulties, not the least of which is how to develop and teach the range of information needed to truly understand any given human being.

RESPONDING TO THE CHALLENGE

So how does one begin? Well, you first need a conceptual framework, a model, to provide a system of linked ideas to explain what it is we are trying to build and, at least in general principles, how it works. When it comes to systems of human knowledge and to psychology in particular, models have been proposed for thousands of years. We have already visited quite a few of them. However, to simplify matters here, and because the earlier chapters have already provided a historical context, we will begin with Engel. He gave us a starting point in 1977 when he proposed the biopsychosocial model. He began with two basic pieces of a conceptual foundation. The first was that it took into consideration multiple sources of information about human behavior – it is *multifactoral*. The second is that it approached human nature, like all of nature, as being *system based*, recognizing the complexity of living things in an environment, which have multiple levels of structure and function, ranging from the atomic to the entire ecosystem. All levels interact with and affect each other in various, complex ways. This constitutes a holistic rather than atomistic approach to human nature. The third part of the foundation, which Engel did not refer to directly, adds the epistemological approach of *social construction*. This embraces the intersubjective nature of nearly all that we hold to be true, especially as it regards human psychology and behavior. In other words, we approach all knowledge about people from the position of and using the tools of the human mind. This affects not just what we think we know but how we organize and conceptualize what we know. The fourth and final part of the foundation is evolution, which provides the conceptual basis for why and how things change over time.

The Integrated Model

With that conceptual foundation in place, we can develop a framework for *organizing* the actual information called for to understand mental health and mental illness. It must provide a relational matrix to understand what types of information are needed and how they are connected to each other systemically. Later in this chapter, we will introduce and explore this framework, which we will call the Integrated Model. With that framework in place, filled in with subfields of knowledge, we can start identifying the specific information we have and need, with a particular focus on creating links between different subfields of knowledge and seeing how they are applied in the real world. In other words, if the framework is valid, it can be activated in the real world of academic study and practical application. This includes existing knowledge subfields, ranging from global studies to molecular biology. It also includes existing application areas like clinical psychology, psychiatry, and social work. Before describing the proposed framework of knowledge areas (Integrated Model), let's say a bit more about the four parts of the conceptual foundation.

Multifactoral Psychology – The four parts of the foundation have all been discussed in previous sections of this text, in various historical contexts. The biopsychosocial model emerged because of the increasingly obvious conclusion that human psychology is the result of many different factors, and focusing exclusively on only one or two of them is misleading, resulting in inappropriately amplifying one factor (for instance, behaviorism) while completely ignoring others (for instance, genetics). It's like the old story of the three blind men describing an elephant. One is standing by the ear and says an elephant is thin and smooth, like a large leaf. The second is standing by the tail and says it is long and thin, like a vine. The third is standing by a leg and says it is thick and upright, like a table pedestal. We need to take a wide-angle view of human nature. This was how premodern people approached human nature, and after the atomization of modernity artificially divided knowledge acquisition into separate silos of truth, it is time for a postmodern reintegration of the multiple factors impacting human nature.

Systems Theory – In so doing, we can see that human psychology exists as a system itself, incorporating many areas of knowledge, but also lies within a larger system of human knowledge. This meta-system includes different levels, that interact in complex ways, requiring that in order to understand the human psyche, we must understand the relationships between different levels of the system. This is at least as important as understanding the nature of the subsystems in and of themselves. Therefore, this model incorporates a Complex Adaptive System (CAS) approach to systems theory. It will be described in more detail later in the chapter, but for now can simply be referred to as a theoretical foundation for understanding the dynamic qualities of complex systems like those involving mental health and mental illness.

Social Construction Theory – It is the centrality of the *relationships* (interaction of information and energy) between levels and parts of a system that makes the philosophy of social construction so important in this model. It does not preclude the truth that things, in and of themselves, have a reality but rather that what is most important is what they mean in the context of their functional relationship with each other. For instance, money has reality in and of itself, but outside of a human context, it is simply chunks of metal and pieces of paper. Now that we are living in an electronic society, money can come into existence and be moved about, saved, and spent, without ever having physical existence. It has become pure information – a thing of meaning, without physical form. It has become more a process than a thing, and yet it remains one of the most important elements in human existence. The contextual dynamics are far more important than the individual forms.

Again, that is not to say that individual form does not matter – it does. If I had a million dollars in cash in shed and the shed burned down, destroying the cash, that money would be gone. All elements in a system have specific properties that place constraints and capacities on the system as a whole. These are brute facts, and the relative consideration of them differentiates "weak" social constructs (dominated by brute facts) and "strong" social constructs (dominated by relational dynamics). One could argue that money has become a stronger social construct as it has become more electronic and less connected to physical materials like gold. The principle remains, however, that the value or meaning placed on any brute fact depends on its relationship to other brute facts, as they exist and interact within a given nested system of relational dynamics.

Actually, a number of constructionist epistemological approaches have been proposed. The first is *social causation*, and it is the closest to a modernist view in that it accepts the basic medical model of mental disorders as things "in and of themselves" but then explores the role of social stresses in their etiology, presentation, course, and outcome. This approach parallels the thinking in the DSM, which allows for an influence of sociology on mental illness, but the taxonomy itself is presented as basically universal. The second approach is *social construction* and takes things much further. In this epistemology, reality is not an ontological "given," waiting to be discovered, but rather is largely created by human thought, experience, and imagination. This raises the question of whether any mental disorders actually exist, separate from human conceptualization. It also raises the question of whether any objective reality at all can be accepted within social construction. For the most part, it is. Even within the social construction perspective, the physical world is accepted as real, with its own qualities. Where things become much more "constructed" is in the social sciences. Social constructionists look at how individual thinkers in psychology and psychiatry have been influenced by their own experiences, as expressed in their use of language and symbols – an approach typically referred to as deconstruction. They also consider the way in which scientific knowledge is created based on individual and collective interests and power dynamics. Truth is not necessarily truth but rather a comfortable position for those currently holding power and thus influencing the beliefs of others.

As an alternative to the two polarities of social causation and social construction, there is the middle ground of *social realism*. In this approach, objective reality is accepted but critically interpreted. It proposes that material and social realities exist prior to a given individual encountering them but then emphasizes the role of individual agency and action to align with or change those social realities. That means there is a material reality, so it is not reality itself that is socially constructed, but our theories about it are, which, in a way, is more important because they are what we act upon. Material and social realities constrain or motivate action but do not completely control it. This suggests that the social and natural sciences should utilize different methodologies because the social sciences study phenomena that are relativistically determined. For instance, individual and collective action, inspired by certain beliefs can change social structures, while human activity cannot change the fundamental structure of natural phenomena. So, social realism accepts both objective and subjective data as valid and examines the *relationship* between the two based on the assumption that they must be considered within a *social context*.

Evolution – The question emerges, then: What is the fundamental process underlying these relationships, especially as they change over time? Evolution provides the basic principles for change, centering on adaptation and environmental fitness. It tells us *why* things change the way they do and the basic nature of the relationships between phenomena. At its core, evolution says that species change or do not change, based on how they fit current environmental conditions and are able to survive and procreate within that environmental context.

Evolution is a mysterious natural process that often defies entropy to push life toward ever-more-complex and adaptive forms. This process shows no indication of having designed humans (or anything else) in an intelligent, predetermined way. Our species is the result of the adaptively successful tinkering of existing parts, with our only unique capacity, our X-Men superpower, being our big brains. That is what gave us the edge over the competition. Early humanoids were smarter than their rivals, better able to work together in complex social groups, adjust their behavior to meet the demands of different environments, control fire, build shelters, find food and water, and make friends with or defeat their rivals.

That is why it is important for us to remember that, as discussed in the first chapter, evolution is not just physiological but cultural as well. We evolved ways of thinking and behaving that served us well through the 90% of our history when we lived in small bands of hunter-gatherers, moving often and living in mortal fear of lions, famine, and rival humanoid groups. Because of this, we are quick to anger, quick to panic, and slow to deeply think things through. We are obsessed with food, sex, and money, even when we have plenty of them to survive. Our brains are vulnerable to all manner of problems related to our emotions, our cognition, and our behavior. In short, feeling happy and at peace often seems to be the exception rather than the rule. So much of human life seems to be a desperate attempt to find some form of peace and happiness, which appears for fleeting moments but more often shimmers like a mirage in the distance, beckoning us to do whatever we can to feel good in the moment.

This desperate race for happiness reflects an underlying evolutionary truth. Nature does not care if we are happy; it only cares if we survive to procreate. In fact, as discussed in the previous section, we are "wired" by evolution to easily feel bad in order to motivate us to take action directed toward survival-related goals. We experience deprivation states (hunger, fatigue, thirst, lust) that push us to stay alive and pass on our genes. We experience emotional states (fear, jealousy, disgust, anger) that motivate us to deal with perceived threats in our environment.

Beyond these daily troubles, there are other, more profound difficulties. Many people experience horrific circumstances that make the normal, day-to-day alleviation of these troubles next to impossible. On the deprivation side, this includes people who are caught up in wars, disease, and famine. On the negative emotional state side, it includes people who are highly traumatized, experiencing profound cultural disruptions or oppression, or suffering with severe mental illness. Now, if that was not enough, there is for most of us the reality that toward the end of the road, we will experience old age and medical decline. Finally, at the end of the road, everyone will experience death. It is not pleasant to talk about, but that is the sad truth of the human condition. We are often a rather miserable lot, and in the end, we all lose the biological game. A major part of our misery is that we all know it.

Again, evolution cares nothing about this. It cares only that we pass on our genes. From this perspective, there is no design, no grand intentionality, just a natural process that rewards survival and procreation and punishes failure (Dawkins, 1986). There are evolutionary explanations for aggression, war, rape, antisocial behavior, infanticide, and various forms of selfishness. Thus, evolution wields a double-edged sword. It provides the tools for species survival, including consciousness itself, but in doing so, it also creates a psychology that is often miserable. Because of our big brains, humans are prone to be anxious, depressed, frustrated, disappointed, angry, resentful, jealous, envious, regretful, guilty, ashamed, self-conscious, and self-doubting. Nature, and the consciousness it gave us, can be harsh and unforgiving, but it can also be loving and generous. Human nature is not all dark. Humans evolved to love each other in many different ways, to be altruistic, kind, and thoughtful. We can find joy and pride in our accomplishments, as well as those of people close to us. We can enjoy all manner of sensory delights, including good food, beautiful views, a warm bath, and the sand between our toes. We can enjoy the social relationships in our lives and revel in joy of companionship, play, and sport. We draw comfort, meaning, and purpose from our spiritual, professional, and social communities.

So the initial thrust of evolution drove our adaptive development, providing the edge our species needed to survive, but now it can be seen as a primary source of both mental health and mental illness. It is a foundational element in what makes us human and should be considered a "lens" of understanding human functioning, directly connected to the biological, the psychological, and the social aspects of our nature. It is the *why* to their *how*, and because of that difference, it would not be included in the biopsychosocial approach if that model were only descriptive and structural in nature; but everything changes if we think of it as a process model. What if, instead of considering the biopsychosocial model as a static collection of functional areas, we develop it as a dynamic process of change over time. It must then include not only the functional areas but also the basic dynamic of evolution that is driving the change and shaping the functional areas. This is vital, because the state of the system as it stands at any given point in time is a consequence of its history, and that provides clues as to its movement into future states. That means the model is not just descriptive and prescriptive but also (to a limited extent) prognostic.

The Nest of Being and Systems Theory

Much more needs to be discussed regarding the four-part foundation, but with the basic outline in place, we can start to explore what a framework of knowledge areas should look like. This exploration is not new. A Great Chain of Being has been postulated for at least 3,000 years (Wilber, 2000). In the premodern world, it was typically conceptualized as a spiritual hierarchy of being, starting at the lowest level of basic matter then progressing through plants, animals, humans, angels, and, at the top, God. Each level of the chain was thought to include the qualities of the level below, but with additional, higher qualities. In the Classical era, Aristotle utilized the concept to develop a ranking of animals, with humans on top (of course). This constituted a nonreligious system of organization and directly influenced scientific thinking throughout the Middle Ages.

On the problematical side, this way of approaching reality has supported the creation of hierarchal systems that lack legitimacy but still provide a rationale for oppressive concepts with their related systems, including caste systems, racist hierarchies, etc. However, the misuse of an idea does not invalidate the idea itself. Recognizing that reality consists of nested holarchies does not place any particular moral value on the different levels. It does not say that organs are *better* than atoms just because they are at different levels within a nested system. It has typically been the imposition of a supposed moral hierarchy, driven by the interests of a dominant group to maintain and legitimize its power, that has inspired the creation of unfair and oppressive "chains of being." This temptation needs to be strongly resisted in order to create a model that *accurately* reflects reality to the best of our limited human ability.

With that in mind, we need to develop a logical framework of knowledge regarding mental health and mental illness, as it is embedded within psychology in general, and thus including the full range of human experience. Ken Wilber took this perspective and postulated what he called the Great Nest of Being (2000). It includes five levels of being, each transcending and including the previous one.

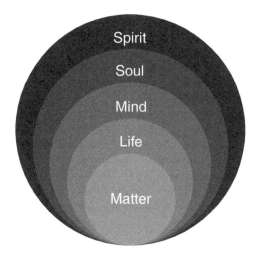

Any particular aspect of life – dealing with the death of a loved one, for instance – can be understood from the perspective of any of these levels. It does assume that moving from a lower level of perspective to a higher one is developmental. Each progressive level takes a wider, more inclusive view that is more conscious and less embedded in the immediate life situation. For instance, minds are consciously aware of and incorporate a much wider range of information than cells.

Part of the aim of spiritual growth, as envisioned and often experienced by many of the world's great sages, mystics, and prophets of history, is to move one's center of being (thoughts, feelings, behavior, attention, and energy) away from the lower levels of matter, life, and even mind and toward soul and eventually spirit, incorporating ever-widening perspectives on reality (Aurobindo, 1949; Huxley, 1944; Wilber, 2000).

In order to understand this model better, we can look at it from the perspective of the study of human beings. The level of *matter* relates to the field of physics. What are the basic laws and materials of the physical universe? How are atoms constructed, and how do they function? *Life* relates to the biological sciences, including neurology and biochemistry. What are the basic structures and processes of biological life, including our own? *Mind* refers to the study of psychology and sociology. What are the processes of human motivation, thinking, feeling, behaving, and interacting with others? *Soul* refers to the study of religion. How have different faiths conceptualized the metaphysical world and humanity's place in it? *Spirit* refers to the study of mysticism. What is the ultimate truth of existence beyond religious systems and their religious institutional agendas?

In considering this model, we realize that almost all subfields of knowledge focus on one or at most two levels of reality. The biological model focuses on the life level, sometimes giving a passing nod to the mind level but rarely giving it equal footing. Conversely, most work in psychology does the same thing to the life level, or biology. People focused on religious studies rarely make any mention of biology and are often too embedded in their own theological model to take a higher spiritual view.

Not only does the Nest of Being recognize that there different levels of a system but that there is dynamic interaction and movement between the levels (Wilber, 2000). It reflects a developmental process. What this is saying is that human wellness does not have to stop at the level of meeting basic biological needs, adjustment or adaptive needs, or even somewhat higher happiness and self-esteem needs. Humans can and often do aspire to higher levels of functioning and experience.

Abraham Maslow was aware of this. His model of a human hierarchy of needs and the goal of self-actualization actually parallels Wilber's in important ways. He saw psychological development as a process that starts in the biological realm then proceeds through basic adjustment/adaption (safety) into higher levels of emotional wellness (love and esteem) and then into spiritual levels of self-experience (self-actualization). He also noted that people who attained high levels of self-actualization became less self-centered. They thought less about themselves and more about others and higher principles of human well-being and spirituality. This reflects a form of self-transcendence, or what Wilber refers to as the *selfless self.*

It also reflects what has been called the *perennial philosophy* (Aurobindo, 1949; Huxley, 1944). The basic idea here is that the human psyche reflects the divine psyche. Each person has within them the potential to know and experience the "spiritual ground of all things." The belief is that most people live in ignorance of this truth and thus continue to suffer the trials and tribulations of everyday life. But there are an uncommon few who become enlightened to the truth and thus free from suffering. They see and experience the transcendent *truth* behind the veil of existence. They experience the *godhead*, both within themselves and present in all existence. While this experience can sometimes come in a flash, it is typically achieved and maintained through hard work. As Huxley wrote, "the nature of this one Reality is such that it cannot be directly and immediately apprehended except by those who have chosen to fulfill certain conditions, making themselves loving, pure of heart, and poor of spirit" (1944, p. viii). Different religions have various terms and processes for this. In Buddhism, it is called enlightenment; in Hinduism, it is called nirvana; in Taoism, it is called balance; in Christianity, it is called Christ-consciousness or grace.

It should be noted here that there is a profound difference between *traditional* Western theology, where God is conceptualized as separate from humanity and nature (the material realm), maintaining this separation until death, and what is typically referred to as esotericism, which centers on the idea that God-consciousness is within us and can be accessed through certain disciplines and practices. For the most part, there has been a split between East and West about the legitimacy of this approach to spiritual growth. In the East, the monks and gurus who pursue such a level of lived spiritual experience are considered high-level practitioners of a mainstream belief, while in the West, individuals who pursue such a goal have generally been considered heretics and often excommunicated from the mainstream faith and, at times, even physically punished or killed. This attitude has softened over the last century and a half, largely as the religious concepts from the East (particularly Buddhism and Hinduism) have filtered into our society, but also because of the influence of African religious traditions, through the slave trade, on Christian practices as they developed in South America and the Caribbean.

Today, in the West, millions now practice meditation, do yoga, and embrace a vegetarian diet. Most of these people do so for various health or "mind-level" reasons (relaxation, fitness, relief of stress or anxiety), with limited understanding of the spiritual purpose of the practices themselves, which is to help the individual transcend the lower levels of consciousness and enter the higher ones. Some in the West are fully aware of these "higher" goals, and a smaller number enthusiastically pursue them for this purpose. Some are even adherents of Western religions and have chosen to add some of these beliefs and practices to their personal theology, despite what the leaders of their churches may say.

In fact, one of the most consistent trends in modern religion in the West is that people are turning away from traditional, mainstream churches and reliance on their theological authority (Pew Research, 2019). Instead, more people are describing themselves as nondenominational or simply spiritual. They are defining religion for themselves and often piecing together various beliefs and practices to create their own religion – the religion of no religion. Over the last decade, the percentage of Americans who identify themselves as Christian has dropped 10% while the percentage who describe themselves as religiously unaffiliated has risen 9%, with a lot of the change coming from younger people. Nearly half of the so-called Millennial generation consider themselves "unaffiliated." It should be noted that there has been almost no increase in the percentage of people who call themselves Buddhists, Hindus, or generically spiritual. Instead, it appears that most of these ostensibly nonreligious people "dabble" in various practices and may have a belief in a spiritual dimension to life but do not commit themselves very strongly to spiritual growth.

This is, of course, probably how it has always been, especially in large, complex societies. Attaining the highest levels of spirituality has always involved a select few. They establish the possibility for its attainment, describe the path, offer to assist others, and model the journey. Few follow. Most remain at the mind level, raise families, work a job or career, have "normal" lives, and their affiliation with a church is more a social and cultural habit than a spiritual calling. They want to be happy and reach their life goals, but those goals typically do not include becoming a priest or monk, walking away from their material lives, and praying or meditating 12 hours a day. Still, the fact that they know that some people do and believe that this is possible for anyone to attempt and that the pursuit is valid – that it reflects reality – is enough to establish the Nest of Being in their minds as real.

There are those who reject all references to a spiritual or nonmaterial level of reality. Some of these folks may be "stuck" at a relatively low level, focused heavily on life (Wilber) or safety (Maslow) issues. They tend to see life in terms of direct threats and the need for either refuge or dominance. Their lives are focused on a "kill or be killed" perspective. This level of existence is very real. Threats are real, danger is everywhere, and some forms of self-protection are appropriate. However, if a great deal of one's consciousness is "caught" at that level of reality, one is likely to miss a lot that lies beyond that perspective. Of course, we also know now that people do not need to satisfy one level of the hierarchy in order to move on to higher levels. More recent research supports Maslow's basic model of different types and levels of needs that are connected to a sense of well-being but has found that many people are able to move on to social and spiritual needs while still struggling with basic material and safety needs (Tay & Diener, 2011). Thus, some who reject nonmateriality are not "stuck at a low level" at all but may be thoughtful, emotionally sensitive, deep thinkers, but have decided the universe is material by nature. This includes, of course, the dynamic of energy ($e = mc^2$, after all) but that is a major step away from traditional religious beliefs (gods and demons, etc.) and at least a half step away from esoteric ones (human nature as pure consciousness, etc.) Many of these nonspiritual people still believe, as Maslow did, that as people move toward self-actualization, they will typically become more loving, accepting of others, selfless, generous, and peaceful. In other words, there is still room for personal growth that moves in the same *psychological* direction as something we call spiritual growth. Thus, we can say the nested model – given its systemic character – is still valid, even if we were to replace the top level of spirit with the concept of pure energy and extraordinary possibilities, which is the ultimate reality of the material universe (Greene, 2011).

Wilber's Theory of Everything

The Great Nest of Being, as conceptualized by Wilber, provides the starting point for a simple, systemic hierarchy for our model, but it does not lay out the functional/content areas we need. Ken Wilber addressed this as well (1995, 1996, 2000). He looked at various models of human development and functioning, including biological, psychological, and spiritual ones. He found them all too one-dimensional. He recognized that any comprehensive model of psychology had to incorporate various models and include both the internal, subjective side of life and the external, more objective side. He also recognized, of course, that it had to incorporate levels. What he developed was a model with four quadrants – including an Interior-Individual (Intentional), an Exterior-Individual (Behavioral), an Interior-Collective (Cultural), and an Exterior-Collective (Social). Wilber came by this differentiation of quadrants by studying hundreds of other models. He found that although they all had some similarities, they were also profoundly different. They were not all describing the same things, but when considered together, what they were describing seemed to always fall into four basic areas. First, they were either describing internal or external phenomena. Second, they were describing either individual or collective phenomena. Thus, there were four basic "streams" of description, what he calls the Intentional, the Behavioral, the Cultural, and the Social. It is a fascinating model and does a great service in providing a map covering far more territory than previous ones.

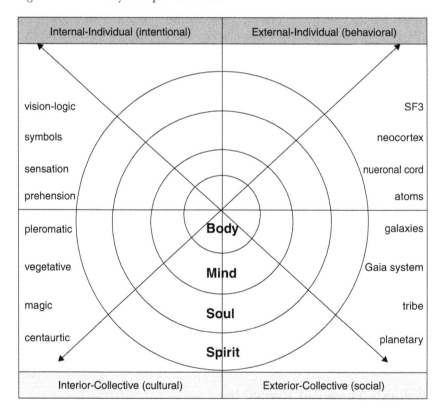

For instance, to use one of Wilber's examples, let's say somebody has a thought: "I want to go to the store." The thought itself exists as a subjective, internal experience (Intentional). The thought also corresponds to a material process embedded in brain activity (Behavioral). The thought also relates to a certain set of cultural meanings. It would not even occur in a culture without stores (Cultural). And finally, that culture will have a set of structures, technologies, and social divisions that shape the values and meanings within it (social). The model is beautiful in its logic and basic simplicity. There are difficulties, however. The primary one is that the differentiation of the four quadrants ends up organizing different types of phenomena in ways that are almost unrecognizable to the large majority of social scientists. For instance, galaxies and tribes are in the same quadrant. Nobody who studies astrology includes tribal dynamics in their work and would not consider the two in any meaningful way related. This is not to say the model does not make sense. But it seems odd at first to include galaxies and tribes in the same category in any system. What Wilber is referring to is the level of collective organization – how they group together. His point is that galaxies are huge, but their collective organization is simple, based on gravity. Tribal society is more complex. However, no matter how logical the model, it helps for it to be translatable in a direct way to existing categorical systems in order to be practical and accepted by a wide range of people.

Ken Wilber is not the only one to attempt to categorize and graph the various areas and levels of a biopsychosocial model. Engel (2003) provided a nested system model similar to Wilber's. It started with the molecule in the center then progressed through the organelle, cell, tissue, organ, nervous system, person, two-person, family, community, culture, society-nation, and finally the biosphere. It reflects an accurate continuum but does not differentiate Internal-Subjective states from physiological material and processes. Thus, the lower levels include the physiological but nothing psychological, and the higher levels are primarily social but not physiological. Wilber's system helps by differentiating the subjective from the objective – the psychological experience from the material elements of that experience. However, the nonintuitive ways it differentiates the social from the cultural and individual from the collective make it hard to translate into current systems or disciplines. What is needed is a model that is systemic, is nested, clearly differentiates types of phenomena, and is intuitively approachable within the various fields that are already busy studying these phenomena.

The Framework of Knowledge Areas

What follows is an attempt at this. For convenience and to emphasize its (subtle) differences from Wilber's model, we will call this the Framework of Knowledge Areas (FKA). Wilber's quadrants are maintained, as are systemic levels and the differentiation of objective and subjective phenomena. Rather than differentiating individual and collective, however, it is separated by Internal and External – this supports the basic human experience of things within us and things outside us while amplifying the concept that all human relationships, from the dyad to world culture, are intersubjective social creations, not physical things like organs. They *use* physical things like various technologies to further their ends, but the ends and processes themselves are a result of social construction. The physical aspects of society, its technologies, including printing presses, phones, and hunting arrows, are in the External-Objective quadrant. Every quadrant (and level) interacts with the others but has its own holistic dynamic (it is a logically identifiable thing in itself) that

makes it fundamentally different than the others. The psychological experience of
the individual (Internal-Subjective) is connected to but different from the physiological structures and processes of the individual (Internal-Objective), including the
brain. There is a dynamic, flowing interplay between the material and nonmaterial
internal world, each affecting the other. They are not the same thing, although they
are systemically entwined. The same is true in the world external to the individual. The physical world (External-Objective) of biology, climate, and ecosystems
interacts dynamically with the subjective world of both human and animal society.
Again, society or culture is a *system* of relationships, rules, beliefs, and values, which
interacts with the physical world and is powerfully impacted by it but can be considered a separate thing of itself.

The separate units at any level and in any quadrant are typically referred to
as holons. This means that they have a separate reality of their own (as previously
described) but are themselves part of larger holons. There really is no limit to the
possible levels, which together constitute a holarchy. We do not know what all the
constituent "parts" of subatomic particles are – they may be made up of tiny bits of
pure energy (string theory). At the other end of the spectrum, we do not know what
lies beyond our universe. There may be a nearly endless series of other universes (a
multiverse). Between the extremes, there is a nearly endless variety of ways one can
parse the different levels within different fields. One discipline may posit 4 levels,
while another may posit 44. The key is the concept of nested holons, making up
holarchies, not the specific number of levels in any particular branch of knowledge.
For those who are more visually oriented, this is what the FKA might look like.

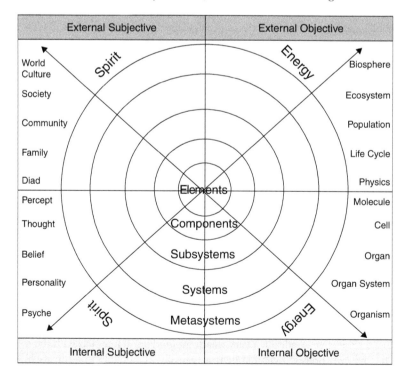

The listing of topics along the left and right "walls" of the FKA are examples of common subfields of academic study that would make sense at its place in a particular nested system. Many others could be put in their places. For instance, a computer engineer would work from the External-Objective but might put plastic and metal at the lowest level then progress through circuits, processor boards, a single computer, and finally whole computer networks. Computer programmers, conversely, work more in the External-Subjective, designing informational processes and relationships. Their work interacts directly with the External-Objective but has its own qualities and characteristics that are unique and different from that of computer engineering.

What each subfield has in common is that it typically exists at a particular level or directly connected levels of systemic organization. Someone who studies human perception of stimuli or basic thought processing is typically not concerned with the overall psyche. People who study molecular biology are not looking at the organism as a whole. Of course, some fields take a wider perspective, often in terms of both levels and quadrants. A computer programmer must consider not just the working of a single computer but how it interacts with a much larger computer network. She focuses on the External-Subjective of information and relationships but also has to produce a material product (External-Objective) in terms of a record of computer code embedded on a recording device. Psychologists often consider multiple levels of both the Interior-Subjective and the Exterior-Subjective, along with some consideration of the Interior-Objective.

In regard to the levels of the FKA, it starts in the middle at the most elemental – meaning the smallest units needed to "build" the overall system that is being considered. Depending on the particular field, this may include quarks or metals or specific mental perceptions. The next level includes combinations of elemental units that serve a *separate functional purpose*, for instance a cell or a thought or a family. These components work together to create subsystems that can perform much more complex work than the components themselves. This includes such things as organs or beliefs or communities. At the next level, these subsystems work together to perform even more complex and integrated tasks. This includes such things as the central nervous system, the personality, and nation-states. These link together to form even more complex systems. For the human being, this means the complete biological organism and the overall psyche. In the external world, this could mean the complete biosphere, an emerging world culture, or it could also refer to the entire universe if one's systemic focus went beyond the Earth. How many areas of knowledge are needed and how many system levels there are depends on the phenomena being considered and why it is being studied. If you are trying to fix a car, you don't need to get more elemental than nuts and bolts, and your largest system would be the one car. If you are designing a traffic system, the most elemental level would be a single car, and the largest would be the entirety of the traffic system being designed.

Each level has its own structural and formal semiautonomy but is subsumed within the overall structure of the higher level. This is not a moral distinction. No level is *better* than another. Molecular biologists are not doing *inferior* work to astronomers. Cars are not morally superior to bolts. At the same time, it must be recognized that higher levels subsume lower ones, so the work at higher levels is taking more phenomena into consideration in its understanding of how the world works. This has important ramifications for the understanding of reality. As a general rule, the outer levels are more inclusive and thus can seem more valuable. It takes an act of moral will, a conscious choice about values, to make an individual more valuable than a group. In nature, a single individual is never more important than the group. However, it is also true that without the individual elements, the collective *cannot exist*, and thus the elemental parts are just as important as the subsystem they make possible.

Outside the system rings are spirit and energy. This is present for two reasons. First of all, the large majority of humans believe in a spiritual level of reality. To exclude this level would be an insult to those people, would fail to reflect the subjectively lived reality in which they exist, and would fail to acknowledge the possibility of realms of reality not immediately apparent at the present state of scientific knowledge. Also, on a nonreligious basis, as was previously pointed out, energy and matter are simply two different "states" of the same reality. Energy is matter moving very quickly. Processes like fire transform something that is currently physical into energy. This reflects the fundamental truth of our universe. So for those who shrink from the idea of Spirit, it can be replaced with the term "Energy." They may well be the same thing, couched in different ideology. They are both conceptualized as the central force and foundation of all creation, lying behind and within the known physical universe (Greene, 2011).

The last aspect of the FKA to consider is the Adaptive Dynamics arrows. They indicate two things, the hierarchal nature of nested systems and the dynamic processes involved. First, relating to natural hierarchies, the outer rings indicate higher levels of complexity and inclusion. As stated before, each subsumes the levels below, and together, they make up a holarchy. This may come as a shock to those who eschew hierarchies. There are many who do so, primarily because humans have a very poor history when it comes to how the more powerful treat the less powerful. It has been brutal, grossly unfair, and profoundly immoral. Personally, I count myself among the humanists who believe that all human beings have equal intrinsic worth and should all be treated as equals, with equanimity and kindness. I also believe we should treat the Earth the same way and develop better ways to sustain our human life while damaging the natural environment as little as possible. As noted before, neither of these moral and philosophical positions contradicts the basic truth that the world exists with nested levels of complexity and integration. Atoms are part of molecules. Molecules are not part of atoms. Trees are part of a forest. A forest is not a part of a tree. Again, this does not place moral values on different levels of a system, but it does reflect on their overall valuation. It is better to sacrifice a tree than a forest or a state over the nation of which it is a part. It also means that because they are directly connected, it usually makes no sense to sacrifice a part to support the whole. More often, the health of the individual parts supports and reflects the health of the overall system. The good of the holon is connected to the good of the holarchy. Damage to a holon negatively impacts the holarchy. Every level is important and can spell vitality or doom for the whole. Environmental conditions that lead to better health for a single tree also impact other trees and thus the entire forest.

This discussion leads us to the other purpose for the Adaptive Dynamics arrows in the FKA. It has to do with the developmental pattern or direction of evolution. The progression of evolution in general, and the human one in particular, begs the question of whether it has what Ken Wilber called a "secret impulse" for greater complexity and transcendence (1996). If it does, then higher levels of spirituality and consciousness are not just "happy accidents" connected to our big brains but are emergent qualities deriving from the evolutionary process itself. Just as sexual reproduction was an "improvement" on previous forms of reproduction, spirituality represents an "improvement" on previous levels of mentation. In that case, spiritual consciousness can be seen as being at the highest level of the nested system, both transcending and including lower levels of mental awareness. The highest possible transcendent awareness, then, may be of all reality. In that sense, consciousness equals depth – through various levels of holarchy. The deepest (or highest) consciousness is one that can include and then transcend all systems and experience itself as part of the Whole of Wholes. This brings us back to the wisdom of the sages, who tell us it is within our reach to experience nirvana, enlightenment, or Christ-consciousness. It is hard to imagine a greater sense of wellness or mental health than that!

Adaptive Dynamics in the Integrated Model – CAS

At the beginning of this chapter our basic model was presented, establishing a combination of multifactoral psychology, systems theory, social construction, and evolutionary theory as the conceptual foundation, with a framework of knowledge areas built on that and specific subfields of knowledge and their practical application resting at the top. That gave us a starting point, with easily recognized tools to begin building a new Integrated Model of human knowledge, again with thanks to Ken Wilber and George Engel's enormous contributions to the subject. We have described the basic elements in the foundation and the FKA and could stop there, but it would leave us well short of a fully functioning model. What we have so far is a structural model with static components. It includes the four quadrants of knowledge and grounds them in evolutionary theory but does not describe how they dynamically interact with each other and change over time. It is like a statue that cannot move. The next section provides the principles of that movement and thus further develops the *foundation of the model* as dynamic and embedded in the history reviewed in the first nine chapters of the text.

What is being proposed here is a model reflecting a Complex Adaptive System (CAS). The basic idea of CAS is that understanding the form or behavior of any particular element(s) in a system does *not* lead to an understanding of the system as a whole (Lansing, 2003; MacLennan, 2007; Miller & Page, 2007). In the spirit of the early Gestalt psychologists, CAS proposes that the whole is more than the sum of its parts. That is because the parts interact in highly complex ways, leading to a different form and/or function than exhibited by any individual part or subsystem of the whole. The key to understanding the whole, then, is to avoid getting lost in the details of the parts themselves and instead focus on the complex *relationships* between the parts. This language should make clear that CAS is not only an extension of systems theory, it is closely related to postmodern, relativistic thought.

The fact that it deals with complexity makes it a good approach to deal with issues involving cross-disciplinary systems, including organization, adaption, robustness, and emergent qualities. These considerations transcend but include the more concrete levels or parts of the system, such as the biological, psychological, and sociological aspects of mental health. It is about finding *patterns and dynamics* of organization and activity within systems that occur spontaneously (i.e., through evolution) and thus have no central control. CAS also allows for a shifting between dichotomous and continuous aspects of various phenomena within a system. Some things are naturally continuous in nature – temperature, for instance – while others are dichotomous, such as something being alive or dead. Models that were developed for dichotomous phenomena often have difficulty dealing with more continuous aspects of reality. This is true for the DSM, which is based on the medical model and works well within the paradigm of medical-style binaries like sick–not sick, broken–not broken, pregnant–not pregnant. However, it turns out that mental health and mental illness, for the most part, are continuous, not dichotomous. Therefore, a model that provides a valid understanding of mental health must be "at home" with both ways of conceptualizing phenomena.

When you add the myriad contributions from the four quadrants, the system becomes overwhelmingly complex. This, of course, is why people (both professionals and everyday folk) seek to simplify any system by considering only a small number of contributing factors to a phenomenon at any one time. The Integrated Model presented here is highly demanding in terms of both the range (cross-discipline) and depth (multilevel) of information areas that one is called upon to consider in order to understand something as challenging as mental health and mental illness. No human can reasonably be expected to know everything he or she *should* know. It requires the three approaches mentioned before: widening the range of coursework in academic programs, doing more cross-discipline research or knowledge building, and utilizing multidisciplinary team approaches to assessment and treatment in human service programs.

It also requires what is being proposed here: conceptual models that are designed to deal with the wide variety of information and high level of complexity involved in this subject. Of course, when you open the door to a model like CAS to understand complex phenomena, you have to consider a new set of variables beyond the ones that may have been standard to the topics themselves. For instance, at no point in the text have we discussed social contagion, but it is a dynamic common to many social phenomena. One has to consider the impact of a person's sense of well-being influencing those around him and her, thus "spreading" the meme of well-being. Conversely, a sense of despair or hopelessness can also influence others and spread.

Another aspect of CAS that is important here is that it is more applicable to large groups of people than to individuals. It is easier to understand and predict the movements of herds of animals than individual ones. That is because the differences between individuals often cancel each other out, so you get an average characteristic. Think about the overall movement of a swarm of bees or flock of birds versus the unpredictable movement of a single bee or bird. This suggests that the underlying dynamics of social behavior can be understood through mathematical modeling, using metadata, based on an analysis of the different factors involved and their relative power to impact a particular dynamic. This is where things get very challenging. How can we know exactly how many and specifically what factors are involved in any given dynamic? And how can we measure the relative impact of various factors? For one individual or group, religion may play a very powerful role in their sense of psychological well-being, while for another, it plays a role but a relatively weak one.

To further complicate things, this dynamic changes over time. The first person or group may experience a "crisis of faith," and the relative strength of this factor decreases. That is why a major element in CAS is adaptation. This implies two things: first, that a central consideration of any phenomenon is its responsiveness to other phenomena that exist around it, and second, that this is a dynamic process that has a history, a current state, and a future state. The dynamic interplay of a phenomenon and its surrounding environment, leading to either adaptive success or extinction, is what we call evolution. This is commonly thought of as a purely biological process, but from a wider perspective, it is really a universal, natural process that occurs in different ways for various phenomena. It is particularly relevant for human psychology, where there is both a biological component and a sociological one.

Another important aspect of CAS is the recognition that interactions between components of a complex set of phenomena do not occur in linear strings, as typically described in narrow research designs or standard conceptual models. In complex systems, components interact through a web of mutual influence. Rather than A >> B >> C, what occurs in large-scale, natural, complex systems is that A, B, C, and a wide variety of other factors all interact with each other at the same time. It begins to look more like a web or a cloud rather than a line of interacting factors.

One of the hallmarks of complexity is the fact that, because it acknowledges the inter-dependence of various parts of the system, the traditional research method of studying various parts of a system separately in order to understand it is not appropriate and can easily provide misleading results. You can't atomize a complex system without grossly distorting its holistic dynamics. This is particularly true in social systems, as individual agents (people) have to predict and react to other agents while trying to meet various goals, and of course the other agents are doing the same thing in the same relational exchange. This quickly leads to nonlinear complexity or what could be called the web of mutual influence, whose reality is lost when being studied with standard methods of research.

The CAS model shows how a system can get "locked into" a suboptimal dynamic because a particular pattern of interaction can emerge, initiated by different parts of the system making "good" choices, but the collective outcome can still be poor. Given the principle of adaptability, while the resulting pattern may be suboptimal, in that one could imagine a better one, it must still be functional and reflect certain advantages. For instance, it could be more difficult to change and improve the pattern than to simply leave an imperfect pattern in place. This can often happen when authority positions exist at certain midpoints in the system but not at the top, so purposeful change can occur at the subsystem level but only have marginal impact on the system as a whole. There may also be competing forces at other points in the system that keep it from changing too much or too fast. An example of these dynamics is how the insurance industry impacts the conception of mental illness through its insistence on a dichotomous categorization of mental disorders. People at midlevels of the insurance system are in an authority position to decide which mental disorders qualify for treatment under a given insurance policy and how to reimburse for services based on industry standards for the type and quantity of treatment for a particular disorder, making it difficult to change the overall system. While this system supports a suboptimal system of categorical diagnosis, it will become much more difficult to conduct business if psychiatry moves toward a dimensional model of mental illness, acknowledging the myriad factors influencing a client's experience and thus complicating the decision regarding the most effective treatment(s) to implement. As noted previously, the APA now recognizes the reality that mental illness is more dimensional than it previously believed, but it feels it should move slowly in that direction so as not to grossly disrupt the existing mental health care system. So the *competing forces* push the system in different directions – sociologists push in one direction, the insurance companies push in another direction, and the American Psychiatric Association pushes in a third.

CAS refers to this as *decentralized interaction*, or what we called the web of mutual influence, and emphasizes the adaptive dynamic involved. Ultimately, all parts of the system are aspects of reality and impact the present state of the system. They are real forces in the "environment" or overarching context within which the parts exist and interact. When change occurs in one part (a new edition of the DSM is published), it sends ripples through the web, impacting the other parts of the system, such as insurance companies, pharmaceutical companies, psychiatrists, psychotherapists, and the consumers of mental health care services. Each of these parts ("agents" in the terminology of CAS) then reacts, sending ripples of their own that impact the original source of the change (training schools criticize the changes to the DSM) and so on and so on. Now picture this web of agents (more like a cloud, really) acting and reacting, causing the entire web to twist and drift. How is it twisting, and what direction is it drifting? This image reflects the adaptive evolution of a complex system.

So how does this idea of the adaptive evolution of a complex system relate to the psychology of mental health and mental illness? It turns out that there really is no historical "starting point" to begin a discussion of the human understanding of mental health and mental illness because every point in time has precedents. That is one of the reasons it was important for us to review the history of these concepts in human society. Every state of belief and practice is the emergent consequence of the time that came before. That is true in the short term and also in the long term. We are the inheritors of our prehistoric forebears, with brains evolved to react with intense fear or anger toward potential threats and intense love and affection toward our children and others close to and important to us. Why? Because mammals evolved *emotions* as flexible behavioral motivators to replace more hardwired instinctual behavior patterns in reptilian neural networks. That gave humans the huge advantage of *behavioral flexibility* in the fight for survival in a hostile and changing environment. It also led us to often being made miserable or euphoric by our own (and others') emotional reactions to the myriad factors in play at any particular point in time.

We can see how a belief or behavior pattern can shift as the variables in the environment (both internal and external) change over time. In relatively simple systems, this is called feedback; in complex systems, as noted previously, we call this decentralized interaction. One important question is how these interactions seek some level of stability, or homeostasis. There is a natural process whereby imbalances in a system create problems that drive change toward rebalance or equilibrium. For instance, in economics, there is the *law of diminishing returns*. In this dynamic, early contributions to a system typically have a strong impact, but as contributions increase, the net impact drops. At a certain point, additional contributions will start to have a damaging effect, for instance causing inflation and thus lowering the value of later contributions. There is typically an optimal balance point. For instance, a bird may benefit from longer wings for greater flight stability, but at a certain point, the wings become too big and start to impede the bird's ability to fly or engage in some other important life activity. The birds with the optimally sized wings for the current environment will be most successful and pass on those genes to the next generation. The key word is *current*, because as the environment changes, as it always does, the optimal wing size will change with it. If a species does not adjust adequately to the changing environment, it will find itself at a disadvantage. Of course, some organisms are so well suited for their environment that they reach a stable point of evolutionary homeostasis and remain prolific and relatively unchanged for a long period of time, Sadly, cockroaches are an example of this!

This foundational process is manifested in many ways, as it involves adaptive feedback. The emergent qualities of a phenomenon lead to feedback from the environment, which provides reward for fitness or pressure for change. What this means is that the universe is always in conversation with itself – an endless process of emergence, contact, reaction, new contact, and new emergence, across many agents, system levels, quadrants, and over time. This suggests that CAS is well suited to help us develop the kind of model we need to understand something as complex as mental health and mental illness. It allows us to understand the dynamic relationships between different variables better and predict multiple possible futures, depending on how different variables impact emerging phenomena.

APPLICATION OF THE STRUCTURAL ELEMENTS OF THE INTEGRATED MODEL

The previous discussion described the foundation and structure, including the evolutionary basis and complex adaptive dynamics, of the Integrated Model. We can now explore the application level of our model, as it *activates the structural elements* (subfields) of the model's framework of knowledge areas that includes the four quadrants of knowledge and thus the variety of subfields within those quadrants. The question now is how we are likely to move forward and *utilize* this model to develop a greater understanding of both mental health and mental illness and put it to practical use in the real world. Reflecting on this question, three basic possibilities emerge. The first involves an *individual learning* as much as he or she can about the various areas of study related to human psychology – especially as it relates to mental health and mental illness. The second involves *building bridges* between those areas of study to reach greater levels of complexity, inclusion, and transcendence regarding the topic. The third involves developing *institutional systems* that are dedicated to the integration of knowledge and practice in order to understand and impact mental health.

Expanding Individual Knowledge Through Content Area Study

The first way of applying the Integrated Model is to expand the content areas that people study, either through the process of formalized learning designed to prepare one for a career working with people or as a program of self-improvement. This means that it can occur in an institutional setting (typically a college or university) or informally at home with carefully selected content material. The basic idea is to learn information from all four quadrants of knowledge, at various systemic levels. This process, whether formal or informal, is not a passive absorption of data. It is important that this be an active process, always reflecting on the personal meanings that are triggered in an individual and how they may change through the integration of new information. As an instructor, I always press my students to reflect on the information they are learning, often through self-reflection essays, so that the learning process is one of integration and growth not just memorization.

At the beginning of this chapter, we listed some of the academic areas that could and should be linked to this model. The question becomes, how much does one need to know to truly understand a person, including oneself? The question needs to refer to both academic knowledge (molecular biology, for instance) and knowledge about the person (history of substance use or romantic relationships, for instance). The answer, of course, is everything. This is unfortunate, because we cannot know everything about anything. We must live with grossly inadequate information. So the better question may be, what is the *minimum* one should know to gain an *adequate* understanding of a person? This depends, in part, on the purpose of the assessment. If you are a bank's loan officer, there are certain areas of knowledge and personal information you need in order to adequately assess a person's qualification for a given loan. Those knowledge areas and personal information requirements will be different if you are a brain surgeon. The assessment issue before us today regards mental health and mental illness, and our current review of history has revealed a variety of answers to the basic questions around that issue. At one point in history, in certain places, a doctor would need to be knowledgeable about the humoral system and would seek information about such things as diet, exercise, and the size, color, regularity, and consistency of the patient's stools. A psychiatrist in more recent times, in most places in the world now, would need a thorough knowledge of the latest edition of the DSM, some working knowledge of neurochemistry, and information about the patient's recent experience of symptoms as they correspond to the DSM nosology.

So what of today and into the future? If the biopsychosocial approach, as expanded in the Integrated Model proposed here, is valid, it dramatically widens the range of knowledge areas required for an adequate understanding of the whole person. It needs to include all four quadrants, at multiple levels, to properly explore and explain various aspects of a person's strengths and weaknesses in a holistic way. We can begin to explicate the necessary academic areas to consider:

External-Subjective:	Sociology	External-Objective:	Earth Systems
	Anthropology		Environmental
	History		Studies
	Global Studies		History and
	Comparative Religion		Philosophy of Science
Internal-Subjective:	Psychology	Internal-Objective:	Biology
	Communication		Genetics
	Philosophy		Neurology
			Psychiatry

The idea here is to propose some basic content areas that would cover the four quadrants without being too overwhelming to a lifelong student of mental health and illness. One of the hallmarks of many of the early psychiatrists, including Freud and Jung, was their intense interest in cultural history and what it had to tell them about universal principles regarding human nature. It is not clear if that is still the case. Part of the problem is that so much information has been developed in the fields of psychology and psychiatry over the last century that it is a Herculean task just for students to get a solid grounding in what we know in just 2 of the 15 listed academic areas. Perhaps what is needed is a series of what are typically called "survey courses." These present a broad overview of an area of study, designed for nonspecialists. What if we designed a series of survey courses, drawn from all four quadrants, addressing issues from all levels, and made them a requirement for all students of human nature – not just psychology majors but also premed students and future teachers? Social workers would know something about genetics. Medical doctors would know something about psychology. Psychotherapists would know something about ecology. All might gain a greater understanding about how virtually all fields of study have something valuable to add to our overall understanding of the human condition.

In a generic way, this reflects what we call general education and is a requirement in most undergraduate programs. There has long been an awareness that it is the proper purpose of higher (postsecondary) education to produce well-rounded individuals who have a solid grounding in the liberal arts and sciences. This required coursework is seen as providing a broad general knowledge about academic areas connected to specifically human concerns, such as psychology, literature, art, and history, as well as introductions to more "hard science" areas such as physics and chemistry. The basic idea was not to develop better scholars but better citizens, better humans. It was intended to expand both a student's range of knowledge and his or her capacity to think critically and communicate effectively, both within and across areas of knowledge. This is thought to be of service not just as a springboard to a more successful career but as enriching for the mind and soul and thus as a betterment to society.

But something has happened on the way to that goal. Somehow, economic and social forces are leading us away from the liberal arts. One after another, colleges and universities are shifting away from general education toward a more "practical and applied" curriculum. This was given a public voice when, in 2015, the governor of Wisconsin, Scott Walker, proposed to change the mission statement of his state college system to cut the words "search for truth" and replace them with "meet the state's workforce needs." That proposed change was met with such protest that it was dropped, and the governor claimed it was a "drafting error," but the sea change in higher education had already been building for at least two decades. Rather than seeking to improve the human condition, the purpose is increasingly to teach trade skills at the loss of even trying to "nurture young minds" or create "worldly and thoughtful citizens" (Dutt-Ballerstadt, 2019).

It is beyond the purview of this book to explore all the dynamics driving this change, but it was important to note because it impacts our thesis in two important ways. First, it affects all people who seek higher education, which is an increasing number of people every year. To the extent this change of emphasis in higher education reduces their exposure to mind-expanding knowledge and better reasoning skills, it can negatively impact their overall mental health. Second, it directly affects our evolving understanding of mental health and mental illness. To the extent the world's colleges and universities deemphasize general education and the liberal arts, they will push students toward courses and programs directly connected to their eventual career choices. This constitutes a narrowing of perspective. It means fewer people who want to be doctors will take courses in psychology or sociology. It means fewer people who want to be psychologists will take courses in physics or physiology. More students will look at a college catalog and ask, "What does this course have to do with my future job?" In other words, the perspective the Integrated Model takes is directly at odds with the current direction of higher education. It wants to broaden the perspective of students wanting to work with people, while academia seems bent on narrowing students' perspectives.

Despite this, one way to deal with the problem is to justify the logic and practical utility of including a wide array of subject areas in the course list of students who are interested in psychology, medicine, or other fields related to working with people. The logic is clear in the Integrated Model presented here. Human functioning is connected to many different academic areas within the four quadrants – the Internal-Subjective, the External-Subjective, the Internal-Objective, and the External-Objective. Knowing a great deal about only one subject area within one quadrant at a single level leaves a person grossly ignorant of much that is required to truly understand themselves or other people.

The practical utility of a wider knowledge base stems from the greater like-lihood of success in helping someone with a mental health problem if one has a wider range of information about that person. An example of this was often asserted by Engel in his original paper on the biopsychosocial approach (1977). As a physician himself, he recognized that many doctors related to their patients by asking only about clinical symptoms. He asserted that doctors could achieve better outcomes if they knew more about psychology and communication, so that they could relate better with their patients and collect more information. The doctor's task should not just be to gather facts about symptoms but to seek to understand the patient's overall unhappiness and dysfunction, what led them to seek medical help, to take on the "sick role" and accept being a patient. To be able to gather this information, the doctor has to be familiar with the various biological, sociological, and psychological factors at work within his patient's life. With a deeper and more complex understanding of what is wrong, he or she can develop a more effective treatment plan. Also, with a wider range of knowledge and expertise, especially in the area of psychology, the doctor can recognize the interpersonal dynamics of the doctor–patient relationship and is likely to form a stronger working relationship, which leads to better treatment compliance on the part of the patient. So more knowledge means better diagnosis, a better treatment plan, and better treatment compliance.

Expanding Cross-Discipline Scholarship and Knowledge

Of course, just because something is a good idea and makes practical sense does not mean it will win out against competing forces. The economic and social forces driving recent changes in the field of higher education are pushing for quickly and efficiently building practical job skills not deeper, wiser students who integrate a wide range of information about human nature or the world in general. Luckily, there is the second way to approach this challenge and build on the Integrated Model. It is best utilized in combination with the required study of a wider range of topics but can be embraced even if that does not occur. This approach is to build bridges across academic areas and focus on cross-discipline scholarship. The more we can create linkages between holons, the better our understanding of holarchies and systemic holism in general.

These linkages have been developing for quite some time. For instance, the Frankfort School, which was associated with the Institute for Social Research, began in the 1920s in Germany. It sought to integrate various fields of thought, ranging from psychoanalysis and sociology to Marxism. Among its best-known members were Eric Fromm, Theodor Adorno, Walter Benjamin, and Herbert Marcuse. They sought to explore the dynamics between individual psychology and social forces and promote what they saw as social progress. Taking a Marxist position, they explicated the dominant social "truisms" of bourgeois society that justified capitalism, an economic philosophy the institute's members generally thought to be damaging to human well-being. The idea was that the ruling class enforces a cul-tural hegemony, managing the thoughts, feelings, and behavior of the rest of soci-ety. It is naive and narrow-minded to consider only the individual psyche outside of such cultural control. In exploring these cultural and psychological dynamics, they were also aware that when studying the social sciences, one should not imitate the methods of natural sciences. One cannot stand outside one's subjective perspective to study human psychology or sociology from an objective position. The result of this combination of ideas was an epistemology that was self-critical, recognizing the limits of its own assumptions, working hypotheses, and conclusions – never claiming to have the absolute or universal truth. Despite this limitation, they sought to link the worlds of individual psychology, sociology, and political economics in meaningful, more integrated ways.

More recently, there have been similar attempts to bridge the academic worlds of individual psychology and sociology. Specifically, in relation to the issue of mental health and mental illness, social scientists have been exploring how these experiences are affected by social stratification, gender, sexuality, race, ethnicity, age, nationality, the professionalism of mental health care, criminal justice issues, and stigma, or how people are treated who are identified as mentally ill. The complex and controversial interplay between the social and individual aspects of mental health is of particular interest in the field of sociology and has led it to embrace both a systems theory and a constructionist perspective in its explorations of the question of mental health and illness (Rogers & Pilgrim, 2014; Scheid & Brown, 2010).

This basic epistemological position of constructivism, combined with systems theory, which is fundamental to the sociological approach to mental health and illness, is reflected in the Integrated Model presented here. It acknowledges the complex of subjective and objective, internal and external realms of understanding, as well as a direct but highly complex interactions between the four basic quadrants of knowledge. What is somewhat different is that unlike the sociological or biopsychosocial perspectives, the Integrated Model does not emphasize any one area of knowledge over the other. They are all seen as co-equal aspects of reality. Sociology has gone a long way to develop connections between the External-Subjective and the Internal-Subjective. It has not, so far, done much to link the Internal-Objective with the Internal-Subjective or the External-Subjective.

To help us explore some of the connections being made between those areas, let us turn to the work being done in genetics and neurology. These knowledge areas represent the Internal-Objective and thus are of paramount importance in the Integrated Model to create linkages with the Internal-Subjective (personally experienced psychology) and the External-Subjective (sociology).

Cross-Discipline Perspectives – The Epigenetic Story

One of the best examples of a cross-disciplinary topic is the area of epigenetics. While ostensibly a subfield within genetics, it relates directly to human behavior and psychology as much as it does to biology. In fact, David Moore defines epigenetics as "how genetic material is activated or deactivated – that is expressed – in different contexts or situations" (2015, p. 14). He makes it clear that by "contexts or situations," he means the lived, behavioral experiences of human life, not their genetic substrates. Of course, genes themselves have an enormous impact on human psychology, but it turns out that what may be even more important is the *interaction* or *relationship* between genetic material and one's experiences. What is happening experientially influences the actions of our genes, so it is more pertinent to ask what our genes are *doing* than what they *are*.

Conrad Waddington first introduced the term epigenetics in the 1940s to refer to the way that genes interact with their environmental context, and for a number of decades, it was recognized that the environment affected gene expression, but nobody knew quite how. Now we are beginning to understand this collaborative process, although much remains to be discovered. One thing we are discovering is that some psychiatric disorders, such as schizophrenia and bipolar disorder, are associated with epigenetic abnormalities. On the other side of our immediate question about mental health and mental illness, many normal psychological functions, such as memory, learning, and sleep, are also impacted by epigenetic processes. Finally, there is a third area of research interest, which is directly associated with *both* mental wellness and illness. This includes such functions as stress tolerance. This raises the possibility that epigenetics is an essential key to understanding the complex interplay of biology, environment, and experience in human beings.

An example of this was revealed in a research project in which the gene activity of baby rats was altered by the behavior of their mothers (Meaney, 2001, 2010). The pups of mothers who spent a lot of time licking and grooming them responded better to stressful events, and this was reflected in increased activity in specific genes associated with stress tolerance. This linkage of maternal caregiving, gene expression, and stress tolerance is profound. It shows that genetic activity is a process, connected to lived experience, and thus people's psychology is not predetermined by our biology. Nor is our psychology predetermined by our experiences. Instead, our experiences and our DNA interact in complex ways to create an unfolding dynamic process. While specific genes don't come into being or go away, how they operate, whether they are turned on or off, whether they are "turned up" or "turned down" does change over time. In other words, the human genome *effectively* changes over time as a result of lived experience.

It is important to note that epigenetics does not occur in some mysterious, nonbiological way. The term refers generally to any non-DNA genetic process, and it occurs at the biological level. The epigenetic mechanisms themselves occur in a number of complex ways, but for our purposes, we can simplify matters and point out that they mainly affect the genome through the processes of DNA methylation and histone acetylation. Methylation refers to the addition of methyl molecules to a DNA sequence, repressing gene transcription and thus decreasing gene activity – turning it down or off. Conversely, histone acetylation alters the structure of the chromatin (the bundle of genetic material in a cell), allowing more access for DNA binding proteins to activate gene transcription and thus increasing gene activity – turning it on or up. As a side note, histones are simple proteins within the cell nucleus that directly contact DNA and influence its activity in various ways. For instance, DNA wraps around histones tightly, thus allowing it to fit in the cell nucleus. If sections of DNA are wrapped too tightly, their activity is choked off, so in this and other ways, histones operate to regulate the activity of DNA.

That was a gross oversimplification of the epigenetic process, and in reality, we should refer to processes, as there are a number of ways it occurs. Since this is not a biology textbook, please allow me to oversimplify through analogy one step further. We can think of DNA as the basic blueprint of life, while epigenetics consists of all the ways that the blueprint is utilized to build a structure. Maybe a better analogy is to think of DNA as a series of light bulbs, all wired together. The system can only produce the light that is capable of being created by those particular light bulbs. However, they are controlled through a series of dimmer switches (the epigenetic structures), and these switches are adjusted by an electrician (life experience). So life experience influences whether different gene mechanisms are turned off and on, up or down.

For instance, we know that human experiences affect the development of epigenetic mechanisms that then continue to influence our psychology and behavior for long periods of time. For instance, if you take two monozygotic twins (identical DNA) and look at their epigenetic markings when they are very young, they are extremely similar – the DNA methylation and histone acetylation patterns are virtually the same. However, when you look again, when they are older, the pattern is quite different throughout their genomes (Fraga et al., 2005). That is why identical twins still develop as unique individuals, with their own personalities, right down to their genetic functioning, and remain quite different their entire lives.

For another thing, we know that epigenetics affects more than subtle personality characteristics. In fact, this process of epigenetic differentiation (genetic twins developing different characteristics) can help explain why one individual in a monozygotic pair of twins may develop schizophrenia and the other does not. I say "help" because this is not the only factor involved, but it is an important one. Even more profound differences in the physiology and behavior of genetic twins can be attributed to epigenetics. For instance, female honeybees in any particular colony are genetic clones, but they don't all develop the same way. Most become workers, while only a rare few grow up to be queens. Since they all started with the same DNA sequence, how can this happen? Well, it turns out that the difference is diet. The youngsters who are destined to be queens are fed an ongoing diet of royal jelly (secreted from a gland in the feeding worker bee's head), which causes profound changes in the development of the lucky future queens. The rest of the young females get switched to a "worker bee" diet early on and become workers themselves. It is important to note that every female has the genetic potential to become a queen, but the epigenetic process is shaped so that they become workers. We know this is true because when researchers manipulated the epigenetic states of young females by injecting them with specialized molecules to cause demethylation of the DNA, they grew into queens (Kucharski, Maleszka, Foret, & Maleszka, 2008). In the language of our lightbulb analogy, the bulbs are there to be a queen or a worker. The feeding worker bees acted as the electrician, providing the chemicals to switch on some lights and turn off others. The point here is that there are no lightbulbs in the bees to become elephants; the genetic potential has to be there, but the potential differences in function and form are still quite profound.

So how do the epigenetic stories about rats and bees translate into other, more human potentialities – our mental health or illness? Well, we already mentioned the connection to schizophrenia. And while there is still a mystery about just how that differentiation occurs, we know that there are many routes by which epigenetic processes can be impacted by environmental experiences. These include diet (more royal jelly, please!), environmental chemicals, exercise, commonly abused drugs, and particular parenting experiences (cited in Moore, 2015). You will notice that some of these "experiences" are chemical (diet) and some are psychological (parenting). It is not clear yet exactly how psychological experiences cause an alteration in epigenetic functioning, but they do.

One way they do is related to the research on rats. Remember that the rat pups that experienced more licking and grooming (LG) grew up to be more stress tolerant and that this was connected to epigenetic mechanisms. It turns out that this is true in humans as well. In sad but fascinating work done by the same lab, it was found that people who had committed suicide *and* had been abused or neglected (AN) as children showed changes in the same areas of the brain as the rats who had received low LG and subsequently had poor stress tolerance. Specifically, they had increased methylation of the glucocorticoid receptor (GR) promotor area of DNA in neurons in the hippocampus, leading to a reduction of the production and release of stress-moderating proteins (McGowan et al., 2009). This means decreased hippocampal GR expression, decreased GR feedback sensitivity, increased hypothalamic corticotrophin-releasing factor expression, and thus stronger hypothalamus-pituitary-adrenal (HPA) stress responses.

Of course, childhood AN affects a number of brain areas and has a variety of negative effects on psychological development and subsequent adult functioning. There are literally thousands of areas in the brain that are impacted by AN, leading to a wide variety of emotional and behavioral problems, stemming from a variety of epigenetic mechanisms, including DNA methylation and histone acetylation, along with other processes (such as changes to rRNA activity) in the parallel central and peripheral systems (Szyf & Bick, 2013).

These authors note that not only is the brain sensitive, especially in early development, to negative impacts of difficult environments, but they suggest that preventive and early intervention programs could be effective in ameliorating such effects. It may even be possible to reverse some of the damaging effects biologically with such substances as TSA (an enzyme associated with histone deacetylase inhibition), but this work is at a very early stage and is complicated by the fact that no substance is "clean" and thus will have a variety of effects on the body and brain, not all of which are beneficial. There is also the challenge of dealing with the blood–brain barrier, which often limits the effectiveness of substances in the CNS areas that are being targeted. Despite these problems, epigenetic treatments are already being explored as a possible way to treat neurological decline and even specific neurological disorders associated with aging (Delgado-Morales, Agis-Balboa, Esteller, & Berdasco, 2017). In the same review of recent findings, the authors point out that other mental disorders are also being explored as possible targets for epigenetic treatment. For instance, schizophrenia is associated with epigenetic dysregulation, and it turns out that many of the pathways already targeted with successful treatments (dopaminergic, serotoninergic, and monoaminergic) are regulated by epigenetic mechanisms and thus offer promising avenues of research.

Together, research in epigenetics is uncovering the etiological roots of psychotic disorders and finding that there are multifaceted issues with genetic structure, genetic expression, and the vital impact of environmental factors. This work is also expanding beyond the realm of overt abuse and mental disorders. Links are being found between societal issues such as loneliness, poverty, and oppression and epigenetic mechanisms leading to depression, anxiety, and health problems (Hackman, Farah, & Meaney, 2010). The connections are not fully clear. After all, in the real world, there is always a confluence of many different factors, and one cannot conduct controlled studies (nobody volunteers to have their babies purposely raised in deprived environments) to establish direct, causal relationships. However, despite these limitations, the early forays into this area have been fruitful, expanding the reach of epigenetics from the genetic through the environmental and psychological out to the sociological and behavioral.

The same is likely true of most other conditions we identify as mental disorders, as well as "shadow syndromes," which reflect more or less normal disturbances in psychological functioning, which we are finding have their roots in genetics, biochemical influences, direct environmental impacts (maternal care in infancy), and less direct but just as powerful environmental influences such as the systemic, historical impacts of racism and sexism. At the other end of the spectrum, it appears that proper epigenetic regulation is an important factor in what we consider wellness, or mental health. As our brief review of the field reveals, epigenetic factors do not necessarily link to specific mental illnesses but rather to more general functional processes such as stress tolerance, memory, and attention/concentration. Thus, epigenetic factors can be linked to psychological resilience, emotional regulation, good stress tolerance, and the resulting adaptive behavioral functioning that serves as a marker of mental health but also as a feedback loop that increases the sense of psychological well-being.

The emerging results of research in epigenetics (as well as other research on the brain) support some major conclusions regarding our central topic. For instance, it appears that the traditional categorical models of mental illness are not easily sustainable – the brain, for the most part, does not organize its structure of functions around discrete mental disease entities. Brain activity appears to exist more along the lines of different general functions (memory, affect regulation, stress management, attention, executive functioning, etc.), working more or less in harmony, with ranges of functionality, each impacting the other. It is a dynamic process not just a structural one. The biology affects the experiential, and the experiential impacts the biological. The internal affects the external, and the external affects the internal. This aligns with the Integrated Model, which asserts that knowledge of the human experience extends through a layered, complex, and dynamic system across the four quadrants of knowledge – the Internal-Subjective, the Internal-Objective, the External-Subjective, and the External-Objective.

Cross-Discipline Perspectives – the Story of the Evolutionary Neurology of Human Behavior

This section draws heavily from the work of Robert Sapolsky, who is a professor of neurology and biology. He has written a number of books, but my personal favorite is *Behave: The Biology of Humans at Our Best and Worst* (2017). In it, he reviews a wide range of research related to human behavior, looking at it from the perspective of time. That is, he considers a given behavior then explores what we know about what is going on in the brain at that immediate moment, then a few seconds before, hours before, months before, from adolescence, from infancy, from fertilization, from centuries before, and from the beginnings of humanity through evolution. And even though his specialty is biology, Sapolsky asserts that "it actually makes no sense to distinguish between aspects of a behavior that are biological and those that would be described as, say, psychological or cultural – utterly intertwined" (p. 5). He admits that it is "hellishly complicated" to explain human behavior, but to do so in any depth requires that we look at virtually every field of the biological and social sciences.

We will explore two patterns of behavior from Sapolsky's perspective, one generally considered "good," representing mental health, and one considered "bad," representing mental illness. The first pattern we will look at is empathetic behavior. The first question, of course, is how to define empathy. It turns out that even doing this is complicated. There are different types and levels of empathy. In a generic sense, the term refers to the capacity to resonate with another's state of being, especially at the emotional level. Empathy exists when one sees a gruesome picture of someone who is injured, and you cringe in discomfort. This provides somatic (felt) information about the other's state. It is typically differentiated from something called sympathy, which indicates a thought or feeling *about* the other's state. The cringe is empathy; feeling pity for the victim is sympathy. It turns out that a basic capacity for empathy exists in many animals. Pack animals like wolves tend to experience a great deal of *emotional contagion*, with waves of fear or rage flowing through the group. Higher-level primates exhibit more specific and nuanced empathy, such as when the loser of a fight between chimps is approached for consolation grooming by others in the group. This type of empathetic behavior is typically restricted to others who are closely related or longstanding members of the group. It typically does not extend to strangers, and this turns out to be a primary issue in many areas of this kind of research. We are powerfully motivated by our identification with a group (us) to be generous, helpful, loving, and peaceful. Conversely, we identify other groups (them) as alien and tend to treat them in far less altruistic ways. On the biological side of the issue, the center of action for empathy is the anterior cingulate cortex (ACC). This structure resides in the frontal cortex and apparently processes interoceptive (inside us) information. This is often the source of what we think of as "gut" reactions to things or intuition. The ACC also reacts strongly to conflict, or experienced difference from what was expected. When things go wrong, the ACC lights up. It also lights up when there is positive emotional resonance – I smile when you smile.

However, the ACC isn't about selfless altruism. It is highly attuned to situations in which we *are* or are *not* getting what we want. Empathy is important for learning and thus adaptive behavior: "Boy, that looks like it hurt. I'm not going to do that!," or on a more subtle, social level: "He looks like he is in pain, and I feel compelled to console him, which is both nice and will solidify my interpersonal bond with him." There are other areas of brain functioning involved as well. The insula and amygdala work together and are funneled through the ACC. It turns out that neural pathways that foster our own awareness of and reaction to danger or pain are also activated when we see others in danger or pain. There is an old adage from psycho-therapy that in order to build empathy for others, one must develop empathy for oneself. Well, it turns out that neurology is confirming that clinical wisdom. Feeling for others goes hand-in-hand with feeling for oneself.

The pathways necessary for empathy, although subtly different from person to person, were laid down in our early evolution, presumably because it fostered both cooperative social behavior and individual safety awareness that was essential to survival. This begs the question about other patterns of thought, feeling, and behavior that developed over time, were essential for survival, but may not be so "good" as empathy. Sapolsky (2017) explores these as well. For instance, human beings (like most other animals) have a strong proclivity to form in-groups and out-groups, *us* versus *them*. From friendship cliques to family bonding to racial and ethnic identifications to political and religious groupings to nation states to spe-ciesism, humans are drawn to group together and see their groups as superior or in natural conflict with others. This happens at a preconscious, neurological level (Knutson, Mah, Manly, & Grafman, 2007). With only a 50-millisecond exposure to a face of a human from another gender, race, or social status, the amygdala is activated within another 100 milliseconds – long before the brain has time to register the image consciously or do any secondary processing of the information. In other words, being prejudiced comes naturally; being accepting of others takes work. This relates to the finding that reciprocal altruism happens more the closer the genetic kinship of the people involved. Humans tend to be more generous, supportive, and self-sacrificing the closer the biological relationship. In general, the further away from *us*, the more negative a cognitive, emotional, and behavioral reaction we have toward *them*. This was good news in evolutionary terms. The more strongly one bonds to a group and fights outsiders, the better one's chances of survival. However, it is bad news for those who consider themselves human-ists and seek world peace. "The world is one" may be a moral aspiration, but it is working against our evolutionarily inherited natural predilections. Sapolsky makes it clear that we developed as a species to be both generous to those close to us and brutal to those we deem our enemies. It may not be morally right, but it is good evolutionary psychology and thus hard to break.

These two neurological-sociological findings are important in relation to our central thesis, the question of mental health and mental illness. Among sociologists, dynamics like racism and sexism have long been considered learned behavior and, by extension, a sort of group mental illness. Among the biological evolutionary crowd, empathy has been approached with suspicion, with many wondering how self-sacrifice could ever evolve, since it precludes the individual from procreating. Now we can begin to see how dynamics involving neurology, evolution, sociology, and individual psychology can converge into a more holistic understanding of human behavior. But it is complicated. As previously noted, racism may be *natural* from an evolutionary perspective, but that does not make it morally *right*. That being said, racism is embraced in many different cultures because it works for group cohesion, so if one were to take an extreme multicultural perspective, it could not be morally condemned; it serves a sociological purpose. One has to *side* with a particular cultural or philosophical belief set like humanism (which I personally do) to take a moral stand against racism, which is at odds with a purely relativistic or postmodern point of view. This means that on many matters, neurology does not bring us much closer to a universal position on mental health or illness, certainly as it pertains to broad issues regarding human values, beliefs, or general behavior. It resides in one of the four quadrants (Internal-Objective) but must be considered just one source of information that interacts with many other sources in order to approach anything like an understanding of mental health.

This is equally true in regard to other complex behavior patterns such as substance abuse. Taking addictive substances changes the way the brain works, partly through the release of dopamine and by promoting synaptic changes in the motivational circuitry (Kauer, 2018). Different drugs can target different molecules, but it appears that a relatively common impact is on the ventral tegmental area and the nucleus accumbens regions, which are thought to be the motivational center of the brain. This circuit is connected to feelings of craving, thus driving the individual to consume the substance, which then triggers the release of dopamine, which induces a feeling of pleasure. Even a single, first-time use of cocaine or opioids will lead to the motivational system being "hijacked" by the drug, strengthening the synapses that drive dopamine producing cells and in effect "rewiring" the brain to experience intense motivation (craving) to ingest more of the drug. This neuroplasticity happens within a few hours of exposure to addictive drugs and can last for months without ongoing exposure. The truly complicated part is that this plasticity does not lead automatically to addiction. Many people experiment with powerful drugs and do not become addicted.

The answer to drug addiction, then, has to come from the complex interaction between various quadrants, not just the Internal-Objective field of neurochemistry. Tommy Saah (2005) reminds us that addiction arises from the interplay of biology, psychology, and social influences, all linked through the overall process of evolution. This correlates with our Internal-Objective, Internal-Subjective, and External-Subjective quadrants. More specifically, Saah posits that from an evolutionary perspective, drug abuse arises as a form of compensation for lack of environmental fitness. For instance, a person who has received poor parental care may tend to focus more on short-term environmental risks. That was an adaptive strategy in the deep past but is not as helpful in a modern context. In other words, evolution has wired the brain so that people are motivated to attain short-term gains (survival) but come at the cost of longer-term gains that would be more valuable (a good career). This wiring leaves humans vulnerable to being "hijacked" by evolutionary drives.

This dynamic is particularly active in the realm of emotions, which evolved as motivators to increase behaviors that promote adaptive fitness. Negative emotions like anger and anxiety are associated with threat response, while positive emotions like joy and excitement are associated with increasing adaptive gains, such as social connections. Drug use can temporarily increase positive emotions and decrease negative emotions, thus compensating for disturbances in the neurological/behavioral process of emotional regulation. For instance, rather than taking appropriate action to reduce threats associated with feelings of anger or anxiety, the person can take a drug to temporarily reduce the negative emotion. This provides a short-term gain, which would normally signal a reduction of environmental risk but, in the case of drug use, has been artificially induced and thus could represent a failure to deal effectively with a risk and have long-term consequences.

This tactic would be particularly compelling if the individual's personal history includes parental neglect leading to poor stress management, as we explored earlier in this chapter. This dynamic is strongly influenced by sociological factors, such as the presence of drug-using peers, the availability of drugs to take, and the lack of supportive resources in the environment. What you have then is the confluence of factors from all four quadrants of knowledge, leading to a compensatory behavior with highly negative consequences. Again, the neurological story relates to one quadrant (Internal-Objective), but to really understand addiction, one needs additional information from the three other quadrants. This includes such things as the possibility of developmental trauma making the person more vulnerable to the short-term rewards of drug use (Internal-Subjective), association with a peer group that supports drug use (External-Subjective), and the easy availability of specific substances in the environment that have addictive qualities (External-Objective).

Empathy/altruism, racism (along with other in-group/out-group dynamics), and drug addiction are just a few of the many areas of human functioning that are increasingly being understood through a multidisciplinary perspective. The work of Sapolsky and many others is revealing the connections between our behavior and its correlates in our immediate neurological functioning, its connection to neurological development, and those roots in our evolutionary and sociological history. They make it clear that when we think of any given psychological state, whether reflecting health or disorder, we must consider what our brains are doing right now, how they developed in the individual's life, and how they developed collectively millennia ago.

Integrating Knowledge and Practice at the Institutional Level

In this book, I have repeatedly promised not to write about the practical application of models of mental health and illness – treatment. Now I am going to break that promise. No model of reality deserves the name unless it can be practically applied to the real world. I may choose to believe I can breathe water, but unless I show that I can, it remains a theory, and one that defies common sense and all available knowledge. So what happens if we apply the Integrated Model to real-world situations? The best way to find out is to look for experiments in which people have sought to understand a person's mental health and illness from a variety of viewpoints – taking into account information from all four quadrants.

The first factor to consider in this is the fact that, as noted before, it is unreasonable to expect any one individual to have a high level of knowledge or expertise in all pertinent areas of human functioning. Therefore, we are looking for institutions or experiments that take a fully integrated team approach to such understanding. Sadly, in the real world, the more experts you have to look at a situation, the more challenging it is to manage and the more money it costs. That limits the availability of such examples. The argument has always been that if there is a greater investment of resources in understanding a human problem at the front end, the subsequent quality of treatment will lead to cost savings in the future. However, budgets and people being what they are, many try to save dollars now and are less compelled by the prospect of future savings. The good news is that this is not always true. Sometimes people succeed in gathering the resources necessary for a more comprehensive assessment of human problems in order to design better interventions to improve mental health.

The Sacramento Assessment Center Story

What follows is a description of one such experiment. The Sacramento Assessment Center (SAC) was a residentially based assessment service utilized by the juvenile justice system in Northern California. This service utilized a multidimensional approach to assessment, looking closely at ten different areas of functioning, including psychological, psychiatric, criminological, substance use, educational, occupational, recreational, social attachment, medical, and placement adjustment (Jenkins, Conroy, & Mendonsa, 2013).

Back in the mid-1990s, many of the youth entering residential placement through the juvenile justice system received psychological screenings at some contact point in the system, but they were often superficial or one-dimensional or failed to examine critical areas of functioning, such as family, education, personality dynamics, or other key areas (Grisso, Vincent, & Seagrave, 2005). Given the tight budgets and large number of youth involved in the system, such brief, superficial screenings may be understandable, but a much more thorough, multidisciplinary assessment had the potential to develop a better understanding of the youth involved, including factors connected to their mental health and illness, and therefore make better choices regarding the interventions needed to reduce their recidivism risk and increase their overall well-being.

SAC was designed to meet this need. It was a collaborative approach, joining group home facilities, probation personnel, and a full range of assessment professionals from relevant disciplines with the mutual goal of gaining a thorough understanding of the placement and treatment needs of adjudicated juveniles. A growing body of evidence supported not only the general efficacy of a thorough assessment in clinical practice (Meyer et al., 2001) but more specifically the importance of accurately identifying the range and severity of risk factors across multiple domains of behavioral and psychological functioning that are known to contribute to juvenile recidivism and to repeated adjudication as a result of placement failures with the resulting cost increases (Cocozza & Skowyra, 2007; Grisso et al., 2005; Petteruti, Walsh, & Valezquez, 2009). In other words, an integrated model was needed.

SAC was designed with this multidisciplinary model in mind and provided a ten-area formal assessment, conducted by a multidisciplinary assessment team that included the assigned probation officer, a clinical psychologist, a child psychiatrist, an educational psychologist, a family specialist, a substance abuse specialist, a pediatrician, an occupational and recreational specialist, and a social worker. This team was led by the assessment director and conducted its work according to a standardized assessment protocol. The assessment included multiple clinical interviews, a standardized battery of tests in the different assessment areas, a family home visit and interview, a careful review of all available background information, and, whenever possible, observation of the client's behavior and functioning on the housing unit. Each professional completed his or her specific assessment duties, culminating in a written report that was presented orally in an assessment team meeting to determine specific recommended services and a general treatment plan for each adolescent. The results were documented in a full assessment report with a single-page evaluation summary.

While the adolescent was undergoing the assessment process, they resided in a level-12 (moderately high level) group home. While the adolescents were there, they were assigned a social worker, who worked with them from entry to discharge. The social worker was part of the assessment team and brought vital information about the day-to-day functioning of the minor while living in the group home. Behaviors in the classroom and in the residential unit (with staff as well as with peers) were seen as vital pieces of information that could give the assessment team an idea of how the adolescent may behave in future group home placements and would also be used to further verify, disconfirm, or corroborate other assessment results. This important insight was a vital factor in deciding the most appropriate level and type of services offered by the minor's subsequent placement setting.

The information from the full assessment report was useful not only to the assigned deputy probation officer but also to the family, to the youth, and to professionals who would be providing treatment. Although this book is not about treatment, it is important to note that SAC was quite effective. The outcomes from SAC were encouraging and provided evidence of the benefits and utility of a comprehensive, multidisciplinary, assessment model (Mendonsa, 2008; Wilcox, 2003). Mendonsa compared the recidivism rate of adolescents who went through the SAC assessment process with a control group who did not. He found the assessment process often led to a much faster initiation of treatment planning, to treatment itself, and thus to shorter placements. He also found that the SAC group had lower recidivism rates than the control group and, when they did reoffend, committed less serious offences and were less likely to need another out-of-home placement.

The Sacramento Assessment Center no longer exists. It was an effective project, and it worked because of its focus on multiple aspects of the clients' functioning and the hard work of a dedicated staff who respected each other's areas of expertise and worked together as a team. The best example of this was Dr. Mark Conroy, who served as the clinical director for more than 15 years. During his tenure, he made sure that all members of the team felt valued for their contributions, worked together smoothly, and shared a holistic vision of the overall well-being of the clients and their families. It was an "all-in" approach that was dedicated to both understanding and action, with as few limits as possible. It was an example of how widening and deepening our perspective leads to greater understanding and better practice.

BRINGING IT ALL TOGETHER: THE INTEGRATED MODEL AND UNDERSTANDING MENTAL HEALTH

Much of this chapter has been quite abstract, and you may be wondering how to utilize the Integrated Model with our central topic, mental health and mental illness. First of all, it is important to remember that there are two basic components in the model, structure and dynamics. In regard to the first, it provides the structural components – the nuts and bolts of human knowledge, organized within four quadrants (reflecting the human-centered organizational perspective of inside/outside and objective/subjective) and across multiple system levels. The complex adaptive systems perspective embedded within evolutionary theory provides the dynamic element, showing how the knowledge areas of the Integrated Model relate and interact with each other, creating emergent qualities and adaptively evolving over time.

In regard to taking it from the conceptual to the practical and applied, we looked at three primary ways to do this. The first has to do with individuals seeking a wider knowledge base, using the model to guide their study to better understand human nature through existing subfields of knowledge within the four quadrants. The second involves cross-discipline studies that help increase linkages between the quadrants and the systemic levels within the quadrants. The third asserts the importance of developing institutional programs and services that involve multiple professionals who are experts in the various knowledge areas directly related to the mental health and mental illness of their clients.

The last way to approach this topic is to begin a process of using the Integrated Model to develop core descriptions of mental health and mental illness, in and of themselves. This project is at its earliest stages, and thus we will only be able to approach the topic in the most general way, with a few examples that can touch on only a very limited number of aspects of the model. So let's dive in. The question is mental health. What is it? To answer that using the Integrated Model, we need to consider what areas of knowledge we need to draw from and at what systemic levels. An initial glance would suggest that such a broad subject will require knowledge from all four quadrants at various systemic levels. Our review of the history of the subject shows that when it comes to mental health, humans have connected it to both internal and external factors, as well as both objective and subjective factors, with connections ranging from the cellular level to the planetary. The next step involves choosing the specific subject areas associated with the issue. At the very least, the following need to be included, and you can easily think of more.

Internal-Subjective	Internal-Objective	External-Subjective	External-Objective
Developmental Psychology	Genetics	Sociology	Nutrition and Health
Positive Psychology	Behavioral Neurology	Global Studies	Environment & Resources
Philosophy	Psychopharmacology	Comparative Religion	Personal Technology
Theories of Personality	Nutrition	Gender Studies	Community Resource Guide

The next step would be to become conversant in all the pertinent areas, at least at a basic level. With that information in place, one could begin to draw connections between different subject areas and explore the dynamic interactions between them. This study would have to be historical in nature, as one can only begin to understand the current interactional dynamics of, say, gender, ethnicity, and the health care system in a particular region by placing them in historical context. Is this starting to sound like an impossible task? It is, or at least a very daunting one. In fact, it is what we have been trying to do throughout most of this book and have only scratched the surface. This takes us back to the three recommendations; learn as much as we can from a variety of subject areas, focus on cross-disciplinary work, and, whenever possible work collaboratively with people from other disciplines.

So we have run into a major hurdle in our attempt to define mental health: the overwhelming amount of knowledge that is required for any kind of solid understanding of the topic. There is a second, perhaps more difficult challenge. As we have seen throughout this text, there are many different perspectives on mental health. In some ways, it is what you think it is. The concept is heavily impacted by culture – the External-Subjective – it is what the people around you think it is. Mental health is what our family, friends, neighbors, community, tribe, religion, ethnic group, age group, socioeconomic group, social media, and television shows all tell us it is. This is particularly difficult when these various influencers are telling us different things, as they inevitably do in our modern world. It is also a constantly moving target, as our sense of what mental health is will likely change during the different stages of our lives. As one broad example, it may be that experiencing a high level of action and excitement may be central to a person's idea of mental health when she is young, but by midlife, the idea of experiencing a sense of relaxation and peace takes over. So knowing as much as we can only gets us so far. We need to be comfortable in a highly subjective atmosphere of constructionist truth that is both personal and collective at the same time. After all, the truth of mental health lies in the context of a combination of internal and external influencers at a current moment in time. That makes it quite difficult to define, and I am certainly not going to let some shrink define it for me.

Is there anything we can hang onto, from an objective standpoint, to help us understand? Well, yes, there are a few things. They do not mean the same things to all people, but they can serve as starting points to explore the subjective reality of any one person or group of people. They come to us from the collective wisdom of many people throughout history and their various approaches to this topic.

Physical Health	It is hard to feel mentally good when one feels physically bad.
Healthy Lifestyle	Nutrition, exercise, sleep, time with nature
Social Functioning	Having close, nurturing relationships with others
Accomplishment	Feeling one is using one's talents/skills in an effective way
Adjustment	Feeling one is in line with an important and esteemed group
Balance	Avoiding extremes of thought/feeling/behavior/attitude
Spirituality	Religious/spiritual beliefs and practice are connected with wellness
Wisdom	Connecting with human knowledge and deep truths about life
Fostering Positivity	Meditation, self-talk, avoiding negativity

Conversely, much the same could be said of mental illness as mental health. It is hard to define, highly subjective in nature, and a moving target through the lifespan. That being said, similar to mental health, there are some starting points that can be explored.

Cognition	Irrational, delusional, negativistic, disorganized, impoverished
Emotions	Dysregulated, overly negative (fear, anger, jealousy, envy, disgust)
Behavior	Impulsive, overly restricted, hurtful of others or self, bizarre
Low Functionality	Work, relationships, self-care
Biology/Genetics	Various neurological dysfunctions, not clearly identified yet

Whether one is considering mental health or mental illness, it is vital to think about what is causing or influencing an individual or group's mental state. This question typically lies at the heart of how people understand and organize mental illness – in other words, models of mental illness. These can be broadly organized within the four quadrants.

Internal-Objective	The range of influences that are physiological, including what is inborn and what is biologically impacted by experience
Internal-Subjective	The range of influences that impact people's psyche through their unique individual experience
External-Objective	The range of influences mediated by interactions within and between various social/religious/ethnic groups
External-Objective	The range of influences mediated by physical, external circumstances such as wealth, technology, physical safety

The first three areas correspond broadly to the biopsychosocial model, while the fourth is added to complete our Integrated Model. As discussed previously, factors present across the four quadrants engage through decentralized interaction to produce emergent qualities. That dynamic of interaction and emergence is experienced in the present moment but is historically mediated by the process of evolution. The meaning given to the present moment's experience is mainly the result of the dynamics of relationship or interaction between the factors present, not so much the objective reality of the factors themselves. Together, these foundational dynamics lead to a felt sense of positivity or negativity, as well as a state of functionality within one's environmental context. When it is going well, people can feel integrated, strong, and "in the flow." When it is not going well, people feel fragmented, weak, and ineffective.

Let's look at this process through the lens of a particular model of mental illness that emerged recently. The diathesis-stress model was first introduced in the 1960s. It proposes that mental illness arises through the interaction between preexisting vulnerabilities and ongoing situational stressors (Ingram & Luxton, 2005; Meehl, 1962). It helps explain why some people with a high level of vulnerability (family history of severe mental illness, for instance) may experience mental illness even if they are not exposed to high levels of situational stress. Conversely, some people with relatively low levels of vulnerability may experience mental illness if exposed to overwhelming levels of stress (in cases of PTSD, for instance). The key is the relationship between the vulnerabilities and the stressors. This corresponds well with the Integrated Model – factors from the Internal-Objective quadrant (genetic vulnerability) dynamically interact with factors from the External-Subjective (family dynamics – loss of a loved one) and the Internal-Subjective (difficulties with the development of healthy attachment) to create emergent qualities (sadness, hopelessness, sleep problems) and a subsequent sense of meaning (depression). Whether or not the difficult experience of depression rises to the level of what someone would choose to call a mental disorder depends on how such a disorder is defined within a specific nosology. In other words, it is a question of language and contextual definition. The most commonly utilized, professional categorical system is the DSM-5, and it has specific criteria for the diagnosis of what it identifies as various depressive disorders.

In the context of the Integrated Model, the DSM itself represents an emergent phenomenon, arising from the dynamic interaction between pertinent factors from all four quadrants of the Integrated Model.

Internal-Subjective	Internal-Objective	External-Subjective	External-Objective
Personality characteristics of task force members	Genetic/bio forces impacting task force members' own individual psychology	Sociocultural forces influencing task force members	The technological tools available to aid the collaborative work of task force members
personality characteristics integrated into diagnostic criteria within the DSM	Genetic/bio forces impacting the conceptualization and diagnostic criteria for disorders	Sociocultural forces influencing the expression or validity of mental disorders	The technological and institutional tools used to disseminate and implement the DSM in practice

As such, it should not be blindly accepted as empirical "truth," nor should it be rejected as "only" a cultural document. The DSM is the result of influences from multiple sources of information or knowledge, with various levels of empirical objectivity and constructionist subjectivity, mediated by evolutionary factors. This means that in some ways, given its widespread use and popularity, the DSM is bound to have some utility and validity, but in other ways, it continues to have the same serious problems that have been explored for some time (Helzer & Hudziak, 2002; Kinderman, Allsopp, & Cooke, 2017; McNally, 2011).

In regard to its utility and validity, the DSM does provide a generic definition of mental illness that has as broad agreement as any. Across recent editions, with relatively minor changes, it has defined mental illness as the presence of signs and symptoms, reflecting either impairment or distress, caused by an underlying disturbance in behavior, emotions, and/or cognition. It stresses that this pattern should not simply reflect a conflict with society unless the syndrome that led to the conflict is caused by an underlying psychological disturbance. I have presented this definition to students for quite a few years, and very few have disagreed with it. It has both the advantage and disadvantage of being very broad and vague. The DSM also describes a number of syndromes that have been accepted as "real" for thousands of years, including psychosis, trauma reaction, depression, and substance abuse. This gives it legitimacy that is both cultural and based in research.

On the other hand, the DSM's problems continue to challenge its basic, foundational validity. I say foundational because there are a number of issues with the DSM, but for this section, I am focusing on those related to the core concept of mental illness. Without going into too much detail, these can be broken down into two major issues: the question of dimensionality and the question of clinical severity, which are actually closely connected. As has been noted before in this text, the research is increasingly supporting the idea that mental illness is more dimensional than it is categorical. This is largely because it turns out that the brain is not organized around specific mental disorders – it is organized around psychological functions, such as memory, attention, emotion, abstract thought, etc. These functions do not turn on or off in the way a medical illness is present or not. Instead, they work at various levels of effectiveness and efficiency. Therefore, any diagnostic system that seeks to align with the way the brain actually works needs to provide a structure reflecting the brains different functions and how they can be compromised at different levels, by different factors, both biological and sociological. Instead of a model that looks like a decision tree:

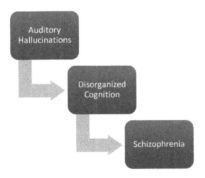

It would look more like this – with a lot more items, of course.

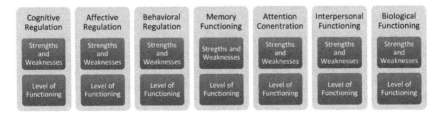

Diagnostics would shift away from focusing on a list of symptoms toward an assessment of different functional areas. Diagnostic labels would still be necessary, for a wide variety of reasons that should be obvious. Our brains categorize information in order to simplify, organize, communicate it to others, and decide on adaptive responses. I need to be able to see an animal and quickly differentiate a cow from a lion, identify it as safe or unsafe, let others know or be informed by others about it, and then decide what to do – run away or milk it. We need to categorize phenomena and do it easily and quickly – it is a functional heuristic in regard to both our own cognition and decision making – but in order to be able to work effectively with others in a group. However, at the same time, it is vital to recognize that while categorization serves important purposes, and in *some* ways, it reflects reality, in other respects, reality is dimensional, with phenomena existing on a spectrum. It has even been asserted that we do not need categorical diagnoses at all and that professionals could communicate better and signify the relational context of mental health problems more effectively if we eschewed diagnostic labels and instead emphasized uniquely personal case formulations (Kinderman et al., 2017).

At the very least, we need a taxonomic system that reflects both ways of understanding and organizing psychological phenomena, the categorical and the dimensional. We still need categories, but they must be linked to naturally occurring patterns of various psychological functions. Plus, in addition to explicating the different functional areas of the brain/psyche, such a categorical matrix should not just identify *disorder* but must also be able to recognize *order*, or wellness within the same areas, and measure, in some way, the current level of functionality in those areas. In this way, it would succeed in reflecting how the brain and the psyche actually work, provide a balanced view of the person's psychological strengths and weaknesses, and include measures of how well the person is doing in various areas of functioning.

This begs the question of what level of functionality moves a person from the category of health to that of illness. It should be obvious by now that the answer from the dimensional perspective is that there is no magic line. In fact, the postmodern, relativistic perspective would conclude that there is *no objective basis* for such a line, and the differentiation between such categories must start with a person's subjectively constructed interpretation of his or her own experience not the supposedly objective assessment of someone else. However, as with the importance of retaining labels for particular mental disorders, societies need to draw a line somewhere. In honoring the External-Subjective, we must recognize the basic legitimacy or right of any culture to make judgments about people's cognition, emotion, and behavior, and thus its contribution to an inclusive and integrated definition of mental health and mental illness.

Or perhaps there should be multiple lines, not just one between wellness and insanity. There used to be a commonly utilized psychiatric model of psychological organization and wellness that had four levels of overall personality functioning; the psychotic, the borderline, the neurotic, and the healthy(Gunderson, 2009). Perhaps it is time to bring the original line of thought back by considering the overall level of organization and functioning of the personality as a central aspect of assessment of wellness. We may not want to use the same labels, and obviously the underlying theoretical conceptualization must be updated, but if we want to move away from strictly categorical models and think more dimensionally, it is necessary that we have a well-developed system for assessing overall mental wellness.

Such a system does not exist outside that psychodynamic model. The only one that enjoyed widespread use was the Global Assessment of Functioning (GAF) that was included in the DSM's multiaxial assessment, but it was dropped in the DSM-5. It had a number of problems associated with it, including the facts that it was so broad-based that it lacked specific descriptive power, it was too closely linked to the DSM disorders themselves, and also that it was clearly a "tag-on" to the DSM without a solid development of its rationale, structure, validity, or reliability.

What is needed is a system of assessment that can address both global and function-specific areas, has some grounding in an objective, empirical epistemology, but also is highly sensitive to the subjective, relativistic, and constructionist reality of human psychology. Such a system would need to be dimensional (perhaps retaining the GAF's 0–100 scoring system) but with categorical anchor points. It would be too confusing to use the ones utilized in the old psychoanalytic system, but for a start, we might suggest Healthy, Average, and Unhealthy. For greater specificity, we could add Superior on one end and Extremely Unhealthy on the other.

The result would be a diagnostic system that incorporates the best of both worlds, the modern and postmodern – the empirical and the relativistic. As alluded to many times in this text, there are aspects of psychological reality that lend themselves to an objective, empirical understanding (the Internal-Objective and External-Objective). These include such things as biology, genetics, and technology. At the same time, there are aspects of psychological reality that lend themselves to a subjective, relativistic understanding (the Internal-Subjective and External-Subjective). These include such things as sense of self and affiliation with a group. As described, an Integrated Model must include all four quadrants of knowledge, understood in the context of a complex adaptive system. It must also be able to support a system of assessing mental health and disorder that integrates both dimensional and categorical aspects of the phenomena – taking into account both specific and global aspects of psychological functioning. After all, the human experience of psychological wellness or illness is ultimately an individual, holistically experienced state of being. To some extent, it can be atomized, but this is always an artificial process that loses the essence of the thing itself. People do not experience one of two states – mental health or mental disorder. They experience a continuously emergent quality of consciousness, which has a holistic essence that can be summarized by a single global measurement, but also has subparts that can be assessed separately. To an extent, functional problems occur in common enough patterns to categorize some disorders (psychosis, depression, and substance abuse come to mind), but what is more important is an individual assessment to identify the unique pattern of strengths and weaknesses a person experiences, across all four quadrants of information.

It is beyond the purview of this book to fully flesh out such a system of psychological assessment. This book was designed to provide a historical background and conceptual foundation for an approach to understanding mental health. The challenge was to help us break out of our habitual and authoritatively enforced ways of thinking about the issue. This is especially true as it regards the tendency to think in simplistic binaries (sane and crazy, biological and sociological, etc.), because the truth lies in dynamic complexity, reflecting the reality and wisdom of both sides of each binary.

Maybe the Epicureans had it right in their understanding that moving to extremes in any areas of life leads to misery. They endorsed an approach of radical acceptance of life as it is and moderation in all one's affairs. This is roughly equivalent to the Buddhist and Taoist approaches – awareness, acceptance, and moderation. If that is a recipe for mental health, can it also be for our *understanding* of both mental health and its binary, illness? Along these lines, in the field of psychotherapy, we have moved beyond the surprisingly recent requirement that therapists be loyal to and practice only within particular schools of psychotherapy, such as psychodynamic or cognitive-behavioral. It has become accepted and even valued to take a more integrated approach to psychotherapy, utilizing, in a thoughtful way, the best ideas and practices of various schools of thought. What is recommended here is that we take the same approach to understanding the foundations of mental health and illness. No single university or hospital department has all the answers, but nearly all have something useful to say. Can we bring their voices together in a harmonic way? Can we integrate our collective wisdom and hard-won truths? Can we find a place of honor and value for multiple perspectives, multiple truths, multiple realities?

We know it is possible to break out of limited and limiting paradigms because we have seen it so often in history. Despite the forces that keep people locked in their silos, some insist on challenging the status quo. They stand up to the authorities of the age and insist on seeing things in new ways. The point here is that we need to keep expanding our vision. Models are, after all, just models. They reflect a particular point of view about something at a particular point in time in a particular place. They are not the thing itself. They are tools of understanding, and when they stop being useful or adequately reflect the things they represent, they must be modified or tossed aside for a new model. The hope is that the new paradigms reflect advances in knowledge and understanding as the human race comes to know itself and its world better.

REFERENCES

Adler, A. (1992). *Understanding human Nature: The psychology of the personality*. London, England: Oneworld Publications. (Original work published 1927).

Aiken, H. (1954). *The age of ideology: The 19th century philosophers*. New York, NY: The New American Library.

Alexander, F., & Selesnick, S. (1966). *The history of psychiatry: An evaluation of psychiatric thought and practice from prehistoric times to the present*. New York, NY: Harper & Row.

Al-Shawaf, L., Conroy-Beam, D., Asao, K., & Buss, D. (2015). Human emotions: An evolutionary psychological perspective. *Emotion Review*, 1–14.

American Psychiatric Association. (2013). *Diagnostic and statistical manual of mental disorders* (5th ed.). Washington, DC: American Psychiatric Association.

American Psychological Association. (2014, June). How many psychologists are licensed in the United States? *Monitor on Psychology*, *45*(6).

Anonymous. (1939). *The big book of Alcoholics Anonymous*. New York, NY: Alcoholics Anonymous World Service.

Attenborough, D. (1966). The land-diving ceremony in Pentacost, New Hebrides. *Philosophical Transactions of the Royal Society B*, *251*(772), 503–505.

Aurobindo, S. (1949). *The life divine*. Twin Lakes, WI: Lotus Press.

Bandura, A., Caprara, G., Barbaranelli, C., Gerbino, M., & Pastorelli, C. (2003). Role of affective self-regulatory efficacy in diverse spheres of psychosocial functioning. *Child Development*, *74*(3), 769–782.

Bao, W., & Haas, A. (2009). Social change, life strain, and delinquency among Chinese urban adolescents. *Sociological Focus*, *42*, 285–305.

Bao, W., Haas, A., & Xie, Y. (2016). Life strain, social control, social learning, and delinquence: The effects of gender, age, and family SES among Chinese adolescents. *International Journal of Offender Therapy and Comparative Criminology*, *60*(12), 1446–1469.

Beck, A., Rush, A., Shaw, B., & Emery, G. (1979). *Cognitive therapy of depression*. New York, NY: The Guilford Press.

Benjamin, J. (1988). *The bonds of love: Psychoanalysis, feminism, and the problem of domination*. New York, NY: Random House.

Benjamin, J. (2018). *Beyond doer and done to: Recognition theory, intersubjectivity and the third*. New York, NY: Routledge.

Benning, T. (2015). Limitations of the biopsychosocial model in psychiatry. *Advances in Medical Education and Practice*, *6*, 347–352.

Ben-Noun, L. (2003). What was the mental illness that afflicted King Saul. *Clinical Case Studies*, *2*(4), 270–282.

Berger, B., & Tobar, D. (2007). Physical activity and quality of life: Key considerations. In G. Tennebaum & R. Eklund (Eds.), *Handbook of sport psychology* (pp. 598–620). Hoboken, NJ: John Wiley.

Bertalanffy, L. (1969). *General system theory: Foundations, development, applications* (revised ed.). New York, NY: George Braziller, Inc.

Birchwood, M., & Chadwick, P. (1997). The omnipotence of voices: Testing the validity of a cognitive model. *Psychological Medicine*, *27*(6), 1345–1353.

Bishop, P. (1995). *The Dionysian self: C.G. Jung's reception of Friedrich Nietzsche*. New York, NY: Walter de Gruyter & Co.

Bolen, J. (1989). *Gods in everyman: A new psychology of men's live and loves*. New York, NY: Harper & Row.

Bonelli, R., & Koenig, H. (2013). Mental disorders, religion and spirituality 1910 to 2010: A systematic evidence-based review. *Journal of Religion and Health, 52*(2), 657–673.

Bowler, P. (2009). *Evolution: The history of an idea (25th Anniversary Edition)*. Berkeley, CA: University of California Press.

Boyce, C. J., Brown, G. D. A., & Moore, S. C. (2010). Money and happiness: Rank of income, not income, affects life satisfaction. *Psychological Science, 21*, 471–475.

Bradshaw, J. (2015). *Healing the shame that binds you*. Deerfield, FL: HCI Books.

Bredstrom, A. (2017). Culture and context in mental health diagnosing: Scrutinizing the DSM-5 revision. *Journal of Medical Humanities, 40*, 347–363.

Brodie, R. (1996). *Virus of the mind: The new science of the meme*. New York, NY: Hay House.

Brown, T., Campbell, L., Lehman, C., Grisham, J., & Mancill, R. (2001). Current and lifetime comorbidity of the DSM – IV anxiety and mood disorders in a large clinical sample. *Journal of Abnormal Psychology, 110*, 585–599.

Bruinius, H. (2006). *Better for all the world: The secret history of forced sterilization and America's quest for racial purity*. New York, NY: Alfred A. Knopf.

Buss, D. (2008). *Evolutionary psychology: The new science of the mind*. New York, NY: Pearson.

Cacioppo, T., & Patrick, W. (2008). *Loneliness: Human nature and the need for social connection*. New York, NY: W.W. Norton.

Campbell, J. (1972). *Myths to live by*. New York, NY: Bantam Books.

Campbell, J. (2008). *The hero with a thousand faces*. Novato, CA: New World Library. (Original work published 1949).

Chafe, W. (2009). *Private lives/public consequences: Personality and politics in modern America*. Cambridge, MA. Harvard University Press.

Chamberlin, J. (2004, July). Survey says: More Americans are seeking mental health treatment. *Monitor on Psychology, 35*(7).

Chomsky, N., & Arnove, A. (Ed.) (2008). *The essential Chomsky*. New York, NY: The New Press.

Clark, K. (1969). *Civilisation*. New York, NY: Harper & Row.

Clifford, T. (1984). *Tibetan Buddhist medicine and psychiatry: The diamond healing*. New Delhi: Motilal Banarsidass Publishers.

Clow, A., & Edmunds, S. (2014). Relationship between physical activity and mental health. In A. Clow & S. Edmunds (Eds.), *Physical activity and mental health* (pp. 3–16). Champaign, IL: Human Kinetics.

Cocozza, J., & Skowyra, K. (2007). *Blueprint for change: A comprehensive model for the identification and treatment of youth with mental health needs in contact with the juvenile justice system*. Delmar, NY: The National Center for Mental Health and Juvenile Justice.

Coleman, D. (2005). *Emotional intelligence: The 10th anniversary edition*. New York, NY: Bantam Books.

Cook, C. (2012). Psychiatry in scripture: Sacred texts and psychopathology. *The Psychiatrist, 36*, 225–229.

Cosgrove, L., Bursztajn, H., Kupfer, D., & Regier, D. (2009). Toward credible conflict of interest policies in clinical psychiatry. *Psychiatric Times, 26*, 1.

Craig, L. A. (2014). The history of madness and mental illness in the middle ages: Directions and questions. *History Compass, 12*(9), 729–744.

Crow, T. (2008). The "big bang" theory of the origin of psychosis and the faculty of language. *Schizophrenia Research, 102*(1–3), 31–52.

Daker, M. (2018). Seeing beyond diseases and disorders: Symptom complexes as manifestations of mental constituents. *Frontiers in Psychiatry*, December (9), 1–6.

Damasio, A. (2003). *Looking for Spinoza: Joy, sorrow, and the feeling brain*. New York, NY: Harcourt, Inc.

Darwin, C. (2004). *The decent of man*. London, England: Penguin Classics. (Original work published 1871).

David, E., & Derthick, A. (2018). *The psychology of oppression*. New York, NY: Springer Publishing.

Davidson, G., Campbell, J., Shannon, C., & Mulholland, C. (2016). *Models of mental health*. New York, NY: Palgrave.

Dawkins, R. (1986). *The blind watchmaker: Why the evidence of evolution reveals a universe without design*. New York, NY: W.W. Norton and Co.

Dawkins, R. (2004). *The ancestor's tale: A pilgrimage to the dawn of evolution*. New York, NY: Houghton Mifflin Company.

Delgado-Morales, R., Agis-Balboa, R., Esteller, M., & Berdasco, M. (2017). Epigenetic mechanisms during ageing and neurogenesis as novel therapeutic avenues in human brain disorders. *Clinical Epigenetics*.

Dennett, D. (2017). *From bacteria to Bach and back: The evolution of minds*. New York, NY: Norton.

Descartes, R. (1998). *Discourse on method and method and meditation on first philosophy*. Indianapolis, IN: Hackett Publishing (Original work published in 1637).

Dishman, R., Washburn, R., & Heath, G. (2004). *Physical activity epidemiology*. Champaign, IL: Human Kinetics.

Draguns, J. (1997). Abnormal behavior patterns across culture: Implications for counseling and psychotherapy. *International Journal of Intercultural Relations, 21*(2), 213–248.

Durant, W. (1926). *The story of philosophy: The lives and opinions of the great philosophers of the western world*. New York, NY: Simon & Schuster.

Durkheim, E. (2008). *The elementary forms of religious life*. New York, NY: Oxford University Press. (Original work published 1912).

Dutt-Ballerstadt, R. (March, 2019). *Academic prioritization or killing the liberal arts?* Inside Higher Education. Retrieved from www.insidehighered.com/advice/2019/03/01/shrinking-liberal-arts-programs-raise-alarm-bells-among-faculty

Eisler, R. (1987). *The chalice and the blade*. San Francisco, CA: Harper San Francisco.

Eliade, M. (1954). *The myth of the eternal return*. New York, NY: Princeton University Press.

Eliade, M. (1957). *Myths, dreams, and mysteries: The encounter between contemporary faiths and archaic realities*. New York, NY: Harper Torchbooks.

Eliade, M. (1958). *Rites and symbols of initiation: The mysteries of birth and rebirth*. New York, NY: Harper Torchbooks.

Ellenberger, H. (1970). *The discovery of the unconscious*. New York, NY: Basic Books.

Ellis, A. (1958). *Sex without guilt in the 21st century*. Oxford, England: Lyle Stuart.

Engel, G. (1977). The need for a new medical model: A challenge for biomedicine. *Science, 196*(4286), 129–136.

Engel, G. (2003). The clinical application of the biopsychosocial model. In R. Frankel, T. Quill, & S. McDaniel (Eds.), *The biopsychosocial approach: Past, present, future*. Rochester, NY: University of Rochester Press.

Ernst, W. (2017). Histories of madness in South Asia. In G. Eghigian (Ed.), *The Routledge history of madness and mental health* (pp. 193–209). Routledge Publishing.

Esquirol, J. (2012). *Mental Maladies: Treatise on insanity*. London, England: Forgotten Books. (Original work published 1845).

Evans, A. (1988). *The god of ecstasy: Sex roles and the madness of Dionysos.* New York, NY: St. Martin's Press.

Faria, M. A., Jr. (2013). Violence, mental illness, and the brain: A brief history of psychosurgery: Part 1 – From trephination to lobotomy. *Surgical Neurology International, 4,* 49.

Fellows, W. (1979). *Religions east and west.* New York, NY. Holt, Rinehart and Winston.

First, M. B. (2003). Psychiatric classification. In A. Tasman, J. Kay, & J. Lieberman (Eds.), *Psychiatry* (2nd ed., Vol. 1, pp. 659–676). New York, NY: Wiley.

Fonogy, P. (2003). Psychoanalysis today. *World Psychiatry, 2*(2), 73–80.

Foucault, M. (1965). *Madness and civilization: A history of insanity in the age of reason.* New York, NY: Vintage Books.

Fraga, M., Ballestar, E., Paz, M. Ropero, S., Setien, F., . . . Esteller, M. (2005). Epigenetic differences arise during the lifetime of monozygotic twins. *Proceedings of the National Academy of Sciences of the USA, 102,* 10604–10609.

Frances, A. (2009). Whither, DSM-V? *British Journal of Psychiatry, 195*(5), 391–392.

Frank, S. (1998). *Foundations of social evolution.* Princeton, NJ: Princeton University Press.

Frankl, V. (1959). *Man's search for meaning.* Boston, MA: Beacon Press.

Frankl Quotes. (n.d.). *BrainyQuote.com.* Retrieved May 29, 2020, from BrainyQuote.com Web site: www.brainyquote.com/quotes/viktor_e_frankl_160380

Freud, A. (1992). *The ego and the mechanisms of defense.* New York, NY: Routledge. (original work published in 1936).

Freud, S. (1950). *Totem and taboo.* New York, NY: W.W. Norton. (Original work published 1913).

Friedman, T. (2005). *The world is flat: A brief history of the twenty-first century.* New York, NY: Farrar, Straus and Giroux.

Fryers, T., Meizer, D., & Jenkins, R. (2003). Social inequalities and the common mental disorders. *Social Psychiatry and Psychiatric Epidemiology, 38*(5), 229–237.

Galton, F. (2005 [1869]). *Hereditary genius: An inquiry into its laws and consequences.* New York, NY: Cismo, Inc.

Gamble, Harvey L., Jr. (1999). Walden Two, postmodern utopia, and the problems of power, choice, and rule of law. *Texas Studies in Literature and Language, 41*(1), 1–15.

Gauld, A. (1992). *A history of hypnotism.* New York, NY: Cambridge University Press.

Gehart, D. (2012). The mental health recovery movement and family therapy, part one: Consumer-led reform of services to person diagnosed with severe mental illness. *Journal of Marital and Family Therapy, 38*(3), 429–442.

Geyer, A., & Baumeister, R. (2005). Religion, morality, and self-control: Values, virtues, and vices. In R. Paloutzian and C. Park (Eds.), *Handbook of the psychology of religion and spirituality* (pp. 412–434). New York, NY: Guilford Press.

Goodall, J. (2010). *50 years at Gombe: A tribute to five decades of wildlife research, education, and conservation.* New York, NY: Abrams.

Gottesman, I. (1991). *Schizophrenia genesis: The origins of madness.* New York, NY: W.H. Freeman.

Gould, S. (1993). *Eight little piggies: Reflections in natural history.* New York, NY: W.W. Norton & Co.

Granello, P. (2013). *Wellness counseling.* New York, NY: Person Education.

Greene, B. (2011). *The hidden reality: Parallel universes and the deep laws of the cosmos.* New York, NY: Random House.

Greene, J. (2013). *Moral tribes: Emotion, reason, and the gap between us and them.* New York, NY: The Penguin Press.

Grinin, L., Markov, A., & Korotayev, A. (2013). On similarities between biological and social evolutionary mechanisms: Mathematical modeling. *Cliodynamics, 4*(2).

Grisso, T., Vincent, G., & Seagrave, D. (2005). *Mental health screening and assessment in juvenile justice.* New York, NY: Guilford Press.

Gunderson, J. (2009). Borderline personality disorder: Ontogeny of a diagnosis. *American Journal of Psychiatry, 166*(5), 530–539.

Gurang, A. R., & Roethel-Wendorf, A. (2009). Stress and mental health. In S. Eshun & A. R. Gurang (Eds.), *Culture and mental health: Sociocultural influences, theory, and practice.* Malden, MA: Blackwell Publishing, Ltd.

Hackett, R., Steptoe, A., & Jackson, S. (2019). Sex discrimination and mental health in women: A prospective analysis. *Health Psychology, 38*(11), 1014–1024.

Hackman, D., Farah, M., & Meaney, M. (2010). Socioeconomic status and the brain: Mechanistic insights from human and animal research. *Nature Reviews: Neuroscience, 11,* 651–659.

Hägele, C., Schlagenhauf, F., Rapp, M., Sterzer, P., Beck, A., Bermpohl, F., . . . Heinz, A. (2015). Dimensional psychiatry: Reward dysfunction and depressive mood across psychiatric disorders. *Psychopharmacology, 232,* 331–341.

Hampshire, S. (1956). *The age of reason: The 17th century philosophers.* New York, NY: New American Library.

Hankins, B. (2004). *The second great awakening and the transcendentalists.* Santa Barbara, CA: Greenwood Press.

Hariri, A., Mattay, V., Tessitore, A., Fera, F., & Weinberger, D. (2003). Neocortical modulation of the amygdala response to fearful stimuli. *Biological Psychiatry, 53,* 494–501.

Harmon, W. (1984). Peace on earth: The impossible dream becomes possible. *Journal of Humanistic Psychology, 24*(3), 77–92.

Harrington, A. (2019). *Mind fixers: Psychiatry's troubled search for the biology of mental illness.* New York, NY: Norton & Co.

Haught, H., Rose, J., Geers, A., & Brown, J. (2015) Subjective social status and well-being: The role of referent abstraction. *The Journal of Social Psychology, 4*(155), 356–369.

Hayes, S. (2004). Acceptance and commitment therapy, relational frame theory, and the third wave of behavioral and cognitive therapies. *Behavior Therapy, 35,* 639–665.

Heinberg, R. (1989). *Memories and visions of paradise: Exploring the universal myth of a lost golden age.* Los Angeles, CA: Jeremy P. Tarcher, Inc.

Heine, S. (2008). *Cultural psychology.* New York, NY: W.W. Norton & Company.

Helzer, J., & Hudziak, J. (Eds.) (2002). *Defining psychopathology in the 21st century: DSM-V and beyond.* Washington, DC: American Psychiatric Publishing.

Herrnstein, R., & Murray, C. (1994). *The bell curve: Intelligence and class structure in American life.* New York, NY: Free Press Paperbacks.

Hillman, J. (1972). *The myth of analysis.* New York, NY: HarperCollins.

Hillman, J. (1979). *The dream and the underworld.* New York, NY: HarperCollins.

Hillman, J., & Ventura, M. (1992). *We've had a hundred years of psychotherapy and the world's getting worse.* New York, NY: HarperCollins.

Hobfoll, S. (1989). Conservation of resources. *American Psychologist, 44,* 513–524.

Horowitz, A. (2002). *Creating mental illness.* Chicago, IL: The University of Chicago Press.

Huitt, W. (2012). A systems approach to the study of human behavior. *Educational Psychology Interactive.* Valdosta, GA: Valdosta State University. Retrieved January 7, 2019, from www.edpsycinteractive.org/materials/sysmdlo.html

Hunt, M. (1993). *The story of psychology.* New York, NY: Doubleday.

Huxley, A. (1944). *The perennial philosophy.* New York, NY: Harper & Collins.

Hyman, S. (2011). Diagnosis of mental disorders in light of modern genetics. In D. Regier, W. Narrow, E. Kuhl, & D. Kupfer (Eds.), *The conceptual evolution of DSM-5*. Washington, DC: American Psychiatric Publishing.

Hymowitz, C., & Weissman, M. (1978). *A history of women in America: From founding mothers to feminists – how women shaped the life and culture of America*. New York, NY: Bantam Books.

Ingram, R., & Luxton, D. (2005). Vulnerability-stress models. In B. Hankin & J. Abela (Eds.), *Development of psychopathology: A vulnerability-stress perspective*. Thousand Oaks, CA: Sage Publications.

Jackson, J., Brown, T., Williams, D., et al. (1996). Racism and the physical and mental health status of African Americans: a thirteen year national panel study. *Ethnicity & Disease, 6*(1–2), 132–147.

Jacobi, J. (1942). *The psychology of C.G. Jung*. Yale, CT: Yale University Press.

Jacoby, M. (1985). *Longing for paradise: Psychological perspectives on an archetype*. Boston, MA: Sigo Press.

Jardina, A. (2019). *White identity politics*. New York, NY: Cambridge University Press.

Jaynes, J. (1976). *The origin of consciousness in the breakdown of the bicameral mind*. New York, NY: Houghton Mifflin.

Jenkins, P., Conroy, M., & Mendonsa, A. (2013). Sacramento assessment center: A comprehensive multi-perspective model for effective assessment of juvenile offenders. *Psychology, 4*(7), 553–558.

Jimerson, S. R., Stewart, K., Skokut, M., Cardenas, S., & Malone, H. (2009). How many school psychologists are there in each country of the world?: International estimates of school psychologists and school psychologist-to-student ratios. *School Psychology International, 30*(6), 555–567.

Johnson, S. M. (1994). *Character styles*. New York, NY: W.W. Norton & Co.

Johnson, S. M. (2007). *Ancient Religions*. Cambridge, MA: Harvard University Press.

Jung, C. G. (1939). *The integration of the personality*. New York, NY: Farrar & Rinehart.

Jung, C. G. (1964). *Man and his symbols*. Garden City, NY: Doubleday & Co.

Karen, R. (1998). *Becoming attached: First relationships and how they shape our capacity for love*. New York, NY: Oxford University Press.

Kasen, S., Wickramaratne, P., Gameroff, M., & Weissman, M. (2012). Religiosity and resilience in persons at high risk for major depression. *Psychological Medicine, 42*(3), 509.

Katschnig, H. (2006). Quality of life in mental disorder: Challenges for research and clinical practice. *World Psychiatry, 5*(3), 139–145.

Kauer, J. (2018). Life experiences and addictive drugs change your brain. In D. Linden (Ed.), *Think tank: Forty neuroscientists explore the biological roots of human experience*. New Haven, CT: Yale University Press.

Keay, J. (2009). *China: A history*. New York, NY: Basic Books.

Keen, S. (1986). *Faces of the enemy: Reflections of the hostile imagination*. New York, NY: HarperCollins.

Kendell, R. (1975). *The role of diagnosis in psychiatry*. Oxford, England: Blackwell Scientific Publications.

Kessler, R., Berglund, P., Demler, O., Jin, R., Merikangas, K., & Walters, E. (2005). Lifetime prevalence and age-of-onset distributions of DSM-IV disorders in the National Comorbidity Survey. EE. *Archives of General Psychiatry, 62*(6), 593–602.

Kessler, R., McGonagle, K., Zhao, S., Nelson, C., Hughes, N., Eshleman, S., ... Kendler, K. (1994). Lifetime and 12-month prevalence of DSM-III-R psychiatric disorders in the United States: Results from the National Comorbidity Survey. *Archives of General Psychiatry, 51*, 8–19.

Kety, S. (1988). Schizophrenic illness in the families of schizophrenic adoptees: Findings from the Danish national sample. *Schizophrenia Bulletin, 14*(2), 217–222.

Keyssar, A. (2000). *The right to vote: The contested history of democracy in the United States.* New York, NY: Basic Books.

Kiesler, D. (1999). *Beyond the disease model of mental disorders.* Westport, CT: Praeger.

Kinderman, P. (2005). A psychological model of mental disorder. *Harvard Review of Psychiatry, 13*(4), 206–2017.

Kinderman, P., Allsopp, K., & Cooke, A. (2017). Responses to the publication of the American Psychiatric Association's DSM-5. *Journal of Humanistic Psychology, 57*(6), 625–649.

Kleinmann, A. (1982). Neurasthenia and depression: A study of somatization and culture in China. *Culture, Medicine, and Psychiatry, 6*, 117–190.

Knutson, K., Mah, L., Manly, C., & Grafman, J. (2007). Neural correlates of automatic beliefs about gender and race. *Human Brain Mapping, 28*(10), 915–930.

Koenig, H. G. (2009). Research on religion, spirituality, and mental health: A review. *Canadian Journal of Psychiatry, 54*(5), 283–291.

Koenig, H. G. (2012). Religion, spirituality, and health: the research and clinical implications. *ISRN psychiatry, 2012*, 278730. https://doi.org/10.5402/2012/278730

Koestler, A. (1990 [1967]). *The ghost in the machine.* New York, NY: Penguin.

Kraepelin, E. (2018). *Lectures on clinical psychiatry.* London, England: Scholar Select.

Kroll, J., & Bachrach, B. (1984). Sin and mental illness in the middle ages. *Psychological Medicine, 14*(3), 507–514.

Kroll, J., & Bachrach, B. (2005). *The mystic mind: The psychology of medieval mystics and ascetics.* New York, NY: Routledge.

Kucharski, R., Maleszka, J., Foret, S., & Maleszka, R. (2008). Nutritional control of reproductive status in honeybees via DNA methylation. *Science, 319*, 1827–1830.

Kuhn, T. (1962). *The structure of scientific revolutions.* Chicago, IL: University of Chicago Press.

Kutchins, H., & Kirk, S. (1997). *Making us crazy: DSM: the psychiatric bible and the creation of mental disorders.* New York, NY: The Free Press.

Lakoff, G., & Johnson, M. (1980). *Metaphors we live by.* Chicago, IL: The University of Chicago Press.

Lambert, E., Wahler, R., Andrade, A., & Bickman, L. (2001). Looking for the disorder in conduct disorder. *Journal of Abnormal Psychology, 110*(1), 110–123.

Lansing, J. (2003). Complex adaptive systems. *Annual Review, 32*, 183–204.

Leahey, T. (2013). *A history of psychology: From antiquity to modernity* (7th ed.). New York, NY: Person Education.

Lebow, J., & Jenkins, P. (2018). *Research for the psychotherapist: From science to practice.* New York, NY: Routledge Publishing.

LeDoux, J. (2000). Emotion circuits in the brain. *Annual Review of Neuroscience, 23*, 155–184.

Lee, N. (2020, August 25). *Nathaniel Lee quotes.* Retrieved from www.goodreads.com/author/quotes/269450.Nathaniel_Lee

LeShan, L. (2002). *The psychology of war: Comprehending its mystique and it madness.* New York, NY: Helios Press.

Levine, D. (2019). The Population of Europe: Early Modern Demographic Patterns. *Encyclopedia of European Social History.* Retrieved November 5, 2019, from

Encyclopedia.com: www.encyclopedia.com/international/encyclopedias-almanacs-transcripts-and-maps/population-europe-early-modern-demographic-patterns

Levy, D. (2010). *Tools of critical thinking: Metathoughts for psychology*. Long Grove, IL: Waveland Press.

Lewis, B. (2006). *Moving beyond Prozac, DSM, and the new psychiatry: The birth of postpsychiatry*. Ann Arbor, MI: The University of Michigan Press.

Lewis-Williams, D. (2002). *The mind in the cave: Consciousness and the origins of art*. London, England: Thames & Hudson.

Linehan, M. (1993). *Cognitive-behavioral treatment of borderline personality disorder*. New York, NY: The Guilford Press.

Lo, M., Hinds, D., Tung, J. et al. (2017). Genome-wide analyses for personality traits identify six genomic loci and show correlations with psychiatric disorders. *Nat Genet, 49*, 152–156.

Lox, C., Martin Ginis, K., & Petruzzello, S. (2006). *Psychology of exercise: Integrating theory and practice*. Scottsdale, AZ: Holcomb Hathaway.

MacLennan, B. (2007). Evolutionary psychology, complex systems, and social theory. *Soundings: An Interdisciplinary Journal, 90*(3–4), 169–189.

Marino, G. (2004). *Basic writings of existentialism*. New York, NY: Random House.

Marmot, M. (2005). *The status syndrome: How social standing effects our health and longevity*. New York, NY: Holt Paperbacks.

Maslow, A. (1967). A theory of metamotivation: The biological rooting of the value-life. *Journal of Humanistic Psychology, 7*(2), 93–126.

Masson, J. (1984). *The assault on truth: Freud's suppression of the seduction theory*. New York, NY: Harper Perennial.

McAuley, E., & Blissmer, B. (2000). Self-efficacy determinants and consequences of physical activity. *Exercise and Sport Sciences Reviews, 28*, 85–88.

McCarthy-Jones, S., Waegeli, A., & Watkins, J. (2013). Spirituality and hearing voices: Considering the relation. *Psychosis, 5*(3), 247–258.

McGowan, P., Sasaki, A., D'Alessio, A., Dymov, S., Labonte, B., Szuf, M., ... Meaney, M. (2009). Epigenetic regulation of the glucocorticoid receptor in human brain associates with childhood abuse. *Nature Neuroscience, 12*, 342–348.

McGuffin, P. (1994). *Seminars in psychiatric genetics*. London, England: Gaskell.

McNally, R. (2011). *What is mental illness*. Cambridge, MA: Harvard University Press.

McNeill, W. (1999). *A world history* (4th ed.). New York, NY: Oxford University Press.

Meaney, M. (2001). Maternal care, gene expression, and the transmission of individual differences in stress reactivity across generations. *Annual Review of Neuroscience, 24*, 1161–1192.

Meaney, M. (2010). Epigenetics and the biological definition of gene x environmental interactions. *Child Development, 81*, 41–79.

Meehl, P. (1962). Schizotaxia, schizotypy, schizophrenia. *American Psychologist, 17*(12), 827–838.

Mellyn, E. (2017). Healers and healing in the early modern health care market. In G. Eghigian (Ed.), *The Routledge history of madness and mental health* (pp. 83–100). New York, NY: Routledge.

Menand, L. (2001). *The metaphysical club: A story of ideas in America*. New York, NY: Farrar, Straus and Giroux.

Mendonsa, A. D. (2008). *Sacramento assessment center: Using comprehensive multidimensional assessments in increasing juvenile offender placement success and reducing recidivism* (Order No. 3321015). Available from ProQuest Dissertations & Theses Global. (304834904).

Merchant, C. (1980). *The death of nature: Women, ecology, and the scientific revolution.* New York, NY: Harper & Row.

Mercier, L. S. (1783). Le tableau de Paris. In M. Foucault (Ed.), *Madness and civilization: A history of insanity in the age of reason* (pp. 202–203).

Meyer, G., Finn, S., Eyde, L., Kay, G., Moreland, K., Dies, R., . . . Kubiszyn, T. (2001). Psychological testing and psychological assessment: A review of evidence and issues. *American Psychologist, 56*(2), 128–165.

Meyer, M. (2017). Madness and psychiatry in Latin America's long nineteenth century. In G. Eghigian (Ed.), *The Routledge history of madness and mental health* (pp. 193–209). Routledge Publishing.

Mezzich, J. (2013). Culturally informing diagnostic systems. In S. Barnow & N. Balkir (Eds.), *Cultural variations in psychopathology* (pp. 137–153). Cambridge, MA: Hogrefe Publishing.

Miles, R. (2001). *Who cooked the last supper: The women's history of the world.* New York, NY: Three Rivers Press.

Miller, J., & Page, S. (2007). *Complex adaptive systems: An introduction to computational models of social life.* Princeton, NJ: Princeton University Press.

Miller, L., & Kelley, B. (2005). Relationships of religiosity and spirituality with mental health and psychopathology. In R. Paloutzian & C. Park (Eds.), *Handbook of the psychology of religion and spirituality* (pp. 460–478). New York, NY: Guilford Press.

Miller, S. (2016, December 13). *One in six Americans takes a psychiatric drug.* Scientific American. Retrieved from www.scientificamerican.com/article/1-in-6-americans-takes-a-psychiatric-drug/

Millon, T. (2004). *Masters of the mind: Exploring the story of mental illness from ancient times to the new millennium.* Hoboken, NJ: Wiley & Sons.

Mineka, S., Watson, D., & Clark, L. E. A. (1998). Comorbidity of anxiety and unipolar mood disorders. *Annual Review of Psychology, 49,* 377–412.

Mitchell, S., & Black, M. (1995). *Freud and beyond: A history of modern psychanalytic thought.* New York, NY: Basic Books.

Mithen, S. (1996). *The prehistory of the mind: The cognitive origins of art, religion, and science.* London, England: Thames and Hudson, Ltd.

Mittal, V., Pelletier-Baldelli, A., Trotman, H., Kestler, L., Bollini, A., & Walker, E. (2016). Schizophrenia spectrum and other psychotic disorders. In J. Maddux & B. Winstead (Eds.), *Psychopathology: Foundations for a contemporary understanding* (pp. 318–340). New York, NY: Routledge.

Moffitt, T., Arseneault, L., Jaffee, S., Kim-Cohen, J., Koenen, K., Odgers, C., . . . Viding, E. (2008). Research review: DSM-V conduct disorder: Research needs for an evidence base. *Journal of Child Psychology and Psychiatry, 49*(1), 3–33.

Moffitt, T., Caspi, A., Rutter, M., & Phil, A. (2001). *Sex differences in antisocial behavior: Conduct disorder, delinquency and violence in the Dunedin Longitudinal Study.* New York, NY: Cambridge University Press.

Mohr, W. (2006). Spiritual issues in psychiatric care. *Perspectives in Psychiatric Care, 42*(3), 174–183.

Moore, D. (2015). *The developing genome: An introduction to behavioral epigenetics.* New York, NY: Oxford University Press.

Moss, Q., Fleck, D., & Strakowski, S. (2006). The influence of religious affiliation on time to first treatment and hospitalization. *Schizophrenia Research, 84*(2), 421–426.

Muller, J. (2018). The tyranny of metrics: The quest to quantify everything undermines higher education. *The Chronicle Review,* January 26, 2018, B11–B13.

Mumford, L. (1961). *The city in history: Its origins, its transformations, and its prospects*. New York, NY: Harvest Books.

Murali, V., & Oyebode, F. (2004). Poverty, social inequality and mental health. *Advances in Psychiatric Treatment, 10*, 212–224.

National Academy of Sciences. (1999). *Science and creationism: A view from the National Academy of Sciences* (2nd ed.). Washington, DC: The National Academies Press.

Neumann, E. (1994). *The fear of the feminine and other essays on feminine psychology*. Princeton, NJ: Princeton University Press.

Neumann, E. (2014). *The origins and history of consciousness*. Princeton, NJ: Princeton University Press. (First published in 1954).

Nietzsche Quotes. (n.d.). *BrainyQuote.com*. Retrieved May 29, 2020, from BrainyQuote. com Web site: www.brainyquote.com/quotes/friedrich_nietzsche_103819

Nolan, P., & Lenski, G. (2015). *Human societies: An introduction to macrosociology* (12th ed.). New York, NY: Oxford University Press.

Nolen-Hoeksema, S. (2016). *Abnormal psychology* (7th ed.). New York, NY: McGraw-Hill Education.

Noonan, M. P., Sallet, J., Mars, R. B., Neubert, F. X., O'Reilly, J. X., Andersson, J. L., et al. (2014). A neural circuit covarying with social hierarchy in Macaques. *PLOS Biology, 12*(9).

Noshpitz, J., & Coddington, R. (Eds.) (1990). *Stressors and the adjustment disorders*. New York, NY: Wiley Interscience.

Okazake, S. (1997). Sources of ethnic differences between Asian American and White American college students on measures of depression and social anxiety. *Journal of Abnormal Psychology, 106*, 52–60.

Olfson, M., Wang, S., Wall, M., Marcus, S. C., & Blanco, C. (2019). Trends in serious psychological distress and outpatient mental health care of US adults. *JAMA Psychiatry, 76*(2), 152–161.

Orr, J. (1955). *The second evangelical awakening*. Wheaton, IL: Van Kampen Press.

Orwell, G. (1949). *Nineteen eighty-four*. London, England: Martin Secker and Warburg Limited.

Otto, R. (1923). *The idea of the holy: An inquiry into the non-rational factor in the idea of the divine and its relation to the rational*. New York, NY: Oxford University Press.

Pagels, E. (1988). *Adam, Eve, and the serpent*. New York, NY: Random House.

Paris, J. (2017). Is psychoanalysis still relevant to psychiatry? *Canadian Journal of Psychiatry. Revue canadienne de psychiatrie, 62*(5), 308–312.

Perls, F. (1972). *In and out of the garbage pail: Joy, sorrow, chaos, wisdom*. New York, NY: Bantam Books.

Peterson, C., Maier, S., & Seligman, M. (1995). *Learned helplessness: A theory for the age of personal control*. New York, NY: Vintage Books.

Petteruti, A., Walsh, N., & Valezquez, T. (2009). *The costs of confinement: Why good juvenile justice policies make good fiscal sense*. Washington, DC: Justice Policy Institute.

Pew Research Center. (2019a). *For Darwin Day, six facts about the evolution debate*. Retrieved from www.pewresearch.org/fact-tank/2019/02/11/darwin-day/

Pew Research Center. (2019b, October 17). *In U.S., decline of Christianity continues at rapid pace*. Retrieved from www.pewforum.org/2019/10/17/in-u-s-decline-of-christianity-continues-at-rapid-pace/

Pilgrim, D. (2002). The biopsychosocial model in Anglo-American psychiatry: Past, present, and future? *Journal of Mental Health, 11*, 585–594.

Pilisuk, M. (2015). Humanistic psychology and peace. In K. Schneider, J. Pierson, & J. Bugental (Eds.), *The handbook of humanistic psychology: Theory, research, and practice* (2nd ed., pp. 149–160). Los Angeles, CA: Sage Publishing.

Pilisuk, M., & Joy, M. (2015). Humanistic psychology and ecology. In K. Schneider, J. Pierson, & J. Bugental (Eds.), *The handbook of humanistic psychology: Theory, research, and practice* (2nd ed., pp. 135–148). Los Angeles, CA: Sage Publishing.

Pinel, P. (1801). *Traite medico-philosophique de l'alienation mentale* (D. D. Davis, Trans.). London.

Pinker, S. (1994). *The language instinct: How the mind creates language.* New York, NY: Harper Perennial.

Pinker, S. (2002). *The blank slate: The modern denial of human nature.* New York, NY: Penguin Books.

Pinker, S. (2011). *The better angels of our nature: Why violence has declined.* New York, NY: Viking.

Pliszka, S. (2016). *Neuroscience for the mental health clinician.* New York, NY: The Guilford Press.

Popper, C. (2002). *The logic of scientific discovery.* New York, NY: Routledge. (first published in 1935).

Porter, R. (2013). *Madness: A brief history.* Oxford, UK: Oxford University Press.

Proctor, E., Vosler, N., & Murty, S. (1992). Child demographics and DSM diagnosis: A multiaxis study. *Child Psychiatry and Human Development, 22,* 165–183.

Proverbio, A., Alberio, A., & DeBenedetto, F. (2018). Neural correlates of automatic beliefs about gender stereotypes: Males are more prejudicial. *Brain and Language, 11*(186), 8–16.

Psychiatry: How many adults in the united states are taking psychiatric drugs? (2016, December 26). *Mental Health Weekly Digest.*

Raglin, J. (1997). The anxiolytic effects of physical activity. In W. P. Morgan (Ed.), *Physical activity and mental health* (pp. 107–126). Washington, DC: Taylor and Francis.

Ralph, R., & Corrigan, P. (2005). *Recovery in mental illness: Broadening our understanding of wellness.* Washington, DC: American Psychological Association.

Raskin, J. (2002). Constructivism in psychology: Personal construct psychology, radical constructivism, and social constructivism. In J. Raskin & S. Bridges (Eds.), *Studies in meaning: Exploring constructivist psychology* (pp. 1–25). New York, NY: Pace University Press.

Ray, I. (1863). *Mental hygiene.* Boston, MA: Ticknor and Fields.

Reagan, R. (1989). *Farewell address to the nation.* Retrieved from reaganlibrary.archives.gov.

Regier, D., Narrow, W., Kuhl, E., & Kupfer, D. (2011). Introduction. In D. Regier, W. Narrow, E. Kuhl, & D. Kupfer (Eds.), *The conceptual evolution of DSM-5.* Washington, DC: American Psychiatric Publishing.

Reik, T. (1970). *Myth and guilt: The crime and punishment of mankind.* New York, NY: Grosset & Dunlap.

Renfrew, C. (2007). *Prehistory: The making of the human mind.* New York, NY: Random House.

Renfrew, C., & Bahn, P. (2016). *Archaeology: Theories, methods, and practice* (7th ed.). London, England: Thames and Hudson.

Rickman, J. (Ed.) (1957). *A general selection from the works of Sigmund Freud.* Garden City, NY: Doubleday Anchor Books.

Robins, L. N. (1999). A 70-year history of conduct disorder: Variations in definition, prevalence, and correlates. In P. Cohen, C. Slomkowski, & L. N. Robins (Eds.),

Historical and geographical influences on psychopathology (pp. 37–56). Mahwah, NJ: Lawrence Erlbaum Associates Publishers.

Rogers, A., & Pilgrim, D. (2014). *A sociology of mental health and illness* (5th ed.). New York, NY: McGraw Hill Education.

Ronson, J. (2011). *The psychopath test: A journey through the madness industry*. New York, NY: Riverhead Books.

Roszak, T., Gomes, M., & Kanner, A. (1995). *Ecopsychology: Restoring the Earth, healing the mind*. New York, NY: Sierra Club Books.

Russell, B. (1945). *The history of western philosophy*. New York, NY: Simon & Schuster.

Ryder, A. (2004). *Cross-cultural differences in the presentation of depression: Chinese somatization and Western psychologization*. Unpublished doctoral dissertation, University of British Columbia.

Saah, T. (2005). The evolutionary origins and significance of drug addiction. *Harm Reduction Journal, 2*, 8.

Saks, E. (2007). *The center cannot hold*. New York, NY: Hyperion.

Sale, K. (1995). *Rebels against the future: The Luddites and their war on the industrial revolution*. Cambridge, MA: Perseus Publishing.

Samuels, A. (1985). *Jung and the post-Jungians*. New York, NY: Routledge.

Sanders, R. (1978). *Lost tribes and promised lands: The origins of American Racism*. Westland, MI: Dzanc Books.

Sapolsky, R. (2017). *Behave: The biology of humans at our best and worst*. New York, NY: Penguin Press.

Sargent, R. (Ed.) (1999). *Francis Bacon: Selected philosophical works*. Indianapolis, IN: Hackett Publishing Company.

Scharbert, G. (2009). Freud and evolution. *History and Philosophy of the Life Sciences, 31*(2), 295–311.

Scheid, T., & Brown, T. (Eds.) (2010). *A handbook for the study of mental health* (2nd ed.). New York, NY: Cambridge University Press.

Schultz, D., & Schultz, S. (2012). *A history of modern psychology*. Belmont, CA: Wadsworth.

Scull, A. (1993). *The most solitary of afflictions: Madness and society in Britain, 1700–1900*. New Haven, CT: Yale University Press.

Scull, A. (2015). *Madness in civilization: A cultural history of insanity from the Bible to Freud, from the madhouse to modern medicine*. Princeton, NJ: Princeton University Press.

Scull, A. (2017). The asylum, hospital, and clinic. In G. Eghigian (Ed.), *The Routledge history of madness and mental health* (pp. 101–114). New York, NY: Routledge.

Seligman, M. (1991). *Learned optimism: How to change your mind and your life*. New York, NY: Vintage Books.

Seligman, M. (2011). *Flourish: A visionary new understanding of happiness and wellbeing*. New York, NY: Free Press.

Senik, C. (2014). Wealth and happiness. *Oxford Review of Economic Policy, 30*(1), 92–108.

Shaw, A., Joseph, S., & Linley, P. (2005). Religion, spirituality, and posttraumatic growth: A systematic review. *Mental Health, Religion & Culture, 8*(1), 1–11.

Shepard, P. (1982). *Nature and madness*. San Francisco, CA: Sierra Club Books.

Shively, S., & Day, S. (2015). Social inequalities in health of nonhuman primates. *Neurobiology of Stress, 1*, 156–163.

Shorter, E. (1997). *A history of psychiatry: From the era of the asylum to the age of Prozac*. New York, NY: John Wiley & Sons.

Siegel, L., & Welsh, B. (2017). *Juvenile delinquency: Theory, practice, and law* (13th ed.). Belmont, CA: Cengage Learning.

Skilton, A. (1994). *A concise history of Buddhism*. Birmingham, England: Windhorse Publications.

Skinner, B. (1948). *Walden two*. Indianapolis, IN: Hackett Publishing.

Skinner, B. (1971). *Beyond freedom and dignity*. Indianapolis, IN: Hackett Publishing.

Smith, S. M. (2018). *Documents and debates in American history and government: Volume one, 1493–1865*. Ashland, OH: Ashbrook Press.

Spencer, H. (1972). *On social evolution: Selected writings* (Peel ed.). Heritage of Sociology Series.

Srinivasan, S., Bettella, F., Hassani, S., Wang, Y., Witoelar, A., Schork, A. J., et al. (2017). Probing the association between early evolutionary markers and schizophrenia. *PLoS One, 12*(1), e0169227. https://doi.org/10.1371/journal.pone.0169227

Srinivasan, S., Bettella, F., Mattingsdal, M., Wang, Y., Witoelar, A., Schork, A., . . . Andreassen, O. (2016). Genetic markers of human evolution are enriched in Schizophrenia. *Biological Psychiatry, 80*(4), 284.

Stein, G. (2011). The case of King Saul: Did he have recurrent unipolar depression or bipolar affective disorder. *The British Journal of Psychiatry, 198*, 212.

Stouffer, S. (1965). *The American soldier*. New York, NY: Wiley.

Sue, D., Sue, D. W., & Sue, S. (2015). *Understanding abnormal behavior* (11th ed.). Stanford, CT: Cengage Learning.

Summers, R., & Barber, J. (2010). *Psychodynamic therapy: A guide to evidence-based practice*. New York, NY: The Guilford Press.

Suzuki, S. (1970). *Zen mind, beginner's mind: Informal talks on Zen meditation and practice*. New York, NY: Weatherhill.

Swartz, S. (2017). Mad Africa. In G. Eghigian (Ed.), *The Routledge history of madness and mental health* (pp. 193–209). New York, NY: Routledge Publishing.

Szyf, M., & Bick, J. (2013). DNA methylation: A mechanism for embedding early life experience in the genome. *Child Development, 84*(1), 49–57.

Tarnas, R. (1991). *The passion of the western mind: Understanding the ideas that have shaped our world view*. New York, NY: Ballantine Books.

Tay, L., & Diener, E. (2011). Needs and subjective well-being around the world. *Journal of Personality and Social Psychology, 101*(2), 354–365.

Teasdale, J., Moore, R., Hayhurst, H., Pope, M., Williams, S., & Segal, Z. (2002). Metacognitive awareness and prevention of relapse in depression: Empirical evidence. *Journal of Consulting and Clinical Psychology, 70*, 275–287.

Tedeschi, R., Park, C., & Calhoun, L. (1997). *Posttraumatic growth: Positive changes in the aftermath of crisis*. Mahwah, NJ: Lawrence Erlbaum Associates.

Tett, G. (2015). *The silo effect: The perils of expertise and the promise of breaking down barriers*. New York, NY: Simon & Schuster.

Thorton, T. (2017). Cross-cultural psychiatry and validity in DSM-5. In R. White, S. Jain, D. Orr, & U. Read (Eds.), *The Palgrave handbook of sociocultural perspectives on global mental health* (pp. 51–70). London, England: Macmillan Publishers.

Thumiger, C. (2017). Ancient Greek and Roman traditions. In G. Eghigian (Ed.), *The Routledge history of madness and mental health* (pp. 42–61). New York, NY: Routledge.

Trenery, C., & Horden, P. (2017). Madness in the middle ages. In G. Eghigian (Ed.), *The Routledge history of madness and mental health* (pp. 62–80). New York, NY: Routledge.

Triandis, H. (1994). *Culture and social behavior*. New York, NY: McGraw Hill.

Triandis, H. (1995). *Individualism and Collectivism*. Boulder, CO: Westview Press.

Triandis, H. (1996). The psychological measurement of cultural syndromes. *American Psychologist, 51*(4), 407–415.

Trommsdorff, G., & Heikamp, T. (2013). Socialization of emotions and emotion regulation in cultural context. In S. Barnow & N. Balkir (Eds.), *Cultural variations in psychopathology: From research to practice* (pp. 67–92). Cambridge, MA: Hogrefe.

Van Gennep, A. (2010). *The rites of passage* (2nd ed.). New York, NY: Routledge Press. (Original work published 1960).

Vartejanu-Jourbert, M. (2017). Representations of madmen and madness in Jewish sources from the pre-exilic to the Roman-Byzantine period. In G. Eghigian (Ed.), *The Routledge history of madness and mental health* (pp. 19–41). New York, NY: Routledge.

Von Bertalanffy, L. (1969). *General systems theory: Foundations, development, applications.* New York, NY: George Braziller.

Walker, A. (Ed.) (1967). *A history of neurological surgery.* New York, NY: Hafner Publishing.

Watson, J. (1913). Psychology as the behaviorist views it. *Psychological Review, 20,* 158–177.

Watts, A. (1957). *The way of Zen.* New York, NY: Pantheon Books.

White, W. (1917). *The principles of mental hygiene.* New York, NY: The Macmillan Company.

Wideger, T., & Samuel, D. (2005). Diagnostic categories or dimensions: A question for the diagnostic and statistical manual of mental disorders, fifth edition. *Journal of Abnormal Psychology, 114*(4), 494–504.

Wiger, D., & Harowski, K. (2003). *Essentials of crisis counseling and intervention.* Hoboken, NJ: Wiley & Sons.

Wilber, K. (1995). *Sex, ecology, spirituality: The spirit of evolution.* Boston, MA: Shambhala.

Wilber, K. (1996). *A brief history of everything.* Boston, MA: Shambhala.

Wilber, K. (2000). *A theory of everything: An integral vision for business, politics, science, and spirituality.* Boston, MA: Shambhala.

Wilber, K. (2000). *Integral psychology: Consciousness, spirit, psychology, therapy.* Boston, MA: Shambhala.

Wilcox, S. (2003). *IMPACT program: Juvenile crime enforcement and accountability challenge grant final report.* Davis, CA: Elsan and Associates.

Wilkinson, R., & Pickett, K. (2009). Income inequality and social dysfunction. *Annual Review of Sociology, 35,* 493–511.

Wilson, E. O. (1975). *Sociobiology: The abridged edition.* Cambridge, MA: Harvard University Press.

Woldt, A., & Toman, S. (Eds.) (2005). *Gestalt therapy: History, theory, and practice.* Thousand Oaks, CA: Sage Publications.

World Health Organization (WHO). (1974). *The international pilot study of schizophrenia.* Geneva: WHO.

Wright, R. (1994). *The moral animal: Why we are the way we are.* New York, NY: Vintage Books.

Zagzebski, L. (2012). *Epistemic authority: A theory of trust, authority, and autonomy of belief.* New York, NY: Oxford University Press.

Zimmermann, J. (2015). *Hermeneutics: A very short introduction.* Oxford, UK: Oxford University Press.

INDEX

abolition 161
Abu Bakr 89
academic psychology: advanced
degrees in 134; behaviorism
and 187; cognitive behaviorism
and 188, 200, 204; emergence
of 134, 136, 143–145, 178;
evolutionary perspective and 143,
146; functionalism and 144, 183;
humanistic 192–193, 204; mental
illness and 145; normal functioning
and 146, 151; philosophy/theology
and 16; psychodynamic 188–192,
204; psychosocial explanations and
146; structuralism and 143, 183
acceptance and commitment therapy
(ACT) 234, 236
accomplishment 240
adaptation 140–141, 144, 281
Adler, Alfred 188, 190, 193
Adorno, Theodor 287
Africa: colonization and 204, 212–213;
human development in 19, 22;
impact of Western practices 213;
nationalism and 207; self-rule and
204; traditional mental health
practices in 166, 212–213; women-
led tribal cultures in 78–80
African-American women 164
Agrippa 90
Alcmaeon 55
alcoholic psychosis 112
Alcoholics Anonymous (AA) 236, 238,
245
Alexander, F. 116, 134, 153
Alexander the Great 63–64
Al Farabi 89
alienation 191–192
Allport, Gordon 193
altered consciousness 80
American Association for Humanistic
Psychology 193
American Psychiatric Association (APA)
159, 220, 263, 282
American Psychological Association
(APA) 184, 195, 239
American Transcendentalists 172
analytical psychology 188

analytic philosophy 182
Anatomy of Melancholy (Burton) 92, 104
Anaximander 138
Andreas-Salome, Lou 176
animal magnetism 116–117
anterior cingulate cortex (ACC) 293
Anthony, Susan B. 163
antipsychiatry movement 203–204
antisocial personality 119
applied psychology 183–184
Aquinas, Thomas 89
Archer, Margaret 11
archetypal psychology 35–38, 190–191,
231, 243
Aristotle 63, 74, 89, 138, 167, 270
Asclepiades 57
Asia: Buddhism and 128–130;
colonialism and 166, 212; cultural
diversity in 212; emotional
regulation and 228; export of mental
health practices 212; integrated
approach to mental health in 130;
interdependence-oriented culture
in 228; social anxiety disorder and
226; Tibetan medicine and 130, 212;
women's mental health in 78
assimilation bias 8
attachment theory 188, 191
Augustine, Saint 76–77, 104
authenticity 215, 228
Avicenna 71, 74, 89
awareness 194

Babylonian doctors 46–47
Bachrach, B. 80–81
Bacon, Francis 89, 99–101, 171
Bahn, P. 24
Bao, W. 258–259
Bauer, Susan Wise 10
Bayle, A.L.J. 146
Beatrice of Nazareth 81–82
Beers, Clifford 160
Behave (Sapolsky) 293
behaviorism: adaptability and 186;
cognitive-behavioral therapy (CBT)
and 187; depression and 186;
dysfunctionality and 187–188;
emotional patterns and 185–186;

empiricism and 114, 135; mental health and 186–187; psychology of education and 184–185; utopian society and 186–187, 233; *see also* cognitive-behavioral model of mental health

beliefs: assimilation bias and 8; authoritative 20–21; authority-based 5; behaviorism and 186–188, 232–233; Buddhism and 128–129; categorization and 2; cognitive archaeology and 24–25; collective 23, 260; confirmation bias and 8; cultural 6–7, 31, 42, 47, 57, 64, 67, 224–227; deductive reasoning and 6, 88; empiricism and 20–22, 89–90; epistemology and 10; flexible 241; free thought and 125–126; hermeneutics and 9; heuristics and 8, 10; holding on to established 7, 10; humanism and 237; rationalism and 6; Reformation and 92; religious 51–52, 65–67, 81, 92–93, 138–139, 169–170, 242–243, 272; sense-experience and 5; skepticism and 61; spiritual systems of 79–80; Taoism in 130; theory of mind and 28; Tibetan medicine and 130; Western assumptions of superiority and 166–167, 205

Benjamin, Jessica 230

Benjamin, Walter 287

Benning, T. 253

Berengarius of Carpi 92

Berkeley, George 5, 89, 102

Bertalanffy, L. von 11, 253

Bible: Adam and Eve story 36–37; Christian truth in 95; creationism and 20; epistemic authority (EA) and 20–21; mental illness in 47–50

bicameral mind 32

biological/medical model of mental health: behavior and 223–224; biological etiology and 217, 221–222; biological interventions and 218; categorical model and 219–222; challenge to biopsychosocial model 250–251; cultural variation and 222; dimensional model and 219–222; doctor authority in 252; DSM and 219–224; identification of symptoms and 251; neurology and psychopathology in 224; personal history and 251; psychiatry and 135,

145–146, 148, 178, 203, 218; testing and 218–219, 222

biopsychosocial model: biological factors and 251, 253; causation/correlation and 252–253; conceptual influence of 253; cross-discipline research and 260; doctor-patient relationship and 251–252; dynamic change and 269; Engel and 250–251; grief and 252; holistic approach of 249, 253; level of complexity and 264; medical psychiatry and 250; mental health and illness in 264–265; Meyer and 250; model of levels in 274–275; multifactorial human behavior and 265; Pinel and 120; psychosocial reality and 251–253; social construction and 265; system-based human nature and 265; unique individuals in 249–250; *see also* Integrated Model

bipolar disorder 32

Birth of Tragedy, The (Nietzsche) 177

Bleuler, Eugen 147–148

Bonaventure 89

Bonelli, R. 243

Bosch, Hieronymus 91

Bowlby, John 188, 191

Braid, James 150

brain: addictive substances and 295–296; anterior cingulate cortex (ACC) 293; cognition and 239; diagnostics model and 303; emotions and 72, 268; empathy and 293–294; Enlightenment study of 116; epigenetics and 291–292; evolution and 22–24, 32, 139–141, 268, 282; Greco-Roman world and 55, 57–58, 60; group identity and 260, 294; humoral model and 71–72; impact of childhood abuse and neglect 291; mental illness and 103, 112–113, 188, 197, 250; neurological science and 146; self-consciousness and 27; *see also* neurology

Brant, S. 91

Brave New World (Huxley) 187

Breuer, Josef 151

Bright, Timothy 92

Brodie, R. 260, 262

Buddha 82–83, 126

Buddhism: eightfold path in 127; enlightenment in 272; Four Noble Truths in 83, 127; Japanese 128;

Middle Way 83; monastic life and 128; nirvana and 127; psychological well-being and 82–83, 127–131; subordination of women in 79; Tibetan psychiatry 130–132; Western adoption of 212; Zen Buddhism 128–130
Burton, Robert 92, 104
Bush, George W. 207
Buss, D. 28
Byzantine Empire 95

Calmiel, J.L. 146
Cambrian Explosion 19
Campbell, Joseph 40–41, 43–44, 61, 191
Camus, Albert 215
Canon of Medicine (Avicenna) 71
catatonia 147, 226
categorization: labelling of 1; masculine/feminine principles 37; mental illness and 2, 219–222, 303–304; organization and 1–2; oversimplification and 2
causation 228, 236, 252
Celsus 57
cerebral localization 116
Charcot, Jean-Martin 150–152, 156
Chaslin, Philippe 148
Chiarugi, Vincenzo 120
children: alienation and 191–192; behaviorism and 184; clinical psychology and 184; consciousness and 152–153; ego consciousness and 42; emotional regulation and 227–228; evil spirits and 132; impact of abuse and neglect on 291; inferiority complexes and 190; power striving and 190
China: Confucianism and 83–84; cultural order in 85; delinquent behavior in 258–259; depression in 226; psychological well-being and 83–84; spirituality in 83–85; Taoism in 84; treatment of mental illness in 212
Chinese Classification of Mental Disorders 254
Chomsky, Noam 187
Christianity: Bible and 95; demonic possession and 72; demonization of women in 37, 77–79; drop in rates of 272; emergence of 66; evangelical 170; fall of Constantinople and 95; grace in 272; Holy Roman Empire

and 70–71; medieval scholasticism and 74–75; Middle Ages era and 16, 70, 73–82; mystics and ascetics in 80–82; Protestant movement and 94–96; Romans and 65, 69; social activism and 169; subordination of women in 79; suicide and 226; women as nuns in 79, 81
Cicero 57, 64
Civil Rights Act 164
Classical era: classification system for mental illness 56; Hippocrates and 55–56; initiation rites in 67–68; insanity as divine punishment in 53; mental health as good life 54, 59, 61–62; mental health in 16, 58–68; mental illness in 16, 53–58, 68–69; mystery cults in 66–67; naturalistic approaches in 16, 54, 57–60; Neoplatonism and 65–66; Platonism and 60–62; principles of balance/ harmony in 55, 59, 61; psychological well-being and 54, 59–60; Pythagoras and 54; *see also* Greco-Roman world
classical evolution 22–23, 38
client-centered psychotherapy 237–239
Clifford, T. 130, 132
clinical psychology 183–184, 253
cognitive archaeology 24–28, 38
cognitive-behavioral model of mental health: academic psychology and 200, 204; acceptance and commitment therapy (ACT) and 234, 236; dialectic behavior therapy and 234; empiricism and 232; human motivation and 233; mindfulness-based 234; operant conditioning and 232; preexisting beliefs 235–236; realistic thoughts and 188; relational frame theory (RFT) and 234–235; relativism and 236; social learning and 232; talk therapy and 234; third-wave CBT and 233–234
cognitive-behavioral therapy (CBT) 187–188, 233
cognitive development 24–28, 33, 239
cognitive diffusion 236
cognitive fusion 236
cognitive psychology 233
collective unconscious 35, 190–191, 231
colonialism: African 204, 212–213; destruction of tradition and 166–167; enslavement and 161; imposition of Western views in 126, 133, 166,

211–213; Latin American 211;
   mental health and 130, 166–167;
   nationalism and 207; self-rule and
   204; Western cultural superiority
   claims and 166–168; white man's
   burden and 166–167
Complex Adaptive System (CAS):
   adaptation and 281; decentralized
   interaction and 281–283; group
   behavior and 280; Integrated Model
   and 266, 279–281, 299; relationships
   in 279–280
conduct disorder (CD) 223, 255–259
Confessions (St. Augustine) 76, 104
confirmation bias 8, 100
Confucianism 79, 83–84
Confucius 83
connectionism 184–185
Conroy, Mark 298
consciousness: altered states of 80;
   archetypal approach to 36; biological
   utility of 144; children and 152–153;
   conscious mind and 152; ego and
   152–153; Freud on 152–153; id
   and 152; moral categories and 37;
   preconscious and 152; spiritual
   transcendence and 272; superego and
   152; unconscious and 152
conservatism 165, 206–207
Constantine I 77
Constantinople 95
constructivism 288
Cook, C. 49
coping skills training 234
correlation 236, 252
counterculture 203–210
Counterreformation 96, 98
Craig, L. A. 75
creationism 20–21
cross-discipline research: biopsychosocial
   model and 260; Complex Adaptive
   System (CAS) and 280; epigenetics
   and 288–292; for expansion of
   scholarship 287–288; human behavior
   and 292–296; psychology and 17
Crow, T. 33
Cuban Glossary of Psychiatry 254
Cullen, William 119
cultural evolution 140, 167–168, 268
cultural explanations/perceived cause 254
cultural idiom of distress 254
cultural model of mental health:
   defining mental illness through
   224–226; depression and 226; DSM

and 229; emotional competences
   and 227–228; emotional regulation
   and 227–228; human nature and
   225–226; independence-oriented
   cultures and 227–228; institutional
   care and 228; interdependence-
   oriented cultures and 227–228;
   psychological processes and 226–227;
   social causation and 228–229; societal
   response and 228–229; subcultures
   and 225
cultural nostalgia 8, 207–210
cultural parallelism 31
cultural syndromes 225, 254
culture: authority figures in 21; belief
   systems 6–7, 12, 21, 229; conduct
   disorder and 258–259; counterculture
   and 203–209; defining 224–225;
   evolution of 23; homeostasis and 50–51;
   humanistic psychology and 246;
   human nature and 225–226, 285;
   impact of 261–262; independence-
   oriented 227–228; interdependence-
   oriented 227–228; mental health
   impacts and 213, 254; mind and
   23; modernism and 183, 203;
   mythological systems and 42, 44–46;
   nationalism and 207; personal growth
   movement and 206; postmodern
   approach to 12; postmodern changes
   in 203–211; repression of women
   and 37, 43; romantic humanism and
   203–204; silent majority and 206;
   Western mental health ideas and
   254–261; Western superiority claims
   166–168, 206; *see also* non-Western
   mental health
cyclothymia 146, 148

Darwin, Charles 22, 34, 139–142
Darwin, Erasmus 139
decentralized interaction 282–283
deductive reasoning 6, 88
delinquent behavior 258–259
demonic possession 71–72, 92
depression 186, 226, 239
depth psychology 231–232, 243, 247
de Sauvages, François 119
Descartes, René 5–6, 116, 122–124
Dewey, John 7, 175
DeWitt, R. 10
*Diagnostic and Statistical Manual of the
   American Psychiatric Association* (DSM):
   categorical system and 220–221, 224;

conduct disorder and 255–258; cultural grounding of 229, 254; cultural syndromes in 225, 254; culture of mental illness in 255; development of 263; dimensional approaches in 220, 256; expansion of disorders in 255–256; Integrated Model and 302; medical-style binaries in 280; mental illness definitions in 223, 257–258, 302–303; nosology problems in 263–264; not otherwise specified (NOS) criteria 221; professional education and 14; reorganization of shared symptoms in disorders 222; symptom-based system 202–203; *see also* DSM-5; DSM-III; DSM-IV

dialectic behavior therapy 234

diathesis-stress model 301–302

Dix, Dorothea 159–160

Douglass, Frederick 163

dreams 56, 149

drug addiction 295–296

DSM-5: categorical model criticisms and 219, 221, 263, 302; changes in 220, 224, 263, 305; conduct disorder and 257–258; dimensional approaches in 222; mental illness definition in 223; removal of cultural syndromes in 225, 254; *see also Diagnostic and Statistical Manual of the American Psychiatric Association* (DSM)

DSM-III 203, 220, 263

DSM-IV 223

Durant, W. 176

Durkheim, Emile 46

dysfunctionality: attachment to the self and 131; behaviorism and 188; cognitive-behavioral therapy (CBT) and 187–188; conduct disorder and 223; evolution and 28; mental asylums and 120, 156; mental hygiene movement and 160; mental illness and 49, 148; observable behavior and 93; schizophrenia and 31

ecology 246–248

ecopsychology 247–248

educational psychology 184–185

ego 152–153, 189

ego consciousness 42

ego psychology 188–190

Eleusinian Mysteries 66–67

Ellis, Albert 243

emotional contagion 293

emotional intelligence 227

emotional regulation 227–228, 241

emotions: attachment theory and 191; behavioral flexibility and 282–283, 295; behavior and 185–186, 220; brain and 72, 268; conjoined perspective and 123; culture and 227–228; deviancy and 108; distortions of reality and 236; empathetic behavior 293; functionalism and 144; heart activity and 103; humoral model and 91; personality and 60, 148; positive 239, 241–242; postmodernism and 182–183; psychological processes and 29; psychological suffering and 131–132; psychological theory and 135–137, 157–158; psychological well-being and 239; religion and 51, 169; self-consciousness and 26; social 26, 34

empathetic behavior 293–294

Empedocles 138

empiricism: emergence of 21–22, 87; Enlightenment and 103–104, 117; evolution and 20–21; medicine and 92–93; mental illness and 87, 90–94, 106–107, 114, 119; psychiatry and 103; psychology and 5–6; Renaissance era and 87–94; sensory experience and 89; subjective experience and 102; truth-finding and 5–7, 20, 87, 99

engagement 240–241

Engel, George L.: biopsychosocial model and 13, 250–251, 253, 265, 287; nested systems model and 275, 279

Enlightenment: abolitionist writing and 161; birth of nosology 117–121; birth of psychiatry in 102–104; empiricism and 103–104, 117; evolution of psychiatric theory in 115–117; help-seeking in 117, 122; intellectual movement in 89; medicalization of mental illness 110–112; medicine in 103–104; mental asylums and 103–115; mental health philosophy during 122–126; mental illness in 16, 102–122; non-Western approaches to mental illness 126–133; population increase and 105–106; reason and faith in 122–125; sense perceptions and 102; urbanization and 105–106

Epicurean philosophy 64–65, 99

epigenetics 288–292

epistemic authority (EA) 20–22, 31

epistemology: antidogmatic approach to 124–125; deductive reasoning and 88; inductive reasoning and 99–100; pragmatism and 7, 144–145; reliance on authority 87–88; Renaissance era and 87–88; transcendental 171; truth-finding and 2, 5, 10–11, 99–100

ergasiology 250

Esalen Institute 212

esotericism 272

Esquirol, Jean-Etienne-Dominique 120–121, 145–146

eugenics movement 167, 169

Europe: anti-intellectualism in 73; demonization of women in 77–79; Holy Roman Empire and 70; humanism and 94; intellectual movement in 89; medieval scholasticism and 74–75; mental health and illness in 71–82; mental hospitals in 73; Middle Ages and 70, 72–82; mystics and ascetics in 80–82; population increase and 105–106; Reformation and 94–95; Saint Augustine and 76–77; spread of Christianity in 71; technological development in 74; Thirty Years' War 95; universities and 75

evolution: brain and 22–24, 32, 139–141, 268, 282; classical 22–23, 38; cognitive development and 22; controversy and 142, 154; cultural 140, 167–168, 268; emotions and 282–283, 295; empiricism and 20–21; Freud and 154; human development and 22–23; Integrated Model and 268–269; mental illness and 28–30; mental traits and 141; mind and 23–24; nature versus nurture 34; neurological 32–33; physical traits and 140–141; psychological traits and 140–142; race and 142; resistance to 7, 17, 22; schizophrenia and 31–33; scientific basis for 7, 17, 22, 138–139; selective breeding and 139; self-identity and 142–143; sexual selection and 141–142; social 23, 38, 142; theory of 139–141

evolutionary psychology 28–30, 38, 140–141

existentialism 136–138, 175, 192, 215–216, 237

Fanon, Frantz 167

feminine principles 37

feminist psychoanalysis 230

Foucault, Michel: on asylum populations 107–109; on conceptualization of mentally ill 104, 110–112, 114–115; on great confinement of the insane 107, 109; on insanity and human nature 110; on language and madness 111; on mental illness in the Middle Ages 75–76; on ship of fools trope 91; on silencing of madness 108

Framework of Knowledge Areas (FKA) 275–279

Frances, A. 224

Frankfurt School 287

Frankl, Victor 175, 192–193

Freidman, Thomas 207

Freud, Anna 188–190

Freud, Sigmund: on childhood sexuality 158, 190; conception of mental illness 153–158; criticism of 189–191, 235; dimensional concepts and 155–156; ego defenses and 189; evolutionary theory and 154; on human autonomy 97; human development and 121; hypnosis and 156; hysteria and 151–152; influence of Charcot on 150, 152, 156; influence of Galton on 143; influence on Jung 35; model of the psyche 152, 189–190; mythologies and 178; neurology and 151, 154–155; on neurosis 158; personality theory and 153–155; pleasure principle and 122, 193; psychiatry and 135; psychoanalytic theories of 145, 152, 155, 158, 188–190; psychodynamic psychology and 230; on psychological conflict 155–156; psychological wellness theories and 152; psychopathology theories and 152; psychosexual stages and 153; psychotherapy and 156–157; on religious belief 242–243; seduction theory and 158; on structure of conscious 152–153; unconscious mind and 53, 56, 149, 152–153, 156–157

Frisch, Karl von 140

Fromm, Erich 193, 287

functional contextualism 234

functionalism 144, 183

fundamental attribution error 236

Galen 57–58

Galilei, Galileo 74, 89

Gall, Franz Joseph 116–117

Galton, Francis 143, 168
Gamble, Harvey, Jr. 187
Gehart, D. 245
Gellender, M. 10
geometry 61–62
Gestalt psychology 193–195, 215–216
Global Assessment of Functioning (GAF) 305
globalism 207
Goddess worship 79
God/gods: Biblical stories and 36–37, 48–50; Chinese folk religions and 83; cultural belief systems and 51, 87–88; demonic possession and 72; depersonalization of 62; divine punishment and 53–56, 58–59; epistemic authority (EA) and 21; hero's journey and 41–44; individual relationship with 81, 85; knowledge of self and 123; male gods of war 248; participation mystique and 36; patriarchal shift in 79; Platonism and 138; predestination and 98; Roman Catholic Church and 94–95; romantic idealists and 172
godhead 272
Golden Age 41, 210
Goldstein, Kurt 194
Granello, Paul 239, 241
Great Chain of Being 269–270
Great Nest of Being 270–273
Greco-Roman world: Christianity and 65, 69; collapse of Roman Empire 70; development of science in 54–56; Epicurean philosophy and 64–65; gods and madness in 53–54; humoral model of biological/mental functioning 58, 71; influence of 53; mental illness and 54–58, 68–69; mystery cults in 66–67; naturalistic approaches in 16, 54, 57–59; Neoplatonism and 65–66; observable phenomena and 63; Platonism and 60–62; plurality in 68; psychological well-being and 54, 59–60, 62–65; Stoic philosophy and 64–65; tension in worldviews 56–57; weakening of religion in 58
grief 252
Griesinger, Wilhelm 146
Grinker, R. 11
group identity 67, 260
Gutenberg, Johannes 74
Guyart, Marie 163

Haas, A. 258
happiness: Classical era approaches to 59, 61, 63–65; Epicurean philosophy and 64; equality and 165; intellectual foundation for 125; nature versus nurture 34; search for 268; Stoic philosophy and 64; virtue and 63; well-being and 239; Western approach to 86
Harrington, A. 224
Harvey, William 103
Hayes, S. 234–236
hebephrenia 147
Hecker, Ewald 147
Hegel, Georg 172–173, 175
Heine, S. 224–225
Heinroth, Johann Christian 145, 149–150
Hereditary Genius (Galton) 143
hermeneutics 9–10
hero's journey 41–46
heuristics 8, 11, 21
hierarchy of needs 193, 271, 273
hikikomori 225
Hillman, James 231–232
hindsight bias 8
Hinduism 212, 272
Hippocrates 55–56, 59
Hobbes, Thomas 102, 123, 167
Hoffman, Friedrich 116
Holt, John 161
Holy Roman Empire 70
Homer 59
Horney, Karen 193
House of Medici 97–98
human behavior: adaptive 29; cognitive archaeology and 24–25; cross-discipline research and 292–296; empathetic 293–294; evolution of flexibility in 282; group identity and 294–295; medical model and 223–224; multidetermination of 264; multidisciplinary perspectives and 296; multifactoral 265; nature versus nurture 34–35; rank order and 26; self-consciousness and 26–27; socially undesirable 29–30; social norms for 22, 25, 28, 223; system-based 265
human body 55, 71, 74, 92
human desires 76–77
human development: evolution and 22–23, 38; language development 24–25; nature versus nurture 34–35;

personality and 154; Prehistoric
era 19–20; sedentism and 24; self-
consciousness and 26, 33; social/
cultural change and 23; speciation
phase of 23; tectonic phase of 23–24;
vulnerability to psychotic symptoms 32
human freedom 215
humanism: academic psychology and
192–193, 204–205; mental health
and 94; Postmodern era and 205;
psychological well-being and 59,
205; received authority conflicts
125; religious opposition to 96;
Renaissance era and 87, 94–98;
romantic 203–204; wellness and
125–126
humanistic pragmatism 63
humanistic psychology: client-centered
psychotherapy and 237–239;
cultural dynamics and 246; ecology
and 246–248; ecopsychology and
247–248; existentialism and 192,
237; feminine power and 247; as
foundation for therapeutic practice
237–238, 246; Gestalt psychology
and 194; goals and values in 193,
237; holistic understanding and 237;
hope and meaning in 192–193, 237;
motivation and 193; non-Western
religious beliefs and 243; peace
and war 248–249; phenomenology
and 192, 237; positive psychology
and 239–242, 246; psychological
well-being and 239–242; recovery
movement and 244–246; religious
beliefs and 243–244; self-actualization
and 192, 237; self-will/autonomy and
237; strengths-based perspective in
244; world concerns in 246–248
human mind: beliefs and 171;
distortions of reality and 236;
evolution and 23–24; opposing ideas
and 61–62; personal memory and
236; rational analysis and 60–61
human nature: culture and 225–226,
285; holistic approach to 265–
266; positive approach to 239–;
psychological models and 229;
system-based 265; violence and 248
human potential movement 205,
210, 237
Hume, David 5, 89, 102, 171
humoral model of mental illness:
demonic possession and 92; emotions

and 91; frenzy in 72; Greco-
Roman world 58, 71, 91; mania
in 72; medical doctors and 91–92;
melancholy in 72; Middle Ages era
71–73; purging and 72; Tibetan
Buddhist psychiatry 131
Husserl, Edmund 138
Huxley, Aldous 187, 272
Hyman, S. 263
hypnosis 150–152
hysteria: Charcot and 150; charismatic
healers and 117; Freud and 151–152;
Galen on 58; Hippocrates on 56;
hypnotism and 150–151; mind and
104; Sydenham on 104; women and
"wandering uterus" 55

Ibn Tufail 89
id 152, 189
individual psychology 188
inductive reasoning 6, 89–90
inferiority complex 190
insanity: in the ancient world 46–47,
50; antisocial personality and 119;
biologically-based 71–73, 112–113;
Christianity and 111; in the classical
era 53, 55, 111; demonic possession
and 71–73; as divine punishment
55, 59; expulsion and 91; hero's
journey and 44; medicalization of
111; mental illness and 76; in the
Middle Ages 71–72, 111; Renaissance
representations of 90–91; ship of
fools trope 91, 108; see also madness
Institute for Social Research 287
Integrated Model: application of
283–287; Complex Adaptive System
(CAS) approach in 266, 279–283, 299;
content area study and 284–287; core
mental health descriptions 299–301;
core mental illness descriptions
301–304; cross-discipline research and
280, 287–288; diagnostics model and
303–304; dimensional perspective and
304; DSM and 302–303; dynamics
and 299; evolution and 268–269;
Framework of Knowledge Areas
(FKA) 265–266, 269, 275–279;
individual learning in 284–287;
institutional practice and 296–298;
levels in 274; multifactoral psychology
and 266; Sacramento Assessment
Center (SAC) and 297–298; social
construction theory and 266–267;

structural components 299; systems theory and 288; *see also* biopsychosocial model
International Classification of Diseases (ICD) 255
interpersonal relationships 240–241
intersubjective dynamics 234
intersubjectivity 230–232
Islam 72, 74, 79, 106, 226
isonomy 55

James, William 7, 144–145, 169, 175, 183
Janet, Pierre 151
Japan 128–130, 212, 225
Jaynes, J. 32–33, 42
Jefferson, Thomas 124–125
Johnson, M. 1
Johnson, S. 67
Judaism 79
Judeo-Christian tradition 48, 72, 77, 110, 129, 248
Jung, Carl 35, 178, 188, 190–191, 231

Kahlbaum, Karl 146–147
Kant, Immanuel 171–173, 175, 214
Kierkegaard, Søren 137, 175, 193, 215
King, Martin Luther, Jr. 206
Kipling, Rudyard 166
Klein, Melanie 191
knowledge: a priori categories and 171; Christian West and 71; content area study and 284–287; cross-discipline research and 287–290; empiricism and 99; hermeneutics and 10; inductive reasoning and 6; levels of reality in 271; nosology and 117–122; power and 107; pragmatism and 7; sense-experience and 5; systems theory and 11; technological developments and 74
knowledge frameworks: comprehensive biopsychosocial model 273–275; Framework of Knowledge Areas (FKA) 275–279; Great Chain of Being and 269–270; Great Nest of Being and 270–273; hierarchy of needs and 271, 273; perennial philosophy and 271–272
Koenig, H. 243
Kohut, Heinz 188, 191
Koyre, Alexander 10
Kraepelin, Emil 147–148, 168
Kroll, J. 80–81
Kuhn, Thomas 10, 260, 262

labels 1
labor movement 161–162
Lakoff, G. 1
Lamarck, Jean-Baptiste 139
Lambert, E. 257
language development 24–25, 33
Latin America 204, 211–212
Latin American Guide for Psychiatric Diagnosis 254
law of effect 185
law of exercise 185
learned helplessness 239
learning 184–185, 284–287; *see also* knowledge
Leclerc, Georges-Louis 139
Lee, N. 115
Leonardo da Vinci 89
Levy, D. 235
Lewis-Williams, D. 33
liberalism 165, 206
Linehan, Martha 234
Locke, John 5, 34, 89, 102, 123–124, 171
Lombroso, Cesare 147
Lord of the Rings, The (Tolkien) 208–209
Lorenz, Konrad 140
Luddite movement 208
Luther, Martin 94, 96, 111

madness: Biblical examples of 48–50; conceptualizations of 91; as divine punishment 53, 55; external entities and 32–33; language and 111; medicalization of 110–112; Middle Ages era and 76; silencing of 108–109; *see also* insanity
Maimonides 74
Maladies Mentales, Des (Esquirol) 120
males: aggression displays 30; conduct disorder and 258; delinquent behavior and 258–259; patriarchal projections and 78; rites of passage and 67–68, 248–249; sexual selection and 141–142; subordination of women 78–80, 88; violence and 248–249; voting rights and 163
Man's Search for Meaning (Frankl) 192
Marcuse, Herbert 287
Marx, Karl 165, 172
Marxism 165, 287
masculine principles 37
Maslow, Abraham 122, 137, 193, 237, 240, 271, 273
Maslow's hierarchy of needs 193, 271, 273

mathematics 54, 61, 63, 182
Maupertuis, Pierre 139
May, Rollo 237
medicine: alternative 92–93; biological
knowledge and 113; bodily physicians
in 92; classical era and 55–56, 58;
in the Enlightenment 103–104, 113;
experimental approach to 93; heart
activity and 103; Hippocrates and
55–56; humoral system and 71–72,
91–92; impact of religious doctrine
on 71; mental health and 58–59, 68,
146; in the Middle Ages 71–72; in the
Modern era 135–136; mythological
era and 46–47; power and 115,
121; professionalization of 121; in
the Renaissance era 100; spiritual
physicians in 92; Tibetan 130–132
meditation 212, 272
memes 260–262
memory 236
Mendonsa, A. D. 298
mental asylums: changing beliefs on
mental illness and 106; criminals in
91, 105, 109; as cultural punishment
108–109; Enlightenment rise of
104–115; fear of airborne madness
113; great confinement and 107,
109; Islamic world and 106; medical
power and 115, 121; population
increase and 105–106; psychiatry
and 103, 111–112, 114–115; reform
movement and 104, 121; treatment
of the insane in 91, 109
mental health: behaviorism and
186–187; biological/medical
model of 217–224; categorization
and 2; conceptual foundation
for 14–15, 265–266; cultural
conformity and 25–26; cultural
impact on 213–214, 254; cultural
model of 224–229; diagnostic
system for 304–306; emotional
regulation and 227; Enlightenment
philosophy and 122–126; as good
life 54, 59, 61–62; higher-order
goals and 193; historical approach
to 15–18, 24; Integrated Model and
299–301; multicultural approaches
to 237, 254; nature versus nurture
34–35; non-Western cultures and
82–84, 126–133, 213–214; normal
functioning and 218; organization
of information for 265; paradigm

shift in 263–264; physical activity
and 241–242; professionalization of
17; psychodynamic approach to 150;
psychological model of 229–249;
quality of life and 164–165; religion
and 75–76, 170, 242–244; sense of
self and 164; subjective experience
and 214–216; worried well and 117,
121–122
mental health care 244–246
mental health recovery movement
244–245
mental hygiene movement 159–161
mental illness: alcoholic psychosis
and 112; archetypal approach
to 35–37; assumptions of 3;
biological viewpoint and 12, 155;
biopsychosocial model of 120;
categorization and 2, 219–222,
303–304; classification of 56, 117,
148; conceptual foundation for
2–3, 14–15, 265–266; cultural belief
systems and 12, 21, 225, 254; as
cultural creation 107–108; defining
218–220, 223, 225; deviancy of 108;
diagnostics and 303–304; diathesis-
stress model 301–302; dimensional
model and 219–222; empiricism
and 87, 90–92, 106–107, 114, 119;
epigenetics and 291–292; epistemic
authority (EA) and 21; etiology
of 120; evolution and 28–30; fear
of airborne 113; Foucault on 75,
91, 107–112, 114–115; Freud on
153–158; heuristics and 21; historical
approach to 12–18, 24; increase in
112–113; institutional care for 112;
Integrated Model and 301–304;
mechanisms/dynamics of 219–221;
medicalization of 110–112; medical
tests for 218–219, 222; mistreatment
and 105; multicultural approaches
to 254; nature versus nurture 34–35;
neurosyphilis and 112; non-Western
approaches to 126; as ontological
entity 107–108; organization of
information for 265; physical
explanations 121; professionalization
of 114–115, 121; psychodynamic
approach to 150; psychological basis
for 121, 158; psychological tests for
219; psychopathology and 218; public
responsibility for 106–107; quality of
life and 164–165; shared symptoms

in disorders 222; silo effect and
12–13; sociocultural context of 251;
subjective relativity and 3–4; systems
theory and 11–12; theories of 14–15;
treatments and 14; urbanization and
105–106; Western approach to 70
Mercuriale, Girolamo 92
Mesmer, Franz 116–117, 122, 150
mesmerism 150
metacognition 241
Meyer, Adolph 148–149, 160, 250
Middle Ages era: Christian worldview
in 16, 70, 73–75; cultural change and
85; demonic possession and 72–73;
demonization of women in 77–79;
Europe in 70–82; free thought and
75; humoral model of mental illness
in 71–73; influence of Greco-Roman
rationalism 73–74; insanity in
71–72, 76; Islam and 70; medicine
in 71–72; medieval scholasticism
and 74–75; mental health in Europe
75–82; mental health in non-Western
cultures 82–85; mental illness in 70–
75, 85; mystics and ascetics in 80–82;
naturalism and 73–74; Platonism and
89; projected judgment in 77–78;
religion and 75–82, 85; religious
heretics in 77; roots of Western
culture in 85–86; Saint Augustine
and 76–77; Scholastic movement in
88; spiritual transcendence in 80;
technological development in 74
Middle East 89
Miles, R. 79
milieu therapy 156
mind see human mind
mind-body dualism 251
mindfulness 212, 236
mindfulness-based meditation 234
Mithen, S. 28
Modern era: academic psychology
and 144–145; birth of psychology
135–138; birth of the unconscious
149–158; colonization and 166–167;
cultural evolution and 167–168;
eugenics movement and 167–169;
evolutionary theory and 138–143;
Freudian theory and 149–158;
functionalism and 144–145; industrial
revolution and 135; mental health
and illness in 16, 134, 179; mental
hygiene movement and 159–161;
mental illness classification systems

and 146–149; philosophy and
religiosity in 169–179; pragmatism
and 144–145; progressive movement
and 159–166, 179; psychiatrists
and 145–149; romanticism
versus scientism 134–135; social
reform movement and 161–166;
technological development in 134
modernism 181–183, 205
Moore, D. 288
moral therapy 156
Moreau de Tours, J. 145, 149–150
Morel, Benedict 147
motivation 233
Mott, Lucretia 163
multifactoral psychology 266
mystery cults 66–67
mystics and ascetics 80–82
Mythological era: Babylonian doctors
and 46–47; Biblical examples
of mental illness 47–50; cultural
homeostasis and 50–51; documented
insanity in 46–50; hero's journey
and 41–44, 46; mental health and
illness in 15–16, 40, 43–44, 46–52;
mythological systems in 40–44, 46
mythological systems: culture and
42, 44–46; hero's journey and
41–44; human life and 40–41,
44; nondifferentiation and 41–42;
patriarchal demonization of women
and 43; religion and 44; rites of
passage in 44–46

Napier, Richard 92
National Committee on Mental Hygiene
160
nationalism 207–208
National Women's Rights Conventions
163
Native Americans 163, 166
natural reality 4
natural world: archetypal feminine
in 79–80; Neoplatonism and 65;
preconsciousness and 41; rational
understanding of 65; scientific
understanding and 138–139; systems
theory and 11
nature versus nurture 34–35
Nazism 168, 172, 183, 203
Neolithic Revolution 15, 24, 26, 31
Neoplatonism 65–66, 74, 89
Neumann, E. 35, 37, 42
neurasthenia 168, 225–226

neurological evolution 32–33
neurology: advances in 146–147;
    Charcot and 150–151; Freud and
    151, 154–155; psychasthenia and
    151; psychiatry and 145–148;
    psychopathology and 224; *see also*
    brain
neuroscience 217
neurosis 158, 189
neurosyphilis 112
New Age movement 59, 204–205, 209,
    212, 237
Nietzsche, Friedrich 175–178, 192, 215
nihilism 176–177
Nineteen Eighty-Four (Orwell) 187
*Ninety-Five Theses on the Power and Efficacy
    of Indulgences* (Luther) 94
nirvana 44, 127–128, 174, 272
Nixon, Richard 206
nondifferentiation 41–42
non-Western mental health: African
    166, 212–213; Asian 212; Buddhism
    and 82–83, 126–130, 212; Chinese
    religions/philosophies 83–84, 212;
    collectivist cultures and 129–130;
    colonization and 126, 130, 133,
    166–167; Confucianism and
    83–84; cultural differences in
    213–214; cultural norms and
    254; Enlightenment era 126–133;
    eugenics movement and 167–169;
    export of practices to the West 212;
    impact of Western approach to
    211–213; integrated approach to
    130; Japanese Buddhism 128; Latin
    America 211–212; meditation and
    212; Middle Ages era 82–84; in
    the Modern era 166; Postmodern
    era 211–214; Shinto religion 128;
    social conditions and 212; Tibetan
    Buddhist psychiatry 130–132; Zen
    Buddhism 128–130
nosology: development of 117–121;
    psychiatry and 146–148

objectivity 3–5
object-relations theory 191
operant conditioning 232
oppressed groups: impact of capitalism
    on 165; mental hygiene movement
    and 161; mental stress and 164, 167,
    174–175
Oration on the Dignity of Man (Pico della
    Mirandola) 96

Orwell, George 187
Ottoman Turks 95

Paleolithic Period 24
Paracelsus 90, 92
paradigms 2, 260, 262
Paré, Ambroise 92
participation mystique 36
Pavlov, Ivan 185, 232
peace and war 248–249
Peirce, Charles Sanders 7, 144
perennial philosophy 271
Perls, Fritz 59, 194
Perls, Laura 194
personal growth 206
personality disorders 147
personality theory: cognition and 60;
    conflict and 230; desire and 60;
    emotion and 60; evolutionary theory
    and 154; Freud and 153–155, 230;
    human development and 154; three-
    part structure of 149
pharmacotherapy 152
phenomenology 9, 136–138, 192, 237
philosophy: analytic 182; Bacon
    and 99–101; Buddhist 128;
    Christian worldview and 174, 179;
    Confucianism 83; Enlightenment 118,
    122–126, 171; Epicurean 64–65, 99;
    epistemological relativism 171–172;
    Greco-Roman 55, 57, 60, 64–65,
    74, 95; Hegel and 172–173, 175;
    hermeneutics and 9; human will and
    173–174, 176; idealism and 172–173,
    175; Kant and 171–172, 175;
    Kierkegaard and 175; mathematics
    and 182; misogynistic attitudes in 174;
    modernism and 181–183; natural
    55; Neoplatonism 65–66, 74, 89;
    Nietzsche and 175–178; nihilism
    and 176–177; Platonism 60–62, 138;
    postmodern 181, 215; pragmatism
    and 144–145; relativism and 172,
    175–176; Schopenhauer and 173–175;
    social change and 182; Stoic 64–65,
    99; Taoism 130; Tibetan Buddhist 130
phrenological theory 116
physiological well-being 241–242
Pico della Mirandola, Giovanni 95–96
Pinel, Philippe 118–121, 145–146
Pinker, S. 34, 262
Plato 60, 62–63, 89, 91, 138
Platonism 60–62, 138
Plotinus 65

Popper, Carl 10, 11
Porter, R. 109
positive emotions 239, 241
positive psychology: accomplishment
    and 240–241; emotional regulation
    and 241; engagement and 240–241;
    healthy relationships and 240–241;
    humanistic psychology and 237;
    meaning and purpose 240–241;
    positive emotion and 239–241;
    psychological well-being and
    239–241; success and 247; wellness
    counseling and 241–242
Postmodern era: cultural change and
    203–211; cultural nostalgia and
    207–210; Gestalt psychology and
    193–195; humanistic psychology
    and 192–193; industrial revolution
    and 181; mental health and illness
    in 16, 211, 214–216; modernist
    philosophy and 181–183, 214–216;
    non-Western mental health and
    211–214; postmodern philosophy
    and 181, 215; psychoanalysis and
    188–192; social change and 181–182;
    story of psychiatry in 196–203; story
    of psychology in 183–196; subjective
    experience and 214–216; systems
    theory and 193–195
postmodernism 7–8, 215
pragmatism 7, 63, 144–145, 234
preconscious 152
Prehistoric era: archetypes and 35–38;
    auditory/visual "hallucinations"
    in 33; cognitive archaeology and
    24–28, 38; evolutionary psychology
    and 28–30, 38; human development
    and 19–20; mental health and
    illness in 15, 24–38; nature versus
    nurture 34–35; role of women in 79;
    schizophrenia and 31–33; trepanation
    and 30–31
Prichard, James 147
progressive movement: liberalism and
    165; mental health and 164–165;
    mental hygiene movement and 159–
    161; public responsibility for well-
    being and 160–161, 165–166; quality
    of life improvements in 164–165;
    social change and 164; social reform
    movement and 159, 161–166; voting
    rights and 162–164
projection 77–78, 100
Protestant movement 94–96

psychasthenia 151
psychiatry: antisocial attitudes and
    147; biological/medical model in
    135, 145–146, 148, 178, 203, 218,
    250–251; brain and 116; catatonia
    and 147; classification of mental
    illness in 119–120; cyclothymia
    and 146, 148; development of 16;
    deviancy of mental illness and 108;
    early evolution of theory 115–117;
    empiricism and 103; Enlightenment
    birth of 102–104; hysteria and
    104; mental asylums and 103–105,
    111–112, 114–115; mind/body
    integration in 103; neurology and
    145–148; nosology and 146–148;
    observational 114; personality
    disorders and 147; phrenological
    theory and 116; in the Postmodern
    era 196–203; psychiatrists and
    146–149; psychoanalysis and 178,
    188; regressive behavior and 147;
    Romanticism and 134–135, 145;
    schizophrenia and 147; symptom
    complex and 147; Tibetan Buddhist
    130–132; unconscious mind and 185;
    worried well and 148
psychoanalysis: attachment theory
    and 188, 191; dimensional concepts
    in 155–156; ego psychology and
    188–190; feminist 230; Freud and
    145, 152, 155, 188–190; Jung
    and 190–191; object-relations
    theory and 191; psychiatry and
    188; psychodynamic psychology
    and 188–191, 204–205, 231;
    psychotherapy and 156–157;
    religious beliefs and 243; therapeutic
    relationship and 157–158;
    unconscious mind and 178
psychodynamic psychology: academic
    psychology and 188–192, 204;
    assessment of wellness 304–305;
    depth psychology and 231–232;
    development of 150; Freud and 230;
    intersubjectivity and 230–232; Jung
    and 231; psychoanalysis and 188–
    192, 204–205, 231; self-psychology
    and 191–192
psychological functions (PF) 219–220
psychological model of mental
    health: cognitive-behavioral 229,
    232–237; depth psychology and
    231–232; humanistic 229, 237–249;

intersubjectivity and 230–232;
psychodynamic 229–232
psychological well-being:
accomplishment and 240–241;
balance of the humors and 55,
71; Buddhism and 128–129;
consciousness and 144; cultural
belief systems and 42; emotional
regulation and 241; engagement
and 240–241; in the Enlightenment
122, 124–125; equality and freedom
in 205–206; in the Greco-Roman
world 60; healthy relationships and
240–241; hedonism and 209; human
concerns and 41; humanism and 59,
205; human potential movement and
205; meaning and purpose 240–241;
mystery cults and 67; personal growth
and 206; philosophical beliefs and
124–125; physical fitness/exercise
and 241–242; positive emotion and
239, 241; psychotherapy and 158;
public responsibility for 160–161,
165–166; religious beliefs and 51, 86,
170, 242–244; rites of passage and
46; self-actualization and 240; social
status and 26, 46; spirituality and
242–244
psychology: 20th century impact of
195–196; adaptation and 140–141,
144; analytical 188; applied 183–184;
archetypal 190–191, 231; attachment
theory and 188; behaviorism and
114, 135, 184–188, 203; birth of
135–138; comprehensive models of
274–275; cross-discipline research
and 17; depth 231–232, 243, 247;
educational 184–185; ego 188–190;
empiricism and 5–6; evolutionary
140–141; existentialism and 136–138;
gestalt 193–195; humanistic 192–194;
human mind and 179; individual 188;
inductive reasoning and 6; mental
illness and 3, 16; normal functioning
and 183, 203; phenomenology and
136–138; positive 237, 239–242;
in the Postmodern era 183–196;
psychiatry and 179; psychodynamic
150, 188–191; rationalism and 6;
research challenges of 5; self 188,
191–192; self-efficacy and 124; silo
effect and 13, 259–260; specialization
in 13; systems theory and 193–195;
trauma theory and 158; see also

academic psychology; clinical
psychology
psychopathology: cultural model and
226–227; defining 218; Freud's
theories of 152; medical model
of 103; neurology and 224;
Romanticism and 145
psychotherapy: abreaction and
157; client-centered 237–239;
development of 136; Freud and
156; humanistic psychology and
237–239; integrated approach to 306;
milieu therapy and 156; mindfulness
and 212; moral therapy and 156;
psychoanalysis and 152, 156;
residential settings and 156; theories
of 15; therapeutic relationship and
157–158; worried well and 157
Pyrrho of Elis 65
Pythagoras 54–55

race 142, 161, 163–164
racism 294–295
rank order 26
rationalism 5–6, 73–74, 134–135
Ray, Isaac 159
Reagan, Ronald 207, 210
realism 187
recovery-oriented approach 245–246
Reformation 92, 94–96, 98
regressive behavior 147
Reil, Johann 120, 136
relational frame theory (RFT) 234–235
religion: attitudes of psychology towards
242–243; collective behavior and
51; emergence of Christianity 66;
Freud on 242–243; Goddess worship
79; Greco-Roman world and
66–68; homeostasis and 51; human
development and 25, 28, 33; human
experiences and 46; humanistic
psychology and 243–244; mental
health and 75–76, 170, 242–244;
mystery cults and 66–67; mytho-
cultural systems and 44; philosophical
idealists and 172; psychological
problems and 244; psychological
well-being and 51, 86, 170; rites of
passage and 67–68; Second Great
Awakening and 169–170; self-image
and 170; self-inflicted punishment and
170; spiritual transcendence in 80;
subordination of women in 37, 77–80;
Third Great Awakening and 169–170;

turn from traditional churches 272;
see also spirituality
Renaissance era: alternative medicine
in 92–93; artistic movement
in 96–97; Bacon and 99–101;
Counterreformation and 96, 98;
empiricism and 87–94; epistemology
and 87–88, 99–100; fall of
Constantinople to Ottoman Turks 95;
hedonism and 98; House of Medici
and 97–98; humanism and 87, 94–98;
human right to truth-finding in 97;
inductive reasoning and 89, 100;
intellectual movement in 89; medicine
in 100; mental health in 16, 94–101;
mental illness in 90–94; Reformation
and 92, 94–96, 98; religion and
mental illness in 92; religious
pluralism in 101; representations
of insanity in 90–91; Scholastic
movement in 96; scientific method
and 89–90; sense of self in 97–99
Renfrew, C. 23–24
Republic (Plato) 91
Rhazes 74
rites of passage 44–46, 67–68
Rogers, Carl 137, 193, 236–237
Roman Catholic Church:
challenges to authority of 94–95;
Counterreformation and 96; division
in 96; European universities and
75; opposition to humanism 96;
Ptolemaic views and 74; Reformation
and 92, 94–96; religious authority of
74–75; sale of indulgences and 94
romantic humanism 203–204
Romanticism 134–135, 145, 172
Romberg, Moritz 146
Roosevelt, Theodore 166–167
Rousseau, Jean-Jacques 137
rural life 114
Rush, Benjamin 120
Russell, Bertrand 182
Rynd, Francis 134

Saah, T. 295
Sacramento Assessment Center (SAC)
297–298
Sapolsky, R. 34–35, 262, 292–294, 296
Sappho 55
Sartre, Jean-Paul 176, 215
Saul, King 47–49
schizophrenia: biological origins of
32; cultural manifestations of 226;

evolution and 31–33; genetic markers
for 33; hallucinations and 251;
identification of 147; neurological
evolution and 32–33; Western
cultures and 226
Scholastic movement 88, 96
school psychologists 184
Schopenhauer, Arthur 173–176
science 10, 54–56, 138–139, 260; *see also*
evolution
scientific method 10–11, 89–90, 93
scientific revolution 10–12, 14–15
scientism 134–135
Scull, A. 109
Second Great Awakening 169–170
Secrets of Alessio of Piedmont 92
sedentism 24
Selesnick, S. 116, 134, 153
self-actualization 192–193, 237, 240,
271, 273
self-consciousness: adaptive benefits of
27; cognitive development and 24,
26, 28, 32–33, 35; mental health and
illness 30; neurosis and 26–27
self-efficacy 124, 242
self-fulfilling prophecy 6, 8
self-identity 130–131, 142–143, 170
selfless self 271
self-objects 192
self-psychology 188, 191–192
self-reflective consciousness 21
Seligman, Martin 239–240, 245, 247
Seneca 64
Seneca Falls Convention 163
sense of self 97–99, 164
sexism 294
Sextus Empiricus 65
sexual selection 141–142
Shinto religion 128
ship of fools trope 91, 108
Shorter, E. 105, 108, 109, 112
Siddhartha Gautama (Buddha) 82–83,
126
Sidereus Nuncius (Starry Messenger)
(Galileo) 74
Siegel, L. 258, 259
Sijzi, Abu Said al- 74
silent majority 206
silo effect 12–13, 259–260
skepticism 61
Skinner, B. F. 186–188, 232–233
slavery 161
social anxiety disorder 226
social causation 228–229, 267

social construction theory 265–267
social control theory 258
social evolution 23, 38, 142
social learning 232
social realism 267–268
social reality 4
social reform movement 161–164
social sciences: cross-discipline research
  and 288; cultural embeddedness
  and 261–262; empiricism and 5–6;
  evolution and 34, 139, 142, 154;
  nature versus nurture 34; objectivity
  and 4–5; operationalization of topics
  in 4; rationalism and 5–6; self-fulfilling
  prophecy and 8; silo effect and 13;
  social construction and 267; subjective
  relativity and 3–4, 12; systems theory
  and 11; two-part evolution in 23
social status 26, 46
societal response 228–229
Socrates 59–60
sophistry 61
soul 231–232
Spenser, Herbert 167–168
Spinoza, Benedict 122–123, 171
spirituality: attaining higher levels
  of 271–273; Buddha and 82–83,
  127–128; Confucianism and 83–84;
  esotericism and 272; wellness and
  242–244; see also religion
Srinivasan, S. 33
Stanton, Elizabeth Cady 163
Stoic philosophy 64–65, 99
stress 213–214
structuralism 143, 183, 193
Structure of Scientific Revolutions, The
  (Kuhn) 10
subcultures 225
subjectivity 3–4
substance abuse 245, 295–296
suicide 226
superego 152, 154, 189
Sweetser, William 159
Sydenham, Thomas 103
symptom complex 147
systems theory: brain, mind, and culture
  in 23–24; Complex Adaptive System
  (CAS) approach to 266; as conceptual
  foundation for mental health 11–12,
  52, 253, 266; Gestalt psychology
  and 193–195; human homeostasis
  and 51; human psychology and 266;
  Integrated Model and 288
Szasz, Thomas 12, 107–109, 112

Taft, William Howard 167
talk therapy 212, 234
Taoism 84, 272
Tarnas, R. 63
Telesio, Bernardino 89
temperance movement 162
terrorism 207–208
theory of mind 28
Third Great Awakening 169–170
third-wave CBT 233–234
Thirty Years' War 95
Thorndike, Edward 184–185
Tibet 212
Tibetan Buddhist psychiatry 130–132
Tinbergen, Nikolaas 140
Tolkien, J.R.R. 208
total personality 149
transcendentalism 171–172
trauma theory 158
Treatise of Melancholie (Bright) 92
trepanation 30–31
Trump, Donald 207
truth: assimilation bias and 8; biology
  and 63; confirmation bias and 8;
  cultural belief systems and 6–7;
  empiricism and 5–6, 20, 87; epistemic
  authority (EA) and 20; epistemology
  and 2, 5, 10–11; existing beliefs
  and 10; hermeneutics and 9–10;
  heuristics and 8, 11; hindsight bias
  and 8; mathematics and 54, 61, 63;
  objectivity and 4; paradigms of 2;
  phenomenology and 9; Platonism and
  60–61; postmodern approach to 7–8;
  pragmatism and 7; rationalism and
  5–6; relativism and 175, 181; reliance
  on authority 6–7; Renaissance era
  and 97; scientific method and 10; self-
  fulfilling prophecy and 6; skepticism
  and 65; subjective/objective 175;
  systems theory and 11; theoretical
  frameworks for 11
Twenty-first century: biological/medical
  model of mental health 217–224;
  biopsychosocial model of mental
  health in 249–253; cross-cultural
  world and 254–261; cultural model of
  mental health 224–229; psychological
  model of mental health 229–249

unconscious: collective 35, 190–191,
  231; dreams and 56, 149; Freud
  on 53, 56, 149, 152–153, 156–157;
  hypnotism and 150–152; hysteria

and 150–151; Jung on 190; Modern era birth of 149–158; three-part structure of personality 149–150; total personality and 149
United States: classification of mental illness in 200; delinquent behavior in 259; depression in 226; romantic humanism and 203–204, 237; voting rights and 163–164; women's rights and 163–164
urban life 106, 113–114, 159
utopian society 186–187, 233

violence 248–249
Voltaire 137
voting rights 162–163

Waddington, C. 289
Wagner, Richard 177
Wallace, Alfred Russel 139
Watson, John 185–186, 188
Watts, Alan 212
well-being see psychological well-being
wellness: assessment of 304–306; counseling for 241–242; Freud's theories of 152; help-seeking and 117, 122; humanistic foundation for 125–126; metacognition and 241; physiological 241–242; positive emotion and 239; systems theory and 195
Welsh, B. 258, 259
Western cultures: assumptions of superiority 140, 142, 166–167; authenticity and 228; Christian worldview in 16, 66, 71, 76, 83, 95; colonization and 126, 166–167, 212–214; counterculture and 203–207; Greco-Roman influence and 53, 58, 95; humanistic pragmatism and 63; independence-oriented 227–228; influence of 70; materialism and 247; mental health ideas 254–261; nationalism and 247; rationality and 108, 178; Reformation and 96; schizophrenia and 226;

self-identity and 130; spirituality and 67; subjugation of women in 37; technological development in 21, 181
Weyer, Johann 90–91
White, William 159
White Man's Burden, The (Kipling) 166
Whytt, Robert 119
Wilber, Ken: comprehensive biopsychosocial model 274–275; Great Nest of Being and 270–273; secret impulse for complexity and 279; systems theory and 11
will 173–174, 176
witchcraft 90, 92
Witmer, Lightner 184
Wittgenstein, Ludwig 176, 182
Wolfe, Tom 209
womb envy 80
women: African-American 164; cultural empowerment of 78, 80; goddesses 79, 248; Judeo-Christian demonization of 37, 77–79, 174; Middle Ages era and 77–79; misogynistic attitudes and 174–175; mytho-cultural roots of repression and 43; as nuns 79, 81; patriarchal domination of 30, 37, 43, 77–80; prehistoric era and 79; projected judgment of 77–78; psychological suffering and 78, 174–175; seduction theory and 158; womb envy and 80
women's suffrage movement 162–164
Wooton, David 10
World Health Organization 245, 255
worried well 117, 121–122, 148, 152, 157
Wretched of the Earth, The (Fanon) 167
Wundt, Wilhelm 183–184

Xie, Y. 258

yoga 212, 272

Zagzebski, L. 21
Zen Buddhism 128–130

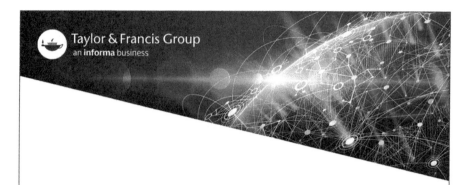

.